COMPUTERS
FOR
TECHNICIANS

ABRAHAM MARCUS
JOHN D. LENK

COMPU

TERS

FOR
TECHNICIANS

PRENTICE-HALL, INC.

Englewood Cliffs, New Jersey

Library of Congress Cataloging in Publication Data

Marcus, Abraham.
Computers for technicians.

(Prentice-Hall series in electronic technology)
1. Electronic digital computers. 2. Electronic digital computers—Circuits. 3. Electronic digital computers—Maintenance and repair. I. Lenk, John D., joint author. II. Title.
TK7888.3.M352 621.3819'58'4 72-5734
ISBN 0-13-166181-7

PRENTICE-HALL SERIES IN ELECTRONIC TECHNOLOGY

DR. IRVING L. KOSOW, EDITOR

CHARLES M. THOMSON, JOSEPH J. GERSHON, AND JOSEPH A. LABOK, consulting editors

COMPUTERS FOR TECHNICIANS

ABRAHAM MARCUS

JOHN D. LENK

10 9 8 7 6 5 4 3

Printed in the United States of America

Prentice-Hall, Inc., Englewood Cliffs, New Jersey

Prentice-Hall International, Inc., *London*
Prentice-Hall of Australia, Pty. Ltd., *Sydney*
Prentice-Hall of Canada, Ltd., *Toronto*
Prentice-Hall of India Private Limited, *New Delhi*
Prentice-Hall of Japan, Inc., *Tokyo*

CONTENTS

I

Introduction 1

III

Practical Computer Circuits *143*

IV

Computer Troubleshooting *369*

PREFACE

This book is the fourth in a series of textbooks for the training of technicians who operate in our industrial plants and scientific laboratories. The first two books of this series, *Electricity for Technicians** and *Electronics for Technicians*† explain most of the basic electrical and electronic principles the technician must know. The third book, *Measurements for Technicians***, is an introduction to the science of measurement with special emphasis placed upon electrical and electronic instruments and methods used for such measurement.

As the title implies, *Computers for Technicians* is written specifically for electronic technicians who plan to enter the highly specialized field of digital computers. The book provides the average technician with all the information needed to understand and service present-day computers.

Computers are no longer limited to the laboratory or government aerospace programs. Computers of all sizes and capabilities have long since moved into every phase of business and industry, creating a need for trained computer technicians. However, technicians have the greatest difficulty in obtaining the specific information they need—in textbook form.

Most existing books on computers are engineering texts for design

*Abraham Marcus, *Electricity for Technicians* (Englewood Cliffs, N.J.: Prentice-Hall, Inc., 1968).

†Abraham Marcus, *Electronics for Technicians* (Englewood Cliffs, N.J.: Prentice-Hall, Inc., 1969).

**Abraham Marcus and John D. Lenk, *Measurements for Technicians* (Englewood Cliffs, N.J.: Prentice-Hall, Inc., 1971).

engineers, data processing books for computer programmers, or a beginner's introduction to the subject for businessmen. Although all of this information can be useful, it still leaves many questions unanswered, and creates a gap for the technician who must service and repair computers. *Computers for Technicians* fills that gap since it is written to serve a threefold purpose. First, it is a textbook for student technicians. Second, it is a training aid for experienced technicians who are familiar with electronics, but have little knowledge of digital equipment, in general, and no understanding of computers in particular. Third, it provides specific, practical information on troubleshooting and servicing computers of all types.

To fulfil the first requirement, computers and associated equipments are explained in basic terms. Coverage logically progresses step-by-step from the evolution of the modern computer, through descriptions of typical computers, as well as covering the "languages" and number systems used in computers, to a discussion of basic electronic circuits found in computers. This is followed by an analysis of a generalized or theoretical computer that contains the basic principles upon which all modern computers operate. A glossary is included at the end of the book to familiarize technicians with terms used in computers.

To meet the second purpose of the book, full technician-level circuit descriptions are provided in a separate section. The circuits discussed are found in actual computers and computer accessories. All sections of the computer—input, output, memory, arithmetic, and control—are described in detail. No attempt has been made to include design data or mathematical equations, except where they are absolutely necessary in the explanation of a circuit.

The third purpose of the book—computer troubleshooting—is covered in the final chapters. The selection and use of computer test equipment, an analysis of computer service literature, and practical computer circuit test techniques are stressed. As is the case throughout the book, particular emphasis is placed on integrated circuits, as they relate to computers.

Whether the problem is one of servicing or simply understanding the equipment, this textbook provides the information necessary for technicians to qualify in the field of digital computers.

ABRAHAM MARCUS

JOHN D. LENK

INTRODUCTION

I

In the most technologically advanced civilization in the history of man, his greatest achievement has been, perhaps, the development of the digital computer. In this section we shall examine how the digital computer evolved and how it is used today. Owing to space limitations, this examination must, of necessity, be rather sketchy.

Also, since the "language" of the computer consists of numbers, we shall consider several number systems. Finally, we shall examine a number of electronic circuits widely used by the digital computer.

EVOLUTION OF THE DIGITAL COMPUTER

1

Of all the types of information that man is able to communicate to his fellowmen, the concept of *quantity* is undoubtedly one of the most important. Primitive man probably learned to count on the fingers of his hand. Thus one unit of anything (man, day, animal, etc.) could be represented by one finger. Two units would be represented by two fingers, three by three fingers, and so forth. It becomes clear that his number world was limited to the ten fingers (digits) of both hands.

As his culture became more sophisticated, his greater needs required a more elaborate counting system. He learned to count by means of symbols drawn in sand, scratched on stone, or marked on a piece of bark. Because his counting system now was not limited to the number of his fingers, it was thus greatly expanded.

Before long it became apparent that in order to cope with the growing complexity of his culture man must do more than count. Hence he learned to add, subtract, multiply, and divide. Thus what started as a simple counting process developed into an elaborate calculating system.

A. EARLY FORERUNNERS OF THE COMPUTER

Throughout the centuries man has sought to invent devices that would relieve him of the tedious work of calculation. Two of the earliest such devices are the **abacus**, known to have been used thousands of years ago, and the **soroban**, a variation of the abacus, which was invented by the Japanese about 900 years ago. These instruments are still used in various parts of the world.

The soroban is illustrated in Figure 1-1. It consists of a rectangular wooden frame carrying several parallel rods or wires upon each of which are strung five movable beads. A bar separates the upper bead from the lower ones. Each column of beads represents a position in the decimal system (units, tens, hundreds, etc.).

Each of the four lower beads has a digital value of 1. The upper bead has a digital value of 5. The positional weight of each bead depends on the column in which it is located. The beads count only as they are pushed toward the central bar. Thus, if all the beads are pushed away

Fig. 1-1. Soroban.

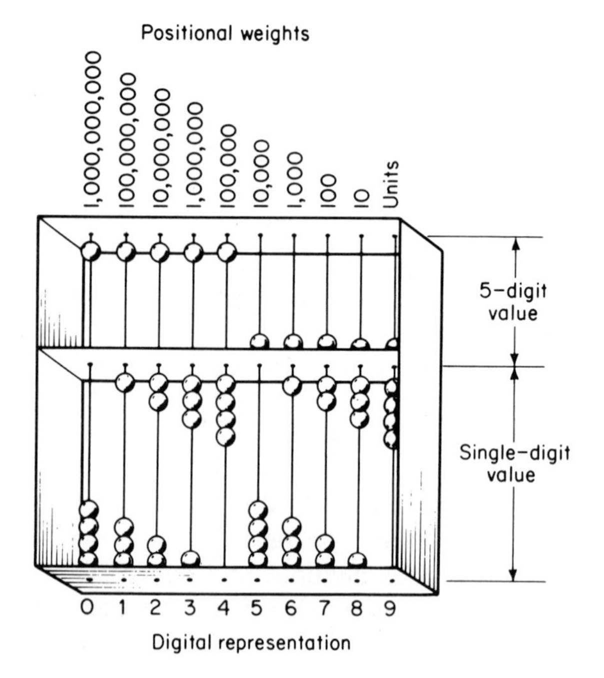

from the bar (down for the lower beads and up for the upper beads), the digital count is zero. For each lower bead pushed up toward the bar the count increases by 1 (multiplied by its positional weight). As each lower bead is pushed down away from the bar the count decreases by 1 (again, multiplied by its positional weight). As the upper bead is pushed down toward the bar, the count is increased by 5 (multiplied by its positional weight). If it is pushed up away from the bar, the count is decreased by 5 (multiplied by its positional weight).

Addition (counting forward) and subtraction (which really consists of counting backward) is performed by manipulating the beads by hand. With this device, a skilled operator may perform addition and subtraction as rapidly as an operator using a modern desk calculator.

In about the year 1642, Blaise Pascal, a French mathematician, devised another type of calculating machine that can be used for addition or subtraction. His device contained a number of ten-toothed cogwheels. The teeth of each wheel are numbered consecutively from 0 to 9. See Figure 1-2.

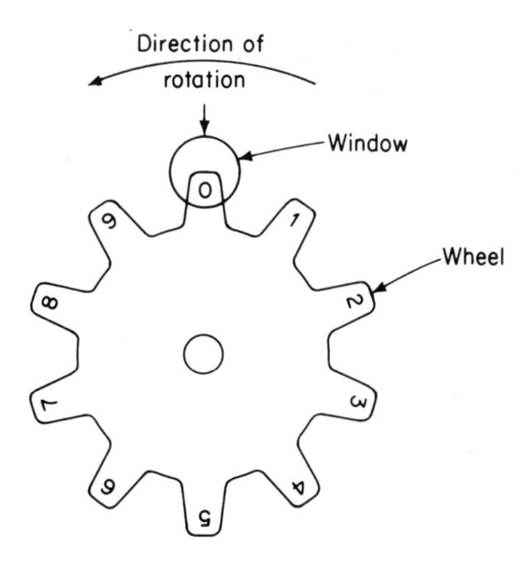

Fig. 1-2. Ten-toothed cogwheel with each tooth representing a digit.

Each time a count is added to the first wheel, which is called the **units** wheel, it is made to turn one-tenth of a revolution in a counter-clockwise direction, thus bringing the next higher digit to the window. Starting from 0, when nine counts are so added, the digit 9 appears;

adding a tenth count brings 0 around again. At the same time, by means of a mechanical linkage, a second similar wheel at its left (called the **tens** wheel) is made to rotate one-tenth of a revolution in a counter-clockwise direction. Thus the digit in the window of the tens wheel changes from 0 to 1. The two wheels now indicate the number 10.

Therefore each time the units wheel passes from 9 to 0, a count, called a **carry**, is added to the tens wheel. Thus the tens wheel rotates one-tenth of a revolution for each complete (ten tenths) revolution of the units wheel. That is, each digit of the tens wheel has a weight of ten unit counts.

In a similar manner, a third wheel (called the **hundreds** wheel) to the left of the tens wheel is made to advance one-tenth of a revolution each time the tens wheel makes a complete revolution. Hence each digit of the hundreds wheel has a weight of 100 unit counts. See Figure 1-3.

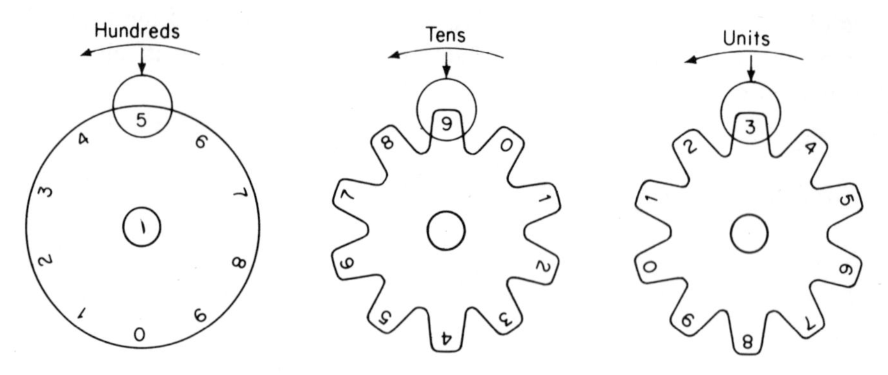

Fig. 1-3. System of three cogwheels indicating a count of 593.

A **thousands** wheel, a **ten-thousands** wheel, and so forth can be added in the same way. Each time a wheel passes from 9 to 0, a carry advances the wheel at its left by one count.

In Figure 1-3, a count of 593 is indicated. Assume that we wish to add 10 more. We can do so by advancing the units wheel ten counts, or one complete revolution. This brings the digit 3 back to the window. But as the units wheel passes from 9 to 0, the carry advances the tens wheel one count from 9 to 0. In so doing, the carry from the tens wheel advances the hundreds wheel one count from 5 to 6. The final figure then stands at 603, an advance of ten counts.

There is an easier way of doing the same thing. Knowing that each digit of the tens wheel has a weight of ten unit counts, all we need to do is advance the tens wheel one count from 9 to 0. Its carry, then, advances the hundreds wheel one count from 5 to 6. The units wheel would be unaffected. Thus the final figure, once again, stands at 603.

Suppose that we wish to add 128 to the original figure of 593. We advance the hundreds wheel one count from 5 to 6. Next, we advance the tens wheel two counts from 9 to 1. In so doing, as the wheel passes from 9 to 0, a carry advances the hundreds wheel from 6 to 7. Then we advance the units wheel eight counts from 3 to 1. Again, as the units wheel passes from 9 to 0, a carry advances the tens wheel from 1 to 2. The final figure, as shown by the digits in the windows, now stands at 721, an advance of 128 counts.

If the machine is to be used for subtraction, the count is backward. That is, the wheels are rotated in a clockwise direction. This time, as a wheel passes from 0 to 9, the wheel immediately to its left is turned **back** one count. This backward cound is called a **borrow**.

To illustrate, suppose that we wish to subtract 78 from the original figure of 593. Turning the tens wheel back seven counts leads us to the digit 2. Note that there is no borrow. Turning the units wheel back eight counts leads us to the digit 5. But as the units wheel passes from 0 to 9, the borrow turns the tens wheel back one count from 2 to 1. Thus the final figure stands at 515.

Here, then, is a counting machine by means of which addition or subtraction may be performed rapidly. Pascal's machine was improved subsequently so that it could be used for multiplication and division as well. (Actually, multiplication involves repeated additions, and division involves repeated subtractions.)

Pascal's calculating machine was the forerunner of our modern desk calculators. Instead of rotating the wheels the required number of counts by hand, appropriately numbered buttons are pressed and the rotation is performed by an electric motor. Also, printing devices, operated by the wheels, are used to print out the final figures.

Let us examine the various components of the calculator that we have just described. First, there is the **input** section, consisting of the various numbered buttons or keys that the operator must press to feed the required information (data) to the machine. Second, there is the **arithmetic** section, consisting of the various wheels and their mechanical linkages whereby addition or subtraction and their carry or borrow functions may be performed.

Third, there is the **control** section, which determines which operation the machine will perform. This control section consists of a button or key that the operator must press and various mechanical linkages that make the wheels rotate in a counterclockwise direction (for addition) or a clockwise direction (for subtraction). These linkages also determine whether there will be repeated additions (for multiplication) or repeated subtractions (for division).

Then there is the **output** section, by means of which the final result is printed on a sheet of paper. Finally, there is the **power** section, which enables the various sections to perform their function. Early calculators obtained their power from a crank turned by the operator. Modern machines obtain their power from electric motors.

Note that the machine also contains a *memory* feature. Assume that we wish to add number B to number A. The appropriate keys are pressed and number A is indicated by the new positions of the various wheels. The positions of the wheels now represent a *memory* whereby number A is **stored** in the machine. Then the keys corresponding to number B are pressed. When the addition operation is performed, the final result, as shown by the positions of the various wheels, represents the sum of A and B.

When it comes to ordinary addition or subtraction, the arithmetic section can perform its operation in about one second (and somewhat longer for multiplication and division). However, each operation requires a much longer period of time because of the need for an operator. He must scan his work sheet, decide what type of operation he desires, and indicate this to the machine by pressing the appropriate control key. He must then decide which numbers to use and feed this information to the machine by pressing the appropriate keys. Finally, he must press the key that applies power to the machine.

All this is not too time-consuming if only a few calculations are involved, but suppose that he is making up the payroll for a large business concern. Thousands of calculations may be required, and the job may take several days. During this time the machine, for the most part, would be idle. How much better it would be if we could eliminate this delay by supplying the necessary information and control to the machine automatically without the need for an operator.

Over 100 years ago, Charles Babbage, a British mathematician, set out to build an elaborate calculating machine, one capable of carrying out any mathematical operation automatically. He failed because of a lack of funds and, primarily, because the technology of his day was not developed enough to produce the high-precision components he required.

Although Babbage died a failure, his ideas lived on and are incorporated in our modern digital computers. One of his main contributions was a method for breaking the bottleneck that we previously discussed. That is, he developed a method for eliminating the human operator from the operation.

Babbage's machine contained three main sections. One was the **store** section, where he entered all instructions (add, subtract, multiply, divide) for each computation, arranged in proper sequence. He also entered there all the data (numbers) required for the various computations, also arranged in proper sequence. Then there was the arithmetic section, which he called the **mill**, where the various computations were performed. Finally, there was the **control** section, which determined the proper transform of instructions and data from the store to the mill.

The instructions and data were stored by means of coded columns of holes punched in a set of cards somewhat similar to the punched cards used by the French inventer Joseph Jacquard in about 1800 for his automatic loom. As the cards were fed into the machine, feeler wires would brush over them. When the holes were in the appropriate pattern, the wires would pass through them and operate the various positions of the control and mill sections. As Babbage visualized it, the machine was to perform, automatically and in sequence, the instructions on the cards, stopping only when the complete series of instructions had been completed.

Assume that the first compilation required the addition of number *A* and number *B*. The wire passing through holes in the first card would actuate the ADD portion of the control section. As a result, the mill section would be prepared to perform addition. The control then would call upon the store to supply the data (numbers *A* and *B*) to the mill. This would be done by means of wires passing through the appropriate holes in the next card. Then the control would call upon the store to supply the next instruction. The mill would be instructed to perform the addition operation.

The addition completed, the control would call upon the store to supply the next instruction—an instruction for the printer to print out the result in the mill. After this instruction was carried out, the control would call upon the store for the next instruction. Thus, by arranging the cards in proper sequence well in advance, the machine would run rapidly through a large series of calculations without the need for a human operator.

B. THE MODERN DIGITAL COMPUTER

This first modern digital computer was built by the engineers of the Bell Telephone Laboratories in 1940. It was a special-purpose type designed to aid the operation of telephone systems. In 1944, Professor Howard Aiken of Harvard built the first digital computer designed to handle a variety of mathematical problems.

Like Babbage's machine, these computers had an external **storage** section consisting of punched cards wherein were stored all the data and instructions, arranged in sequence. They also had **arithmetic** and **control** sections. The **output** section was an electric typewriter, which, upon instruction from the control section, would type out the results of the computations.

Unlike Babbage's machine, which operated mechanically, these computers were electrically operated. Instead of gears and mechanical linkages, they used electric relays, electromagnetic clutches, etc., for the arithmetic and control sections. As a result, these computers could function at a much higher speed than the Babbage machine.

The step-by-step instructions that tell the computer what to do is called a **program**. In 1945, the mathematician Dr. John von Neumann proposed that this program be stored in an internal memory instead of using the external punched-card system. Thus, for example, the complete instruction for an ADD operation could be stored in this internal memory. Then, when the computer was instructed to perform the ADD operation and supplied with the necessary data (also stored in the memory), the control section would automatically search the internal memory for the various consecutive steps and data to perform the operation.

In 1946, J. W. Manchly and J. P. Eckert of the University of Pennsylvania constructed a digital computer, called ENIAC, which used faster-acting electron tubes instead of electric relays in the arithmetic and control sections. Soon a series of computers was built that contained both the internal memory to store data and instructions and electron tubes for the arithmetic and control sections. With these improvements the computer was speeded up so that it could perform an operation in microseconds (a microsecond is one-millionth of a second).

By 1958, digital computers were using transistors instead of electron tubes. These computers were smaller, required less power, and needed no elaborate heat-removal systems. The most modern computers today use microelectronic circuits (integrated circuits) that are even smaller than transistor-type circuits. The result, then, is that the computers are much smaller in physical size. Also, they are faster in their data-processing capabilities. Modern computers are able to perform an operation in nanoseconds (a nanosecond is one-billionth of a second).

Figure 1-4 is a photograph of a modern digital computer system.

Fig. 1-4. RCA Spectra 70 Computer and associated equipment. (Courtesy of RCA.)

Although the digital computer is a direct descendant of the familiar adding machine, it would be wrong to consider it only as an elaborate calculating machine. The computer can, of course, perform calculations at fantastic speeds, but the digital computer also has built into it the capability of making **logical decisions**, that is, decisions based on **yes-or-no**, or **true-or-false**, answers. Because of this capability, the computer is able to perform a large variety of **data-processing** operations, such as the sorting, selecting, matching, merging, classifying, and analyzing of all types of data.

All modern digital computers contain the same five basic sections:

1. The **input** section.
2. The **internal memory** section.
3. The **control** section.
4. The **arithmetic** section.
5. The **output** section.

The memory, control, and arithmetic sections form the **control processing unit** of the computer. The input and output sections comprise the peripheral portions of the computer. This arrangement is shown in Figure 1-5.

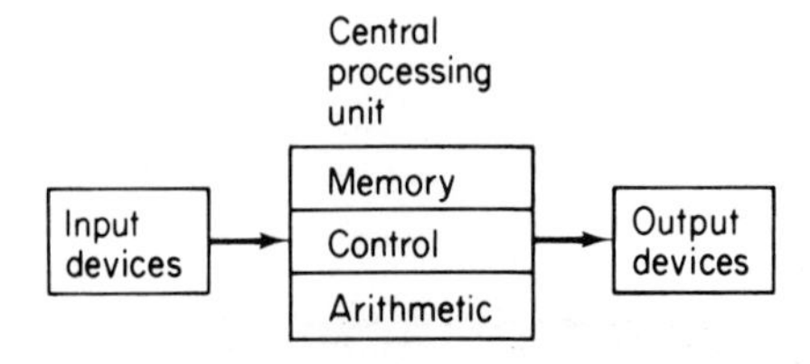

Fig. 1-5. Block diagram of the digital computer system, showing the basic sections.

The data to be processed may be of several types: numbers formed by groups of digits; words formed by groups of alphabetic letters; symbols such as punctuation marks and dollar signs; or combinations of all three types.

The input section accepts the raw data and converts them into a *machine language* that the computer can understand. These converted data are stored at certain locations (called **addresses**) in the memory section of the computer, where the program, a set of instructions in sequential form that indicates how the computer is to process these data, is also stored.

The control section, always acting under these instructions, directs the transfer of appropriate data from the memory section to the arithmetic section to perform the appropriate operations (mathematical and logical) upon the data it contains.

Having completed the operation, the arithmetic section is directed by the control section to store the result at a specific address in the memory section. Finally, the control section directs the memory section to transfer this result to the output section. It is the function of the output section to translate the result from the machine language of the computer to the language of its human operator and to display it to him.

In the world outside the computer, information is conveyed by means of numbers and symbols. Inside the computer, information is conveyed by electric pulses.

Thus the ten digits of the decimal number system can be represented by separate electric pulses having ten different and discrete voltage levels. Alphabetic letters may be coded into number equivalents (for example, $A = 1$, $B = 2, \ldots, Z = 26$) and these numbers may then be converted to pulses of equivalent voltage levels in the computer. Similarly, symbols may be coded as numbers and these numbers may then be converted to equivalent pulses.

The difficulty with such a system is that it uses ten different digits and thus requires pulses of different voltage levels in the computer for conveying information from one section to another. Not only does this make for an excessively complicated machine, but the necessity for distinguishing among the ten different voltage levels introduces a great chance for error. For example, any slight electrical disturbance within the machine could produce changes in these levels.

Accordingly, digital computers use pulses having only two discrete voltage levels. For example, the computer may use a pulse having a 5-V (volt) level and a pulse having a 0-V level (which, in effect, means the absence of a pulse). Thus the chance for error between a pulse and no pulse is much less than the chance of error among pulses of ten different levels. The information is converted into equivalent combinations of pulses and no pulses for use within the computer.

A system of this type is known as a **binary** system, that is, a system using two states—pulse and no pulse. If we indicate a pulse by the digit 1 and no pulse by the digit 0, the system becomes a two-digit (binary) number system. (The binary number system is discussed fully in Chapter 3.)

The Morse International Telegraph Code used by radio telegraphers is a familiar type of binary system. Here, the two states are represented by a short pulse called a **dot** (·) and a long pulse called a **dash** (–). Numbers, letters, and symbols are converted into combinations of dots and dashes. Information is exchanged by means of these combinations of short and long pulses.

For example, the letter A is represented by · – (dot, dash), the digit 3 by · · · – – (dot, dot, dot, dash, dash), and a comma by – – · · – – (dash, dash, dot, dot, dash, dash). Even instructions may be sent by this code. For example, the instruction "send more slowly" is first changed to the code letters QRS and then converted to – – · – · – · · · · (dash, dash, dot, dash, space, dot, dash, dot, space, dot, dot, dot).

The machine language of the computer, then, is binary in nature. Information is converted to combinations of pulse (binary digit 1) and no pulse (binary digit 0) according to some code. Different computers use many different codes. However, all digital computers in common use have the same binary characteristics.

Digital computers fall into one of two general categories—the **special-purpose computer** and the **general-purpose computer**. Special-purpose computers are designed for a particular type of problem, such as handling airline ticket sales or regulating traffic. The program for the solution of a problem to be solved is wired permanently into the machine. The only variable, then, is the data required for the solution of the problem. The same problem is solved over and over, using a different set of data for each solution.

The general-purpose computer, on the other hand, is able to handle a large variety of problems. Both the program and the pertinent data are *read in* to the machine and stored in its memory. If a new type of problem is to be solved, a new program and set of data are read in. Thus the computer is not limited to only one type of problem.

The special-purpose computer generally is smaller and lighter. Hence it may be used where space and weight are limited, for example, in aircraft guidance systems. Where space and weight are not limiting factors, the general-purpose digital computer is usually used because of its greater flexibility.

C. THE ANALOG COMPUTER

Whereas the digital computer operates on information that is presented in discrete steps, the **analog computer** operates on information that is continuously changing. To understand this more clearly, let us consider, for example, a computer that is counting a number of objects passing before it on a movable belt. Each time an object passes, a pulse is produced, causing the counter to advance abruptly one count. This is an example of a digital device.

A room thermostat, on the other hand, is an analog device. The bending of the bimetallic strip in the thermostat is analogous to the temperature of the room. That is, the higher the temperature, the more the strip bends. As the temperature falls, the strip tends to straighten out. The temperature changes gradually, not in discrete steps. Hence the curvature of the strip changes gradually. Likewise, the speedometer in an automobile continually computes the auto's speed as it moves. Thus the speedometer is an analog computer of sorts.

The analog computer can solve mathematical equations by setting up electrical circuits that are analogous to the equations. As a result of these circuits, voltages and currents are produced at levels proportional to the values of the equations. Changes in the variables of the mathematical equations can be duplicated by changes in the values of the electrical components, which cause corresponding changes in the voltages or currents.

Within the computer, these voltages or currents may be manipulated by various amplifiers, voltage dividers, electromechanical devices, etc., to produce the required output. The output may consist of one or more voltages indicated on meters or display tubes, or else the output may be the movement of a pen over a chart to produce a graph showing various numeric relationships. Physical problems that can be converted to mathematical equations may be solved in this way.

In the analog computer the incoming information produces an immediate corresponding output. In the digital computer, on the other hand, the incoming information must first be stored in a memory and then processed in the discrete steps of the program to produce the proper output. Hence the analog computer is faster-acting. Since the analog computer can furnish a continuous solution to a changing problem, the analog computer is well suited to work in *real time*. This is especially important in certain operations, such as missile guidance, for example, where changes take place at an extremely rapid rate.

The digital computer, however, has a number of advantages over the analog computer. The digital computer is more accurate and has both logic and memory systems. Also, the digital computer is more flexible since it can solve different types of problems by the substitution of a different program. In the analog computer, the wiring must be changed for each new problem. Furthermore, if the problem to be solved becomes more complex, the digital computer requires only a more complex program, whereas the analog computer requires a more complex (and usually larger) machine.

In recent times, the analog and digital computers have been combined into a single system called the *hybrid computer*. Here the complementary capabilities of both types are joined, producing a system that is capable of solving real-time problems with great accuracy.

HOW THE DIGITAL COMPUTER IS USED

2

Basically, the digital computer is a data-processing machine. The digital computer can perform mathematical operations (addition, subtraction, etc.) and logical operations (analysis, sorting, rearrangement, etc.) upon the data fed to it, producing new data resulting from these operations. There is hardly an area of human endeavor where the computer is not used.

Digital computers are used to keep track of ships at sea, trains on rails, and planes in the air. Computers are used to coordinate far-flung radar defenses and to regulate traffic in the streets. A few of the other uses include making weather predictions, routing long-distance telephone calls, solving commercial and scientific problems, controlling industrial processes, and storing and rapidly retrieving information.

The computer is able to store tremendous amounts of information in its memory with practically instantaneous recall. Digital computers can perform mathematical computations hundreds of thousands of times as rapidly as the human mind and with far fewer errors. More significant, the computer can make logical decisions.

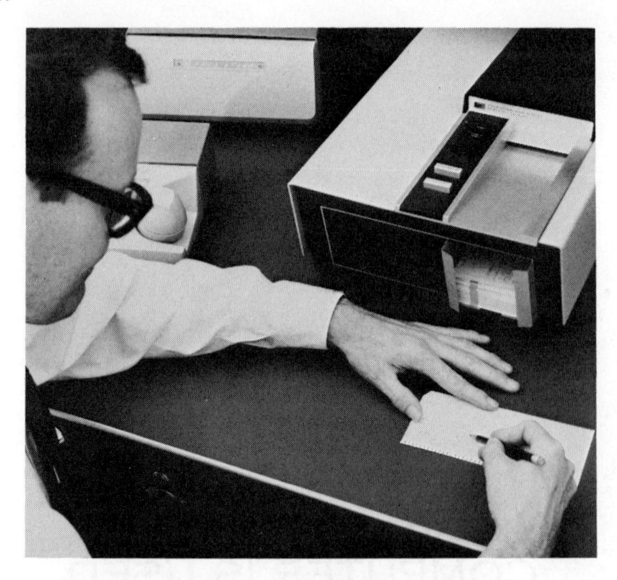

Fig. 2-1. Portable-size optical reader. (Hewlett-Packard). Optical reader reads marked cards. New desk-top optical mark reader from Hewlett-Packard reads standard tabulating cards. Cards may be marked simply with ordinary soft lead pencil. Keypunch bottlenecks are bypassed.

It is little wonder, then, that we tend to give the computer mystical powers, calling it an "electronic brain" with potentialities as great or greater than the human brain. Actually, it is nothing of the kind. The computer is a tool to be used by man as he sees fit and under his direction. Just as the steam engine, gasoline engine, and electric motor are tools to be used to extend man's mechanical ability, so the computer is a tool to be used to extend his mental ability.

The computer's prodigious memory need not fill us with awe. We long have had books that also can store unlimited amounts of information. As for the computer's calculating ability, we are quite accustomed to the various types of adding and calculating machines used in business offices. Nor is there anything mystical in the fact that the computer can calculate faster than the human brain. The power crane, for example, can lift loads thousands of times as great as human muscle can.

Even the computer's decision-making ability becomes commonplace upon examination. Since these decisions are based upon numbers, they are quantitative rather than qualitative. That is, the computer can be directed to compare two numbers and decide if one is larger than the other, or the computer may decide whether the result of a series of

Fig. 2-2. Computerized calculator provides instant answers to complex scientific and engineering problems (Hewlett-Packard).

calculations is a positive or negative number. In the final analysis, from a technician's view, the computer can decide only if an electrical pulse is present or absent.

The digital computer must be told exactly how to make any decision. It is up to the human operator to decide how to interpret this decision. Based upon the decisions made by the machine, the operator can decide whether to add more or less chemicals to an industrial process, whether to give the order to fire a rocket, or even whether a certain scientific theory is true.

For an example of the decision-making property of a digital computer, consider its use for inventory-control purposes. The operator reads into the memory of the machine the last-known quantity of each item of the inventory. He then reads in the total number of each item that has since been taken out of stock. As the computer processes each item (upon instructions from the operator), it subtracts from the last-known number for each particular item the quantity taken from stock. For a particular item the computer then compares the result with a certain minimum-quantity number, which had been decided upon by the operator. Should the remaining quantity be less than the minimum quantity number, the machine signals the operator that the stock of this item must be replenished.

Therefore the digital computer must be told exactly what it is to do by the human operator, who must carefully examine the problem to be solved, decide upon the method of solution, and prepare a series of logical steps (in sequence), called a *program*, to effect the solution. This program, together with the appropriate data, is stored in the computer's memory. Then, upon a signal from the operator, the computer goes to work. Each step of the program is carried out automatically, using the appropriate data. When the program is completed, the results are printed out for the operator to use.

The necessity for preparing a computer program is a most important by-product of the operation since it requires a close and logical examination of the problem. This leads to greater insight into the problem itself and to better planning techniques. Many commercial and industrial operations have been streamlined simply because certain inefficient methods were found when a computer program was written to describe the operation.

A. COMMERCIAL APPLICATIONS

Within the past few decades, commercial enterprises have grown tremendously, both in number and complexity. The paper work—payroll, inventory, accounting, etc.—needed to keep pace with this growth is staggering. And if we add to this the paper work of the business of government, the total would be overwhelming were it not for the help of the digital computer. More computers are used for business purposes than for any other application.

There are manufacturing plants today where almost the entire operation is run by computers. These computers control billing, shipping, and warehousing. Computers order materials as required and write the checks to pay for them. Based upon incoming orders, computers even decide what to produce and in what quantity.

In commercial applications, the computer must deal with an enormous quantity of data, but the number of operations to be performed is generally small. That is, similar operations are done over and over, using a different set of data for each operation. We have already considered an example of this in the inventory-control operation.

As another example, consider the problem of making up the payroll for a plant employing several thousand employees. For each employee, the basic hours of work must be added and multiplied by the basic rate of pay per hour. To this must be added the product of overtime hours worked, multiplied by the overtime rate of pay per hour. The sum is the gross pay for that employee.

From this figure various deductions, such as federal and state withholding taxes, social security and unemployment insurance deductions, and deductions for various other purposes, must be subtracted. This is the net pay. Then the various figures must be entered into the company's records and onto an employee's pay slip. Finally, a check must be drawn for the employee.

The making up of such a payroll for several thousand employees may take a team of clerks several days. The digital computer can perform the entire operation in several hours.

The impact of the computer on the banking industry is no less dramatic. Millions of checks are drawn every day. These checks must be sorted and sent through a network of central clearing houses where they are sorted again and sent to their banks of origin. There, the amount of each check is deducted from the account of the drawer. Without the aid of computers, teams of clerks are required at the various points along the route to handle each check. So great is the volume of checks that banks were having great difficulty finding sufficient clerical help. With the aid of the digital computer and various types of associated sorting machines, the task may be done quickly by a relatively small clerical staff. Along the bottom of each check is printed a series of numbers in magnetic ink that can be "read" by the computer and the sorting devices. These numbers are the account numbers against which the checks are drawn and a routing-transit symbol that indicates where the check is to be sent for collection.

When the check is deposited, a clerk types the amount of the check along the bottom, using the same type of magnetic ink. This is the only human operation and from there on the machines take over. All the checks are quickly sorted into bundles according to their routing-transit symbols. At the clearing house, the checks again are sorted according to the number of the symbol that indicates the appropriate bank. There, the computer subtracts the amount of the check from the account and prints out a balance.

B. SCIENTIFIC AND ENGINEERING APPLICATIONS

Mathematics is the "language" used in the solution of scientific and engineering problems. To solve such a problem, the language is first translated into appropriate mathematical equations. Then quantities are substituted for the variables in the equation and these equations are solved by mathematical means. The advantage of the digital computer lies in the fact that the machine can perform these mathematical operations many times more rapidly and with fewer errors than the human mind can.

For commercial purposes, the computer generally uses a great deal of data to perform relatively few operations over and over again. For scientific and engineering purposes, however, the computer generally uses only a small amount of data. The operations, on the other hand, are many, usually requiring a separate program for each operation.

As an example of how the computer is used to solve a scientific problem, assume that you wish to find how far a freely falling body will fall in 5 seconds. Scientists have found that the equation for the solution of such a problem is $d = g \times t^2/2$, where d is the distance in feet that the body will fall, g is the acceleration due to gravity pulling the body to earth (which is equal to 32 ft/sec for each second of fall), and t is the time in seconds. Substituting the various quantities for the variables of the equation we get

$$d = 32 \times \frac{5^2}{2} = 400 \text{ ft.}$$

If we were to use a computer to solve this problem, the program of instructions would appear as follows:

1. Multiply t by t. (This produces t^2.)
2. Multiply the product by g. (This produces $g \times t^2$.)
3. Divide the product by 2. (This produces $g \times t^2/2$.)

The computer would follow these instructions sequentially, substituting the appropriate numeric quantities for the variables.

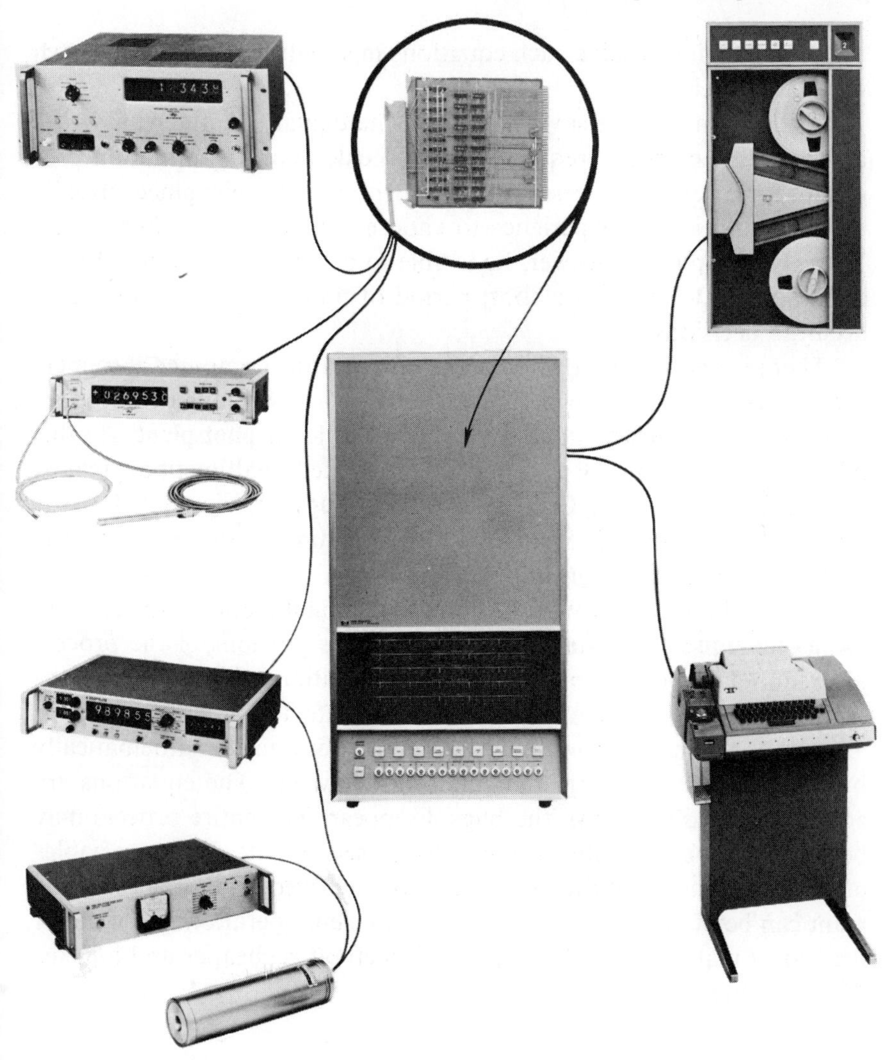

Fig. 2-3. Hewlett-Packard 2116A Instrumentation computer. Interfaces to measuring and recording instruments through buffered, standard I/O cards, with priority interrupt.

Of course, the example shown here is extremely simple and no one would bother using a computer for its solution. But scientific and engineering problems frequently involve much more complicated equations, the solution of which, using paper and pencil, may be long and tedious. For example, the equations involved in sending a manned vehicle to the moon are so complicated that it would take a team of mathematicians many years to solve them. The digital computer, on the other hand, can solve such equations in a matter of days, and much more accurately.

Aside from its time-saving features, the digital computer has other advantages. Engineers frequently must decide upon the optimum procedure for a certain process. Without a computer, the engineer usually draws upon his own experience to choose among several alternatives. With the computer, however, he is able to compare a large number of alternative procedures in a short period of time, thus producing more accurate decisions.

There is another area where engineers find the computer extremely useful. When required to design a plant for a new industrial process, they frequently erect a small-scale model, called a **pilot plant**. As this pilot plant is operated, various unanticipated malfunctions (called *bugs*) usually show up. Only after all the bugs are eliminated is the full-scale plant built. The building and operation of the pilot plant is both costly and time-consuming.

To avoid the necessity for erecting such a pilot plant, engineers may use a technique called **simulation**. The various portions of the process are reduced to equivalent mathematical equations. The interrelationships among these equations (which simulate the interrelationships among the various portions of the process) are examined mathematically by a computer. It is there that the bugs show up. The equations are adjusted accordingly until the bugs disappear. The entire process may be tested by the computer, using different sets of data for the variables of the equations, until the best results are achieved. Then the full-scale plant can be built with the assistance of efficient operation and without the fear of malfunction. Obviously, this method is cheaper and quicker than building a pilot plant.

C. INDUSTRIAL CONTROL

Another area where the digital computer is widely used is in the field of automatic industrial control. Consider an automated plant such as a petroleum refinery. At many points along the process, special devices, called **sensors**, are installed to measure the conditions or state of the process variable at these points. Any deviation from normal must be corrected instantly in order to keep the process flowing without interruption and to ensure that the output from the plant is of proper quality.

The output from each sensor is converted to a corresponding signal (usually electric or pneumatic) that is sent to a **recorder-controller**. This device prints a continuous record of the condition or state of the process variable and compares it with the normal value (called the **set point**) expected at that point. Any deviation from normal produces another signal (again, either electric or pneumatic) that corresponds to the amount of deviation and its phase, that is, whether the condition or state of the process variable is above or below the value indicated by the set point. This signal is sent to an **actuator**, such as an electromagnetic or pneumatic valve, which restores the process variable to its normal value.

The difficulty is that there usually is a complex interrelationship among the process variables. This means that if one variable changes, it usually affects all the other variables. Thus, if one variable changes, the set point of all the controllers should be readjusted to compensate for these changes. So complex is the interrelationship, however, that even an experienced operator cannot make all the readjustments required for the most profitable operation.

It is here that the digital computer comes into use. The signals from the sensors are converted to corresponding numeric quantities that are fed to the computer. Because of its high speed, the computer is able to calculate the effect of every change on the interrelationships among the variables and quickly produce output signals that adjust the set point of each controller to produce the most profitable and efficient operation.

Actually, the computer usually replaces the recorder-controller altogether, continually printing out the condition or state of each process variable, storing the various set points in its memory, and adjusting them as required. It then compares the input signals from the sensors with these readjusted set points and sends appropriate signals to the various actuators.

D. INFORMATION STORAGE AND RETRIEVAL

We are in the midst of an information explosion. Books, articles, reports, etc., are being produced at such a rate that it has been estimated that man's store of information is doubling every 8 years. Surely no one mind can cope with this deluge.

Fig. 2-4. Hewlett-Packard Model 2120A disc operating system with 2100A computer and 7900A moving head disc. Disc storage techniques provide rapid access to information stored for use by computers.

The digital computer gives promise of easing this problem. Entire volumes, articles, reports, abstracts, and even drawings and photographs may be transformed by microphotography to film rolls, glass plates, or plastic cards at the rate of about 10,000 document pages/ft^2. An index may be made of these articles and stored in the memory of the computer, located at some central point. Upon a telephoned information request from a laboratory or study in any part of the country or world, the computer can then search its memory for the location of the pertinent information. It next will seek out the information from the files of films, plates, or cards. Within seconds, an enlarged copy of the required pages or illustrations is available.

Let us consider an example of how such a system might work. A complete library of medical case histories could be set up at some medical center. An ailing patient at his doctor's office would be examined for the significant symptoms together with tests for blood pressure, body temperature, etc., which would be transmitted to a computer at the medical center. The computer would then search its memory and its associated medical files for corresponding case histories. Within seconds the doctor would receive a complete diagnosis of the case, a suggested course of treatment, and, perhaps, a prognosis of the case.

Another example: An attorney seeking to draw up a brief on a certain point of law would telephone to a computer (located at some central law library) a list of significant words and phrases dealing with the case at issue. Within seconds, the computer would reply with abstracts of all laws and rulings upon this point of law, complete with a full list of annotations.

Such information centers are in the process of being set up. There remain, however, a number of problems that must be solved before such systems become fully operative. The making of abstracts and translations from foreign works is a slow and tedious task. So, too, is the making of a comprehensive index. However, a start has already been made whereby the computer will take over these tasks. We may confidently expect a good deal of progress in the near future.

E. THE FUTURE FOR THE DIGITAL COMPUTER

No one can, with any certainty, predict the long-range future for the digital computer. Each day new uses are found and these new applications suggest other new ones. However, present-day research indicates that certain new applications are due in the near future. Some of them have been indicated in the previous section.

Already, computers have been set up at central points to be used by a number of subscribers on a **time-sharing** basis. This enables individuals or concerns that cannot afford to rent or buy a computer to avail themselves nevertheless of the services of the machine. An input device, such as a modified electric typewriter, is set up at the location of each subscriber. These input devices are connected to the computer by telephone or teletype lines or by a microwave radio link. The computer quickly processes the data sent it and returns the answers by the same lines. We may well see networks of such subscriber-computer setups covering the entire country or, perhaps, the world.

A computer can be used to regulate automobile traffic in a large city. Sensors are able to measure the density of traffic at many points and transmit these data to the computer. The computer then determines alternative routes where the traffic is lighter and indicates these alternative routes (by operating regulatory devices such as traffic lights) to direct traffic along the routes. Such traffic systems are already in

Fig. 2-5. Hewlett-Packard Model 5050A digital recorder. Unit prints 18 characters per line at rates up to 20 lines per second.

operation in a number of cities. We may expect to find such a system in every large city.

As another example of the future use of computers, a distant subscriber may dial a central library to indicate a book that he would like to read. At the library, a computer would search its memory and store of files and, within seconds, the book would appear, page by page, on a television screen in the subscriber's home.

The language barrier is a large obstacle to the rapid exchange of information required by our shrinking world. As a start in removing this obstacle, attempts are being made to use the computer for automatic language translation. Much remains to be done before this becomes a practical reality, but substantial progress has been made and we may confidently expect a measure of success in the near future.

A good deal of work is being done to establish better communication between man and the computer and from computer to computer. Computer technology has developed so rapidly that no common computer language has been produced. Instead, each computer has its own language. Descriptions of various computer languages are included in the Glossary. In the early stages of development, computer languages were so different from human languages that direct communication between man and machine was well nigh impossible. However, pseudo-languages have been developed that can be recognized by both man and the computer. At present, computers have nearly reached the point where they can be instructed and can reply in plain English. The time is not far off when an operator will be able to address the computer with the spoken word and receive its reply in kind.

As computers are put into direct communication with other computers by means of telephone, teletype, or radio, the range of all will be extended since each computer will thus have access to the information stored in the memory of the others. Also, most of the correspondence between business firms (bills, statements, checks, etc.) will be eliminated since the computer of one firm will be able to handle all such matters directly with the computer of the other firm.

Work is being done at present on optical scanning devices that would enable computers to read a printed page. In this way, whole libraries might be transferred to the computer's memory. Indeed, computers may become the repository for all information.

Considerable progress is being made in the reduction of computer size. The first electronic computer was a bulky giant containing approximately 18,000 electron tubes, weighing 30 tons, and occupying about 1500 ft^2 of floor space. A tremendous quantity of electrical power was required to operate the machine, mainly to heat the filaments of the tubes, and additional electrical power was needed to operate the cooling devices required to remove the heat so produced.

With the advent of the transistor, the computer shrank in size. Not only is the transistor much smaller than the tube it replaces, but, since it has no filament to be heated, the transistor requires much less electrical power and produces much less heat. Thus there is no need for an elaborate cooling system.

With the development of microelectronic circuits (integrated circuits, or ICs), the computer shrank still further. For example, the General Electric Model A-212 Computer is about the size of a standard typewriter, weighs about 18 lbs, and can perform approximately 160,000 operations/sec.

As the computer shrinks in size, so does its cost. The day may come when all household chores—cleaning, washing, cooking, baking, etc.—will be done by a small computer hidden away in a closet.

NUMBER SYSTEMS

3

The decimal number system is generally used in the world outside the digital computer. Inside the computer, the binary number system is used most often. Therefore, to understand the language of the computer, it becomes necessary to examine number systems in general and the binary number system in particular. In addition, we shall discuss such number systems as the octal, hexadecimal, binary-coded decimal (BCD), and alphanumeric systems. It should be noted that these systems are of more concern to the computer programmer than the technician. However, the technician should have an understanding of the number systems, since they may be needed when performing a checkout of the computer.

A. THE DECIMAL NUMBER SYSTEM

The **decimal** number system uses ten Arabic-Indian symbols, or **digits** (derived from the Latin *digitus*, meaning "finger"). These digits are 0, 1, 2, 3, 4, 5, 6, 7, 8, and 9, in order of ascending or increasing value. In any number system, the number of different digits that may be used is called the **base** or **radix**. Thus in our decimal system, which uses ten digits, the radix is 10.

Each digit has a **digit value**. Standing by itself, the digit 3, for example, has a value of three units. However, when the digit is associated with other digits to form a multidigit number, it also has a **positional weight** in addition to its unit value. The positional weight of the digit at the extreme right of the number (the **least significant digit**, abbreviated LSD) is unity, or 1.

The digit immediately to the left of the LSD has a positional weight that is ten times as great. Thus in the number 43, for example, the digit 3 (the LSD) has a value of 3 and a positional weight of 1. Thus it represents 3×1, or 3 units. The digit 4 has a value of 4 and a positional weight of 10. Thus it represents 4×10, or 40 units. The total number then represents $3 + 40$, or 43 units.

Each time we move one position to the left, the positional weight is ten times the positional weight of the previous position. Thus a digit in the position immediately to the left of the **tens** position has a weight of 100, a digit in the position immediately to the left of the **hundreds** position has a weight of 1000, and so forth. The digit occupying the extreme left position has the greatest positional weight and is called the **most significant digit** (MSD).

Since the positional weights increase tenfold each time we move left one position, we may represent these positional weights in ascending order of the powers of 10. Thus the LSD has a positional weight of 10^0 ($=1$). The next digit to its left has a positional weight of 10^1 ($=10$), the next a positional weight of 10^2 ($=100$), the next a positional weight of 10^3 ($=1000$), and so forth. A partial table showing the positional weights of the ten digits of the decimal system is shown in Figure 3-1.

As each unit is added, the value of the digit in the units position is increased by 1. When the digit 9 is reached, the addition of another unit changes the 9 to a 0 and a **carry** is created, which raises the value of the digit in the tens position by 1. Then the process is continued in the units position with a carry to the tens position each time the units digit changes from 9 to 0.

Similarly, each time the tens digit changes from 9 to 0 (as a result of a carry from the units column), a carry is added to the digit in the hundreds position, raising the value of the latter digit by 1. The process

		Digital positions						
Positional weight	Powers of ten	10^6	10^5	10^4	10^3	10^2	10^1	10^0
	Decimal value	1,000,000	100,000	10,000	1,000	100	10	1
Digit values		0	0	0	0	0	0	0
		1	1	1	1	1	1	1
		2	2	2	2	2	2	2
		3	3	3	3	3	3	3
		4	4	4	4	4	4	4
		5	5	5	5	5	5	5
		6	6	6	6	6	6	6
		7	7	7	7	7	7	7
		8	8	8	8	8	8	8
		9	9	9	9	9	9	9

Fig. 3-1. Partial table showing the positional weights of the ten digits of the decimal number system.

continues with a carry to the digit in the thousands position (raising its value by 1) each time the hundreds digit changes from 9 to 0, and so forth.

So far, we have been considering whole numbers, or **integers**. When we write a decimal **fraction** (that is, a value less than 1) we place a dot, called a **radix point** (in the decimal system it is called a **decimal point**), between the integers and the fraction to separate the two sets of digits. Then each digit of the fraction has a positional weight that is one-tenth the weight of the position to its left.

For example, consider the decimal fraction 0.5273. The digit 0 has a positional weight of unity, or 1. (Note that the digit 0 in the number system does not mean "nothing." It is a digit just as the other digits, except that its value is zero.) The digit 5 has a positional weight of $\frac{1}{10}$. We may write this in terms of **negative** powers of 10 as 10^{-1}. The digit 2 has a positional weight of $\frac{1}{100}$, or 10^{-2}. The digit 7 has a positional weight of $\frac{1}{1000}$, or 10^{-3}. The digit 3 has a positional weight of 1/10,000, or 10^{-4}.

Thus our fraction becomes

$$(0 \times 10^0) + (5 \times 10^{-1}) + (2 \times 10^{-2}) + (7 \times 10^{-3}) + (3 \times 10^{-4}),$$

which is equal to

$$0 + \frac{5}{10} + \frac{2}{100} + \frac{7}{1000} + \frac{3}{10{,}000}.$$

Solving, we get

$$(0 \times 10{,}000) + (5 \times 1000) + (2 \times 100) + (7 \times 10) + (3 \times 1)$$
$$= \frac{5273}{10{,}000},$$

which is equal to 0.5273.

We may have numbers that contain both integers and fractions. Thus, for example, the mixed number 302.95 really means

$$(3 \times 10^2) + (0 \times 10^1) + (2 \times 10^0) + (9 \times 10^{-1}) + (5 \times 10^{-2}).$$

Note that each digit has a positional weight that is ten times that of the digit at its right and one-tenth that of the digit at its left. Powers of 10 are used because this is the decimal system with a radix of 10. If any other system with a different radix were used, the changes would be in terms of the powers of that radix.

For example, there is a **duodecimal** system with a radix of 12 that employs 12 digits. There also are systems such as the **octal** system with a radix of 8, the **quinary** system with a radix of 5, the **binary** system with a radix of 2, and so forth. Keep in mind, however, that the basic principles governing all number systems are the same regardless of radix.

In the following paragraphs we shall discuss the basic arithmetic functions (addition, subtraction, multiplication, and division) using the decimal system. This may seem quite simple to the average technician. However, the material should be studied since it forms the basis for understanding the operation of circuits and components in the arithmetic section of a digital computer (such as the operation of adders, registers, and accumulators).

1. Decimal Addition

The addition process is, in reality, a counting process. Assume that we wish to add 278 to 637. The number to which we add (637 in this example) is called the **augend**. The number that is to be added (278) is called the **addend**. The total of the two is called the **sum**. A plus sign (+) is used to indicate the process of addition.

What we mean is that we are to count 278 beyond 637. In making this count, we add a unit to the LSD of the augend (7) 278 times. Each time the digit in that position reaches the highest digit of the system (9), an additional count changes it to the lowest digit (0) and the count starts up the scale again. Every time the digit changes from 9 to 0, a count, called a carry, is added to the digit next to it in the tens position, advancing it one digit. Thus as a carry from the units position is added to the 3 in the tens position, it is changed to 4.

This process continues, and when the digit in the tens position reaches 9, the next carry changes it back to 0, just as in the units position. As this change takes place, a carry is produced, which advances the digit in the hundreds position (6) to the next higher value (7). This action continues until the full 278 counts have been made.

An easier method is counting the digits in each position separately, taking into account any carry. Thus in the units position we count eight units from 7. This brings us to the digit 5, with a carry as we passed from 9 to 0. In the tens position, the 3 has been changed to 4 by the carry from the previous position. Counting ahead 7 brings us to 1, with a carry as we passed from 9 to 0. In the hundreds position, the 6 has been changed to 7 by the carry from the previous position. Counting ahead 2 brings us to 9.

The final result is then $(9 \times 100) + (1 \times 10) + (5 \times 1)$, or 915. This is usually shown as

$$
\begin{array}{rl}
{\scriptstyle +1\ +1\ \ } & \text{(carry)} \\
6\ 3\ 7 & \text{(augend)} \\
+\,2\ 7\ 8 & \text{(addend)} \\
\hline
9\ 1\ 5 & \text{(sum).}
\end{array}
$$

For practical purposes, outside the computer, we do not go through the tedious process of counting for each digit. However, most addition in computer circuits is done by counting (since a computer can count at very high speeds).

2. Decimal Subtraction

In the process of subtraction, we really count backward. Thus in subtracting, say, 3 from 8, we count backward three units, reaching 5. The number from which we subtract (8, in this example) is called the **minuend**, the number subtracted (3) is called the **subtrahend**, and the resulting number (5) is called the **difference**. A minus sign (—) is used to indicate the process of subtraction.

When dealing with multidigit numbers, each digit of the subtrahend is subtracted from its corresponding digit of the minuend, starting with the LSD and proceeding in sequence to the MSD. If the value of the subtrahend digit is greater than that of the minuend as the backward count goes from 0 to 9, a **borrow** is taken from the digit of the minuend immediately to the left, reducing that digit by 1. Thus

```
  -1     (Borrow)
  826    (minuend)
- 375    (subtrahend)
-----
  451    (difference).
```

If the subtrahend is greater than the minuend, the position of the two are reversed and the subtraction takes place as before, only this time the difference is a negative quantity. Thus, if we were to subtract, say, 826 from 375, the procedure would be as follows:

```
  -1     (Borrow)
   7
 ┌>826   (subtrahend)
 └>375   (minuend)
-----
 -451    (difference).
```

There is another method for subtraction that uses a form of addition (adding numbers of unlike signs). For example, subtracting 23 from 54 is the same as adding +54 and −23. In both cases, the result is +31. This method uses the device of **complements** and often appears in digital computer circuits.

In every number system there are two types of complements. One is the **radix-minus-1 complement**, which is formed by subtracting each digit of the number under consideration from the radix minus 1 of the number system. In the decimal system (where the radix is 10), the radix-minus-1 complement is called the **nine's complement**. The nine's complement of, say, 563 is found by subtracting 563 from 999, which produces 436.

The other complement is the **true complement** and is formed by adding 1 to the LSD of the radix-minus-1 complement. In the decimal system, this is known as the **ten's complement**. The ten's complement of 563 is equal to the nine's complement (436) plus 1, which is equal to 437.

As an example of how the complement is used, suppose that we wish to subtract 132 from 897. By ordinary subtraction we get

897	(minuend)
−132	(subtrahend)
765	(difference).

The same result may be obtained by adding the nine's complement of the subtrahend to the minuend and adding the final carry resulting from this operation to the sum. The nine's complement of the subtrahend (999 − 132) is 867. Thus

+1 +1 +1	(carry)
8 9 7	(minuend)
+ 8 6 7	(nine's complement of subtrahend)
① 7 6 4	(sum)
1	(final carry added)
7 6 5	(result).

If we wish to use the ten's complement for this example, we first obtain the ten's complement of the subtrahend (999 − 132 + 1 = 868) and add it to the minuend. Thus

	+1 +1 +1	
	8 9 7	(minuend)
	+ 8 6 8	(ten's complement of subtrahend)
Dropped ←	① 7 6 5	(sum).

Only in this case the final carry is dropped. The result, then, is 765, the same as before.

As indicated, the subtraction of one positive number from another is the same as the addition of a positive number and a negative one. If the complement method is used, the negative number is always complemented (disregarding the negative sign) and added to the positive number.

However, if the negative number is larger than the positive one, the sum must be a negative number. For example, assume that we wish to add −897 and +132. (This is the same as subtracting +897 from +132. The result is −765.) First, we obtain the nine's complement of the negative number, disregarding the negative sign (999 − 897 = 102). Then we add the complement to the positive number. Thus

```
  132    (positive number)
 +102    (nine's complement of negative number)
 ----
  234    (result).
```

Note that the result has no final carry. This alerts us to the fact that the answer must be a negative number. We merely recomplement the result and change its sign to get the correct answer. Thus 999 − 234 = +765. The correct answer is −765.

Since the complement method for subtraction is, in reality, an addition process, it is well suited for digital computer use. Instead of having separate electronic circuitry for addition and subtraction, the computer need have only the addition circuitry, in addition to circuits to identify the signs (+ or −) of numbers. This makes for a less complex machine, especially since complementing in the binary system (most often used in computers) is very simple.

3. Decimal Multiplication

Multiplication is, in reality, an addition process. Thus, if we wish to multiply 15 by 5, we may successivly add 15 five times to obtain 75. The multiplication table that we memorize is merely a shortcut in the process. The number that we wish to multiply is called the **multiplicand**, the number representing the number of times the multiplicand is to be added is called the **multiplier**, and the result is called the **product**. A multiplication sign (×) is used to indicate the process of multiplication. Thus

15	(multiplicand)
×5	(multiplier)
75	(product).

The memorized multiplication table is particularly useful when we do multidigit multiplication. Suppose that we wish to multiply 423 by 32. Of course, we could successively add 423 thirty-two times, but this is a tedious process. Instead, we perform the following:

423	(multiplicand)
× 32	(multiplier)
846	(first partial product)
+12,690	(second partial product)
13,536	(final product).

Let us examine our procedure more closely. First, we multiplied the multiplicand by the LSD of the multiplier (the units digit 2). This gave us **the first partial product** (846). Then we multiplied the multiplicand by the tens digit of the multiplier (3). But keep in mind that the 3, because it is in the tens position, really stands for 30. Thus, multiplying the multiplicand by 30, we get the **second partial product** (12,690). Next, the two partial products are added to produce the **final product** (13,536).

Note that when it came to the addition of partial products we did not use the number of the second partial product (12,690). Instead, we dropped the zero and *shifted* the remaining number (1269) one position to the left. The dropping of the final zero divides a number by 10. But shifting a number one position to the left has the effect of multiplying by 10. So, since the number was divided by 10 and then multiplied by 10, there was no change in the value of the number. This shifting process is of particular importance in the arithmetic section of a computer, as is discussed in later chapters. The shift register is a classic example of a computer circuit using the shift technique.

4. Decimal Division

We have seen that multiplication is an addition process. Similarly, division is, in reality, a subtraction process. Thus, if we wish to divide 15 by 5, we successively subtract 5 from 15, noting the number of times we can make such subtractions. Examination will show that this can be done three times. The result of this division, then, is 3.

The number to be divided is called the **dividend**, the number the dividend is divided by is called the **divisor**, and the number of times the divisor can be subtracted from the dividend is called the **quotient**. If after the divisor is subtracted from the dividend an appropriate number of times a number is produced that is less than the divisor, this number is called the **remainder**. The division sign (÷) is used to indicate the process of division.

When we divide multidigit numbers, we use a sort of trial-and-error method. Assume, for example, that we wish to divide 8346 by 26. The ordinary paper-and-pencil method is as follows:

```
      321
26) 8346
    -78
     54
    -52
      26
     -26
       0.
```

Thus the quotient is 321 and the remainder is 0. The division may also be carried out as follows:

```
2600 ) 8346
      -2600
       5746
      -2600
       3146
      -2600    (first quotient digit = 3)
        546
       -260
        286
       -260    (second quotient digit = 2)
         26
        -26    (third quotient digit = 1)
          0    (remainder).
```

Let us analyze the operation just performed. First, the divisor has been multiplied by 100 by shifting it two positions to the left and adding a zero to fill in the empty positions. (In a digital computer, the shifting process is done by a shift register in the arithmetic section.) The shifting is necessary so that the divisor can conform to the four-digit dividend. (Later in the operation the divisor will be divided twice by 10 to bring it back to its original value.)

The divisor is successively subtracted from the dividend three times, leaving a remainder of 546. The first quotient digit is thus 3. Next, the divisor is divided by 10 by shifting it one position to the right and dropping the final zero.

The divisor is now subtracted twice from the previous remainder (546), leaving a new remainder of 26. The second quotient digit, then, is 2. Again, the divisor is divided by 10 and subtracted from the remainder. This can be done only once, leaving a remainder of 0. The third quotient digit is 1, and the full quotient is 321.

The subtraction involved can be carried out, of course, by the complement-addition process described in the previous section.

B. THE BINARY NUMBER SYSTEM

The **binary** number system has a radix of 2 with the digits 0 and 1. The positional weights increase from right to left as in the decimal system, only this time the increase is in ascending powers of 2. Thus the digit at the extreme right (the LSD) has a weight of 2^0, or decimal 1. A digit in the position immediately to the left has a weight of 2^1, or decimal 2. The next digit to the left has a weight of 2^2, or decimal 4, and so forth. A partial table showing the positional weights of the two digits of the binary system is shown in Figure 3-2.

Hence, binary number 1011, for example, may be interpreted as

$$(1 \times 2^3) + (0 \times 2^2) + (1 \times 2^1) + (1 \times 2^0) \qquad \text{or as}$$

$$(1 \times 8) + (0 \times 4) + (1 \times 2) + (1 \times 1) \qquad \text{or as} \qquad 8 + 0 + 2 + 1$$

or as decimal number 11. Note that binary number 1011 is not read as "one thousand eleven" but as "one, zero, one, one."

The counting method for the binary system is the same as for the decimal system, except that we use only the two digits 0 and 1. Thus, starting with 0, if we add one count, we get 1. Adding another count, we go back to 0 again, and a carry is added to the next position at the

		Digital positions						
Positional weight	Powers of two	2^6	2^5	2^4	2^3	2^2	2^1	2^0
	Decimal value	64	32	16	8	4	2	1
Digit values		0	0	0	0	0	0	0
		1	1	1	1	1	1	1

Fig. 3-2. Partial table showing the positional weights of the two digits of the binary number system.

left, producing 10. (This number is read not as "ten" but as "one, zero.") Adding another count produces 11 (one, one), and if another count is added, we get 100 (one, zero, zero). The next count produces 101 and so forth.

When we come to binary fractions, we use the same rules that we apply to decimal fractions. A **binary point** (the radix point) is used to separate the integers from the fraction. The weight of the digit to the right of the binary point is 2^{-1}, or decimal $\frac{1}{2}$. The next position to the right has a weight of 2^{-2}, or decimal $\frac{1}{4}$; the next position to the right has a weight of 2^{-3}, or decimal $\frac{1}{8}$; and so forth. A partial table of binary fractions showing their decimal equivalents is shown in Figure 3-3.

Thus the binary fraction 0.101 may be interpreted as

$$(0 \times 2^0) + (1 \times 2^{-1}) + (0 \times 2^{-2}) + (1 \times 2^{-3}) \quad \text{or as}$$
$$0 + \tfrac{1}{2} + \tfrac{0}{4} + \tfrac{1}{8} \quad \text{or as} \quad 0 + 0.5 + 0 + 0.125,$$

which is equal to the decimal fraction 0.626.

Fig. 3-3. Partial table of decimal equivalents of binary fractions.

Binary fractions		Decimal equivalents	
Digits	Powers of 2	Fraction	Digits
0.1	2^{-1}	$\frac{1}{2}$	0.5
0.01	2^{-2}	$\frac{1}{4}$	0.25
0.001	2^{-3}	$\frac{1}{8}$	0.125
0.0001	2^{-4}	$\frac{1}{16}$	0.0625
0.00001	2^{-5}	$\frac{1}{32}$	0.03125
0.000001	2^{-6}	$\frac{1}{64}$	0.015625

If we have a mixed binary number containing integers and fractions, such as 101.101, we may find the decimal equivalent by means of the following tabulation:

Binary digit		Positional weight		Decimal equivalent
1	×	2^2	=	4
0	×	2^1	=	0
1	×	2^0	=	1
1	×	2^{-1}	=	0.5
0	×	2^{-2}	=	0.0
1	×	2^{-3}	=	0.125
				5.625

1. Binary Addition

As in the case of decimal addition, binary addition is essentially a counting process. However, binary addition is simpler than decimal addition. There are only four simple rules for binary addition:

1. $0 + 0 = 0$ with no carry.
2. $0 + 1 = 1$ with no carry.
3. $1 + 0 = 1$ with no carry.
4. $1 + 1 = 0$ with a carry of 1.

For example, suppose that we wish to add binary numbers 11101 and 1011:

Binary								Decimal equivalent
+1	+1	+1	+1	+1			(carry)	+1
		1	1,	1	0	1	(augend)	29
+			1,	0	1	1	(addend)	+11
1	0		1,	0	0	0	(sum)	40

The same rules apply to the addition of binary fractions and the addition of binary mixed numbers. Care must be taken so that the binary points of the augend and addend are lined up one below the other; for example,

Binary		Decimal equivalent
+1 +1	(carry)	+1
1 0 1 . 1 0 1	(augend)	5 . 6 2 5
1 . 0 0 1	(addend)	1 . 1 2 5
1 1 0 . 1 1 0	(sum)	6 . 7 5 0

2. Binary Subtraction

Binary subtraction has four simple rules:

1. $0 - 0 = 0$ with no borrow.
2. $1 - 1 = 0$ with no borrow.
3. $1 - 0 = 1$ with no borrow.
4. $0 - 1 = 1$ with a borrow of 1.

For example, suppose that we wish to subtract binary 0111 from binary 1001:

Binary		Decimal equivalent
−1 −1	(borrow)	
1 0 0 1	(minuend)	9
−0 1 1 1	(subtrahend)	−7
0 0 1 0	(difference)	2

Note that when the first borrow is subtracted from the 0 of the minuend it leaves a 1, with a borrow from the digit at the left. When the 1 of the subtrahend is subtracted from the resulting 1 of the minuend, the difference is 0 with no borrow.

Binary fractions and binary mixed numbers are subtracted in the same way, taking care to place binary points below each other; for example,

Binary									Decimal equivalent					
−1	−1	−1		−1			(borrow)		−1		−1		
1	0	1	.	0	0	1	(minuend)		5	.	1	2	5
−	1	1	.	1	1	1	(subtrahend)		−3	.	8	7	5
0	0	1	.	0	1	0	(difference)		1	.	2	5	0

As in the decimal system, binary subtraction can be performed as an addition process using the complement method. Also, as in the decimal system, there are two types of binary complements, the **one's complement** (the radix-minus-1 complement) and the **two's complement** (the true complement). The one's complement of any binary number is found by subtracting each digit of that number from 1. The two's complement is found by adding 1 to the LSD of the one's complement.

As an example, suppose that we wish to find the one's complement of binary 10101:

$$\begin{array}{r} 11111 \\ -10101 \\ \hline 01010 \end{array} \quad \text{(one's complement).}$$

Note that where the binary number has a 1, the one's complement has a 0. Where the binary number has a 0, the one's complement has a 1. Thus, to find the one's complement of any binary number, simply reverse the digits of the number. Because of this simplicity, the one's complement generally is used in a digital computer.

As an example of the use of the one's complement method, assume that we wish to subtract binary 01011 from binary 11010. The ordinary subtraction method is as follows:

Binary						Decimal equivalent
−1	−1	−1	−1		(borrow)	
1	1	0	1	0	(minuend)	26
−0	1	0	1	1	(subtrahend)	−11
0	1	1	1	1	(difference)	15

Using the complement method, we first find the one's complement of the subtrahend (01011) by reversing its digits (10100). Then the one's complement is added to the minuend as follows:

+1	(carry)
11010	(minuend)
+10100	(one's complement of subtrahend)
101110	(sum).

The final carry beyond the five digits of the problem is added to the sum as follows:

① 01110	(sum)
⟶ +1	(carry is added)
01111	(difference).

As previously explained, when two positive numbers are subtracted from each other, it is the same as an addition between a positive minuend and a negative subtrahend. Where the complement is used, it is always the negative number that is complemented. If, as in the example just considered, the minuend is larger than the subtrahend, the result is a positive number. But if the subtrahend is larger than the minuend, a negative number results.

For example, suppose that we wish to subtract binary 10110 from binary 01101. (This is the same as adding −10110 and +01101. In both instances the result is the same, −01001.) We first find the one's complement of the negative number (−10110), neglecting its minus sign and reversing its digits (01001). To this we add the positive number as follows:

+1 +1	(carry)
0 1 0 0 1	(one's complement of negative number)
+0 1 1 0 1	(positive number)
+1 0 1 1 0	(sum).

The fact that there is no final carry beyond the five digits of the problem indicates that the final result must be a negative number. Accordingly, we then complement the sum (by reversing its digits) and change its sign. This produces the correct final result (−01001).

3. Binary Multiplication

Binary multiplication has three simple rules:

1. $0 \times 0 = 0$.
2. $0 \times 1 = 0$.
3. $1 \times 1 = 1$.

The binary multiplication process is simple. If the digit of the multiplier is 0, the partial product is 0. If the multiplier digit is 1, the partial product is the same as the multiplicand. Then the partial products are summed as follows:

Binary		Decimal
1 0 1 0 1	(multiplicand)	21
× 1 0	(multiplier)	× 2
0 0 0 0 0	(first partial product)	42
1 0 1 0 1	(second partial product)	
1 0 1 0 1 0	(final product)	

From this, it will be seen that the process of multiplying binary numbers in a digital computer requires addition (by means of adder circuits) and a shift (by means of a shift register). The same process applies to multiplication of fractions or mixed numbers; for example,

Binary		Decimal
10.01	(multiplicand)	2.25
× 1.01	(multiplier)	×1.25
10 01		11 25
0 00 0	(partial products)	45 0
10 01		2 25
10.11 01	(final product)	2.81 25

4. Binary Division

Since division by zero is meaningless, there are only two rules for binary division:

1. 0 ÷ 1 = 0.
2. 1 ÷ 1 = 1.

As an example, suppose that we wish to divide binary 101101 (decimal 45) by binary 101 (decimal 5). Then

Binary	Decimal
1001	9
101) 101101	5) 45
−101XXX	−45
0101	0
−101	
0	

Binary fractions and mixed numbers are divided as in the decimal system. Thus suppose that we wish to divide binary 10.01 (decimal 2.25) by binary 1.1 (decimal 1.5). We first move the binary points of both the dividend and the divisor one position to the right. Thus

Binary	Decimal
1.1) 10.01 = 11) 100.1	1.5) 2.25 = 15) 22.5

Then we perform the division process:

Binary	Decimal
1.1	1.5
11) 100.1	15) 22.5
− 11X	−15X
001 1	7 5
− 1 1	− 7 5
0	0

5. Conversion Between Decimal and Binary Numbers

To convert binary numbers to decimal numbers, we may use the method previously described. That is, we multiply each binary digit by its positional weight and add all the products. A simpler method for converting binary numbers to decimal equivalents (sometimes called the **double-dabble** method) is to double the most significant binary digit, add the next lower-order binary digit, and record the sum. Then we double this sum and add the next lower-order binary digit and record this new sum. We continue this process until the least significant binary digit has been added to the previously doubled sum. The final sum is the decimal value sought.

For example, to convert binary number 11010 to its decimal equivalent, we may proceed as follows:

$$
\begin{array}{rlll}
1\ (\text{MSD}) \times 2 + 1 & (\text{next lower-order digit}) & = 3 & \\
3 \times 2 + 0 & (\text{next lower-order digit}) & = 6 & \\
6 \times 2 + 1 & (\text{next lower-order digit}) & = 13 & \\
13 \times 2 + 0 & (\text{LSD}) & = 26 & (\text{decimal equivalent}).
\end{array}
$$

To convert decimal to binary integers we may use a direct method. With this method, we subtract the highest power of 2 that can be subtracted from the decimal number. From the remainder of this subtraction we subtract the next highest power of 2. This is continued until there is no remainder. For each power of 2 thus subtracted, a 1 is written, and a 0 is written for those powers of 2 not used, in the order in which the subtractions were performed.

For example, to find the binary equivalent of decimal 29,

Subtraction		Binary digit	
29 – 4(2^4 or 16)	= 13	1	(MSD)
13 – (2^3 or 8)	= 5	1	
5 – (2^2 or 4)	= 1	1	
1 – (2^1 or 2)	(cannot be done)	0	
1 – (2^0 or 1)	= 0	1	(LSD)

Thus the binary number equivalent of decimal 29 is 11101.

There is another method for converting decimal to binary integers that is especially useful where large numbers are involved and that is similar to the double-dabble method. With this method, the decimal number is divided by 2, and the remainder (if any) becomes the LSD of the binary equivalent. The quotient of this division is divided again by 2 and the remainder (if any) becomes the next significant digit. This process is continued until the quotient becomes 0 and the remainder of this division becomes the most significant binary digit.

For example, to find the binary equivalent of decimal 29,

Division		Binary digit
$29 \div 2 = 14$	(with remainder 1)	(LSD)
$14 \div 2 = 7$	(with remainder 0)	
$7 \div 2 = 3$	(with remainder 1)	
$3 \div 2 = 1$	(with remainder 1)	
$1 \div 2 = 0$	(with remainder 1)	(MSD)

Thus the binary number equivalent of decimal 29 is 11101.

To convert a decimal fraction to its binary equivalent, first multiply the decimal fraction by 2. The integral portion of the product becomes the first digit of the binary fraction. If there is no integral portion, a 0 is inserted in place of the first digit. The remainder of the product (the fractional portion) is again multiplied by 2 and the integral portion of this product becomes the next binary digit. (As before, if there is no integral portion, the binary digit is 0.) This process is continued until the fractional part of any product becomes 0 or, in case of any nonterminating fraction, until the required number of binary digits is obtained.

For example, to find the binary equivalent of decimal 0.6875,

Multiplication	Binary digit	
$0.6875 \times 2 = 1\,.3750$	1	(first digit)
$0.3750 \times 2 = 0\,.7500$	0	
$0.7500 \times 2 = 1\,.5000$	1	
$0.5000 \times 2 = 1\,.0000$	1	

Thus the binary equivalent of decimal 0.6875 is 0.1011.

For an example of a nonterminating binary fraction, convert decimal 0.9283 to its binary equivalent, carrying the binary fraction to six digits:

Multiplication	Binary digit	
0.9283 × 2 = 1 .8566	1	(first digit)
0.8566 × 2 = 1 .7132	1	
0.7132 × 2 = 1 .4264	1	
0.4264 × 2 = 0 .8528	0	
0.8528 × 2 = 1 .7056	1	
0.7056 × 2 = 1 .4112	1	

Thus the binary equivalent of decimal 0.9283 is 0.111011+.

To convert a mixed decimal number (whole number and fraction) to its binary equivalent, convert the whole number and fraction separately and then combine the results.

C. THE OCTAL NUMBER SYSTEM

The **octal** number system has a radix of 8, using eight digits from 0 to 7 in ascending order. When a count is added to the largest digit, 7, the count goes back to the start (0) and a carry is added to the next position to the left. Thus decimal 8 would appear as octal 10 (pronounced "one, zero," not "ten"). A list showing the octal equivalents of the ten digits of the decimal system appears in Figure 3-4.

Fig. 3-4. Table showing the octal equivalents of the ten decimal digits.

Decimal digit	Octal equivalent
0	0
1	1
2	2
3	3
4	4
5	5
6	6
7	7
8	10
9	11

As in other systems, the digits of an octal number are arranged in positions of ascending powers of the radix, reading from right to left. A partial table showing the positional weights of the octal system is shown in Figure 3-5.

Digital position							
8^3	8^2	8^1	8^0	8^{-1}	8^{-2}	8^{-3}	Powers of 8
512	64	8	1	1/8	1/64	1/512	Decimal equivalents

Fig. 3-5. Partial table showing the positional weights of the octal number system.

Thus octal number 1305.1 really means $(1 \times 512) + (3 \times 64) + (0 \times 8) + (5 \times 1) + (1 \times 0.125)$, which is equal to 709.125 in the decimal system.

The octal system is of special interest since its radix (8) is a power of the binary radix (2). Hence the octal number system is frequently used as an aid in programming a digital computer.

Where numbers of different number systems are used, it is conventional to differentiate between these numbers by applying a subscript that indicates the radix being used. Thus 101 in the binary system would appear as 101_2, 523 in the octal system as 523_8, and 983 in the decimal system as 983_{10}.

1. Conversion of Octal-Decimal Numbers

To convert an octal number to its decimal equivalent, multiply each digit by its positional weight expressed in decimal equivalents and add the products. For example,

$$123_8 = (1 \times 8^2) + (2 \times 8^1) + (3 \times 8^0)$$
$$= (1 \times 64) + (2 \times 8) + (3 \times 1) = 83_{10}.$$

To convert a decimal number to its octal equivalent, divide the decimal number by 8 and record the remainder, even if it is 0, which becomes the LSD of the octal number. Divide the quotient by 8 again and record the remainder of this division, which becomes the next significant octal digit. Continue this process until the quotient becomes 0. The remainder from this division process is the MSD of the octal number.

For example, to convert 759_{10} to its octal equivalent,

$$
\begin{aligned}
759 \div 8 &= 94 \quad \text{with remainder } 7 \text{ (LSD)} \\
94 \div 8 &= 11 \quad \text{with remainder } 6 \\
11 \div 8 &= 1 \quad \text{with remainder } 3 \\
1 \div 8 &= 0 \quad \text{with remainder } 1 \text{ (MSD).}
\end{aligned}
$$

Thus $759_{10} = 1367_8$.

2. Conversion of Octal-Binary Numbers

To convert an octal number to its binary equivalent, convert each digit of the octal number to its binary equivalent using three binary digits per octal digit. Then combine these binary groups in proper order. For example, to convert 213_8 to its binary equivalent,

2	1	3	(octal digits)
010	001	011	(binary equivalents).

Thus $213_8 = 010001011_2$.

To convert a binary number to its octal equivalent, divide the digits of the binary number into groups of three, starting from the right. If necessary, fill out the last group (at the left) by placing 0s in front. Then convert each binary group to its octal digit equivalent and combine these digits in proper order.

For example, to convert 10110110_2 to its octal equivalent,

Added ⟶	010	110	110	(binary)
	2	6	6	(octal).

Thus $10110110_2 = 266_8$.

3. Conversion of Decimal-Binary Numbers Using Octal Numbers

An easy way to convert decimal numbers to their binary equivalents or vice versa is to use an octal conversion as an intermediary step. Thus, to change a decimal number to a binary, first convert the decimal number to its octal equivalent and then change this octal number to its binary equivalent. The same procedure may be applied in going from binary to decimal numbers.

To change a decimal fraction to its octal equivalent, multiply the decimal fraction by 8. The integer of the resulting product, even if 0, then becomes the first digit of the octal fraction. The fractional portion of the product is then multiplied by 8 again. The integer of its product becomes the next digit of the octal fraction. Carry out this procedure one place beyond the required number of places for the octal fraction. Then, if the final octal digit is less than 4, ignore it. If the final digit is 4 or more, add 1 to the digit preceding it.

For example, to convert 0.794_{10} to its octal equivalent (carried out three places),

$$
\begin{aligned}
8 \times 0.794 &= 6.352 \qquad &&\text{(integer is 6, first digit)}\\
8 \times 0.352 &= 2.816 &&\text{(integer is 2)}\\
8 \times 0.816 &= 6.528 &&\text{(integer is 6)}\\
8 \times 0.528 &= 4.224 &&\text{(integer is 4).}
\end{aligned}
$$

Thus $0.794_{10} = 0.6264_8$. Since we wish to carry the octal fraction to only three places and the final digit is 4, we round out our answer to 0.627_8.

If we wish to convert an octal fraction to its decimal equivalent, we multiply each digit of the fraction by its positional weight and add all the products. For example, to convert 0.627_8 to its decimal equivalent,

$$
\begin{aligned}
0.627_8 &= (6 \times 8^{-1}) + (2 \times 8^{-2}) + (7 \times 8^{-3})\\
&= (6 \times \tfrac{1}{8}) + (6 \times \tfrac{1}{64}) + (7 \times \tfrac{1}{512})\\
&= \tfrac{6}{8} + \tfrac{2}{64} + \tfrac{7}{512}\\
&= \frac{384 + 16 + 7}{512} = \frac{407}{512} = 0.794.
\end{aligned}
$$

Thus $0.627_8 = 0.794_{10}$.

When dealing with mixed numbers, if converting from decimal to octal or octal to decimal, we must treat the integer and fraction separately and then recombine them. This is not required when converting binary mixed numbers to octal or vice versa.

For example, to convert 425.03_8 to its binary equivalent,

4	2	5	.	0	3	(octal)
100	010	101	.	000	011	(binary).

Thus $425.03_8 = 100010101.000011_2$.

Similarly, to convert a binary mixed number to its octal equivalent, we break up the binary number into groups of three digits, starting at the binary point and proceeding to the left for the integers and proceeding to the right for the fractional portion. Then each group is converted to its octal equivalent.

For example, to convert 11000100.010001_2 to its octal equivalent,

Added ⟶	⓪11	000	100	.	010	001	(binary)
	3	0	4	.	2	1	(octal).

Thus $11000100.010001_2 = 304.21_8$.

D. THE HEXADECIMAL NUMBER SYSTEM

One problem with binary numbers is that they are difficult to manipulate, particularly when large values are involved. This problem is overcome by use of the octal number system, previously described, where three binary digits are represented by one octal digit ($3_8 = 011_2$, $7_8 = 111_2$, and so forth). The hexadecimal number system goes one step further. Each digit in the hexadecimal system represents four binary digits.

Unlike the base 10 of decimal numbers, base 2 of binary numbers, or base 8 of octal numbers, the hexadecimal number system uses a base of 16. Since the familiar decimal system has only ten digits or characters (0, 1, . . . , 9), six additional characters are required for the hexadecimal system—the first six letters of the English alphabet (A, B, C, D, E, and F). Letter A represents a value of 10, letter B a decimal value of 11, and so forth, with letter F representing decimal 15.

Figure 3-6 shows the relationship among the decimal, binary, octal, and hexadecimal number systems.

Note that the carry occurs at 16 in hexadecimal numbers. Thus additional digits are required when the count goes beyond 16. For example, a decimal 16 is hexadecimal 10, decimal 17 is hexadecimal 11, and so forth. This means that

$$\text{Hexadecimal } ①① = (1 \times 16) + 1, \qquad \text{or decimal 17.}$$

Likewise,

$$\text{Hexadecimal } ⑦③ = (7 \times 16) + 3, \qquad \text{or decimal 115.}$$

From this it will be seen that it is possible to represent a large decimal number with a hexadecimal number of fewer digits.

Fig. 3-6. Partial table showing the relationship of decimal, binary, octal, and hexadecimal number systems.

Decimal	Pure binary	Octal	Hexadecimal
0	0	0	0
1	1	1	1
2	10	2	2
3	11	3	3
4	100	4	4
5	101	5	5
6	110	6	6
7	111	7	7
8	1000	10	8
9	1001	11	9
10	1010	12	A
11	1011	13	B
12	1100	14	C
13	1101	15	D
14	1110	16	E
15	1111	17	F
16	10000	20	10
17	10001	21	11
18	10010	22	12
25	11001	31	19
26	11010	32	1A
27	11011	33	1B
32	100000	40	20
33	100001	41	21

1. Conversion Between Hexadecimal and Decimal Numbers

To convert a hexadecimal number to its decimal equivalent (beyond those numbers shown in Figure 3-6), use the following rules:

1. Multiply the most significant hexadecimal digit by 16.
2. Add the next most significant hexadecimal digit to the product and multiply the sum by 16.
3. Continue the process (adding and multiplying) until the least significant hexadecimal digit has been added to the last product.

For example, to find the decimal equivalent of hexadecimal 3C7,

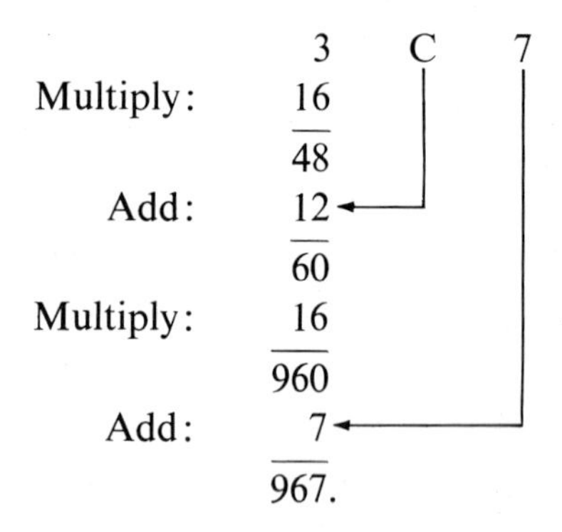

Thus the decimal equivalent of hexadecimal 3C7 is 967.

To convert a decimal number to its hexadecimal equivalent (beyond those numbers shown in Figure 3-6), divide the decimal number by 16 and use the remainder of each division as the hexadecimal number.

For example, to find the hexadecimal equivalent of decimal 967,

967 ÷ 16 = 60 with remainder 7 (LSD)
60 ÷ 16 = 3 with remainder 12 (or C)
3 ÷ 16 = 0 with remainder 3 (MSD)

3 C 7.

Thus the hexadecimal equivalent of decimal 967 is 3C7.

2. Conversion Between Hexadecimal and Binary Numbers

To convert a hexadecimal number to its binary equivalent, convert each digit of the hexadecimal number to its binary equivalent using four binary digits per hexadecimal digit. Then combine these binary groups in proper order.

For example, to convert 3C7 hexadecimal to its binary equivalent,

3	C	7	(hexadecimal)
0011	1100	0111	(binary equivalent).

Thus 3C7 $= 001111000111_2$.

To convert a binary number to its hexadecimal equivalent, divide the digits of the binary number into groups of four starting from the right. If necessary, fill out the last group (at the left) by placing 0s in front. Then convert each binary group to its hexadecimal digit equivalent and combine these digits in proper order.

For example, to convert 11011001011_2 to its hexadecimal equivalent,

Added ⟶	0110	1100	1011	(binary)
	6	C	B	(hexadecimal).

3. Hexadecimal Addition

Hexadecimal addition is also a form of counting, as in other number systems. However, since the carry function occurs at 16, the carry must be added when the sum of digits is greater than F (decimal 15). For example, to add hexadecimal 7 (decimal 7) and hexadecimal A (decimal 10), the sum is hexadecimal 11 (decimal 17).

This may be confusing for those familiar with the decimal system. For that reason, Figure 3-7 is included to aid in adding hexadecimal numbers. Note that Figure 3-7 has 15 rows and 15 columns representing each of the 15 hexadecimal digits. To find the sum of any two digits, note the value at the intersection of the corresponding row and digit.

For example, to add hexadecimal 3 (decimal 3) to hexadecimal C

	1	2	3	4	5	6	7	8	9	A	B	C	D	E	F
1	2	3	4	5	6	7	8	9	A	B	C	D	E	F	10
2	3	4	5	6	7	8	9	A	B	C	D	E	F	10	11
3	4	5	6	7	8	9	A	B	C	D	E	F	10	11	12
4	5	6	7	8	9	A	B	C	D	E	F	10	11	12	13
5	6	7	8	9	A	B	C	D	E	F	10	11	12	13	14
6	7	8	9	A	B	C	D	E	F	10	11	12	13	14	15
7	8	9	A	B	C	D	E	F	10	11	12	13	14	15	16
8	9	A	B	C	D	E	F	10	11	12	13	14	15	16	17
9	A	B	C	D	E	F	10	11	12	13	14	15	16	17	18
A	B	C	D	E	F	10	11	12	13	14	15	16	17	18	19
B	C	D	E	F	10	11	12	13	14	15	16	17	18	19	1A
C	D	E	F	10	11	12	13	14	15	16	17	18	19	1A	1B
D	E	F	10	11	12	13	14	15	16	17	18	19	1A	1B	1C
E	F	10	11	12	13	14	15	16	17	18	19	1A	1B	1C	1D
F	10	11	12	13	14	15	16	17	18	19	1A	1B	1C	1D	1E

Fig. 3-7. Table for addition of single-digit hexadecimal numbers.

(decimal 12), the intersection of the corresponding rows and columns shows hexadecimal F (decimal 15).

4. Hexadecimal Subtraction

Hexadecimal subtraction is similar to other number systems, except that the borrow occurs at 16.

For example, to subtract hexadecimal 1DB (decimal 475) from hexadecimal 3C7 (decimal 967), use the following steps:

```
      1B
  2 ↗ B → 17
  3   C   7     (minuend)
− 1   D   B     (subtrahend)
  ─────────
  1   E   C     (difference).
```

Start with the LSD and subtract B from 7. Since B (decimal 11) is larger than 7, borrow a 1 (decimal 16) from the next higher-order digit C, making the C into a B. The borrowed 1 (decimal 16) added to the 7 makes hexadecimal 17 (decimal 23). The B subtracted from 17 leaves a difference of C.

Next, subtract D from B (middle digits). Since D (decimal 13) is larger than B (decimal 11), borrow a 1 (decimal 16) from the MSD of 3, making the 3 into a 2. The borrowed 1 (decimal 16) added to the B makes hexadecimal 1B (decimal 27). The D subtracted from 1B leaves a difference of E.

Finally, subtract 1 from 2 (MSD). This leaves a difference of 1.

Thus 1DB (decimal 475) subtracted from 3C7 (decimal 967) leaves a difference of IEC (decimal 492).

5. Hexadecimal Multiplication

Hexadecimal multiplication is similar to decimal multiplication. However, since the base is 16, this must be included when the final product is greater than F (decimal 15). For example, 3 multiplied by 8 is 24 in decimal, but this is represented as 18 in hexadecimal. Since this may be confusing, Figure 3-8 is included to aid in multiplying hexadecimal numbers. Note that Figure 3-8 has 15 rows and columns representing each of the 15 hexadecimal digits. To find the product of any one digit multiplied by another digit, note the value at the intersection of the corresponding row and digit.

For example, to multiply hexadecimal 7 (decimal 7) by hexadecimal C (decimal 12), the intersection of the corresponding rows and columns shows hexadecimal 54 (decimal 84).

When there is more than one digit in either the multiplier or multiplicand of a hexadecimal number, the digits must be handled one at a time, with a shift for each digit. Then the product of the two digits is added.

For example, to multiply hexadecimal 7C (decimal 124) by 3(decimal 3), use the following steps:

```
    7  C               (multiplicand)
 ×     3               (multiplier)
 ---------
      24  (3 × C)
 +  15    (3 × 7)
 --------
     174               (final product).
```

1	2	3	4	5	6	7	8	9	A	B	C	D	E	F
2	4	6	8	A	C	E	10	12	14	16	18	1A	1C	1E
3	6	9	C	F	12	15	18	1B	1E	21	24	27	2A	2D
4	8	C	10	14	18	1C	20	24	28	2C	30	34	38	3C
5	A	F	14	19	1E	23	28	2D	32	37	3C	41	46	4B
6	C	12	18	1E	24	2A	30	36	3C	42	48	4E	54	5A
7	E	15	1C	23	2A	31	38	3F	46	4D	54	5B	62	69
8	10	18	20	28	30	38	40	48	50	58	60	68	70	7B
9	12	1B	24	2D	36	3F	48	51	5A	63	6C	75	7E	87
A	14	1E	28	32	3C	46	50	5A	64	6E	78	82	8C	96
B	16	21	2C	37	42	4D	58	63	6E	79	84	8F	9A	A5
C	18	24	30	3C	48	54	60	6C	78	84	90	9C	A8	B4
D	1A	27	34	41	4E	5B	68	75	82	8F	9C	A9	B6	C3
E	1C	2A	38	46	54	62	70	7E	8C	9A	A8	B6	C4	D2
F	1E	2D	3C	4B	5A	69	78	87	96	A5	B4	C3	D2	E1

Fig. 3-8. Table for multiplication of single-digit hexadecimal numbers.

Thus 7C (decimal 124) multiplied by 3 (decimal 3) produces 174 (decimal 372).

E. BINARY-CODED DECIMALS (BCD)

The binary number system is most compatible with the pulses used in digital computers because only two pulse conditions are required to accommodate the two binary digits, 1 and 0. Typically, a binary 1 is represented by the presence of a pulse, while the absence of a pulse represents 0. (However, in various computers, the 1 and 0 digits can be represented by other combinations of pulses, as is discussed in later chapters.)

No matter what number system is used outside the computer (for programming, readout, and so on) the number is converted (or coded) into binary form for use within the computer.

The simplest form of such coding is where decimal numbers (0–9) are converted into binary form using four binary digits, or bits. This **four-bit** system is one of the original codes used in computers and is still used in some business-oriented systems. With this system, decimal 1 is represented by 0001, decimal 2 by 0010, and so forth.

When the decimal number has more than one digit, four binary bits are used for each decimal digit. For example, the decimal number 3739 is represented by 16 binary digits, in groups of four, as follows:

3	7	3	9	(decimal)
0011	0111	0011	1001	(binary)
	0011011100111001			(BCD)

F. ALPHANUMERIC DATA REPRESENTATION

While the four-bit system is adequate to represent any decimal digit from 0 to 9, additional bits are necessary to represent letters of the alphabet and special characters (such as dollar signs, percent symbols, and so forth) that are required for most computers.

Many computer manufacturers have settled on a six-bit system for the coding of letters, characters, and numbers into binary form. The six digits (known as a **frame**) are arranged into A and B digits (known as the **zone**) and the numeric digits (8421), as follows:

$$\underbrace{B \quad A}_{\text{Zone}} \qquad \underbrace{8 \quad 4 \quad 2 \quad 1}_{\text{Numeric.}}$$

Although this follows the system used on some punch cards to represent letters, characters, and numbers, there is no standardization among computer manufacturers as to what character is represented by any given combination. For example, with one system, the letter A is represented by binary 110001, or

B	A	8	4	2	1	(alphanumeric)
1	1	0	0	0	1	(binary).

In some alphanumeric systems, an eight-bit code is used, with four bits for the zone and four bits for the numeric portion. (When eight or more bits are used, the term **byte** is sometimes applied to indicate a string of digits.)

Two eight-bit codes of particular importance are the Extended Binary Coded Decimal Interchange Code (EBCDIC) and the United States American Standard Code for Information Interchange (USASCII). Although most computers now in use are not designed to accommodate these codes directly, there are adapter circuits that convert the computer's code (typically six-bit codes) into either of these codes for interchange of information with other computers.

G. SPECIAL COMPUTER LOGIC CODES

There are many computer logic codes other than those discussed here. Figure 3-9 shows some typical computer logic codes. Note that

Fig. 3-9. Typical codes used in computer logic circuits.

Decimal	Binary	Octal	Hexa-decimal	*BCD*	2421	5421	*XS3*	Reflected grey	2 out of 5	Biquinary 5043210
0	0000	0	0	0000	0000	0000	0011-0011	0000	00011	0100001
1	0001	1	1	0001	0001	0001	0011-0100	0001	00101	0100010
2	0010	2	2	0010	0010	0010	0011-0101	0011	00110	0100100
3	0011	3	3	0011	0011	0011	0011-0110	0010	01001	0101000
4	0100	4	4	0100	0100	0100	0011-0111	0110	01010	0110000
5	0101	5	5	0101	1011	1000	0011-1000	0111	01100	1000001
6	0110	6	6	0110	1100	1001	0011-1001	0101	10001	1000010
7	0111	7	7	0111	1101	1010	0011-1010	0100	10010	1000100
8	1000	10	8	1000	1110	1011	0011-1011	1100	10100	1001000
9	1001	11	9	1001	1111	1100	0011-1100	1101	11000	1010000
10	1010	12	*A*	0001-0000	0001-0000	0001-0000	0100-0011	1111		
11	1011	13	*B*	0001-0001	0001-0001	0001-0001	0100-0100			
12	1100	14	*C*	0001-0010	0001-0010	0001-0010	0100-0101			
13	1101	15	*D*	0001-0011	0001-0011	0001-0011	0100-0110			
14	1110	16	*E*	0001-0100	0001-0100	0001-0100	0100-0111			
15	1111	17	*F*	0001-0101	0001-1011	0001-1000	0100-1000			

most of the codes require four bits for each digit. The 2-out-of-5 (five bits) and biquinary (seven bits) codes are exceptions. In general, four-bit codes yield 2^4 (or 16) possible combinations. However, in certain computer codes, not all combinations are used. When combinations are unused, they are often known as **forbidden** codes.

BASIC ELECTRIC CIRCUITS IN COMPUTERS

4

In digital computers, information (that is, data and the instructions for processing it) is applied as coded groups of electronic pulses (usually in one of the binary codes discussed in Chapter 3). Within the computer, other pulses direct the flow of information from one point to another and initiate and control the various operations. These pulses flow through a network of electronic circuits to specific destinations.

Although many electronic circuit combinations appear in digital computers, there are only four basic circuit elements: gates, inverters (or inverter-amplifiers), flip-flops, and delays. This chapter provides a detailed discussion of the four basic circuit elements. In later chapters, we shall discuss how the four basic elements are connected together to form specific circuit functions (such as how gates are connected to form an adder, how flip-flops are connected to form a counter, and so forth).

It might be helpful to compare the network of electronic circuits of a computer with the network of tracks of a nationwide railroad system. (In fact, one important use of computers is the switching and routing of railroad trains.) In the railroad system, trains run on the tracks. In the computer, electronic pulses flow through the circuit paths. In the railroad system, tracks run between all possible destinations for the trains. In the computer, the circuit paths connect all possible destinations for the electronic pulses.

In the railroad system, each train is routed by opening or closing switches in the tracks. These switches are opened or closed in proper order and at the proper time, in accordance with a logical plan that permits the train to reach its proper destination. In the computer, the electronic pulses are routed by opening or closing electronic switches, called **gates**, in the circuit paths. These gates, too, are opened or closed in proper order and at the proper time, in accordance with a logical plan that directs the pulses to their proper destinations.

Each instruction to the computer requires that certain gates be opened or closed so that the pulses representing the data involved may flow through the prescribed path. The opening and closing of these gates in proper sequence and time are accomplished by the control section of the computer.

As an example, let us assume that the program contains an instruction for transferring some item of data that has been stored in the memory section of the computer to the arithmetic section for processing. Acting upon this instruction, the control section opens all the gates in a path leading from the specific data location in the memory to the arithmetic section and closes all other gates. As the pulses representing that item of data flow through the computer circuits, the pulses encounter these gates. If the gate is open, the pulses flow through. If the gate is closed, the pulses must seek some alternative path where the gate is open. In this way, the pulses are directed to the arithmetic section and to no other point.

It has been stated that the gates are opened or closed according to a logical plan. In a book published in 1854, George Boole, an English philosopher and mathematician, proposed a system of logic based upon two opposite states—*true* and *false*. Not much was heard about Boole's theories until Dr. Claude E. Shannon of Bell Telephone Laboratories in 1938 proposed an analysis of relay-switching circuits based upon two states of relay contacts—contacts closed and contacts open. Since the contacts-closed state of the relay could correspond to the true state of Boole's theories and the contacts-open state to the false state, Boole's system of logic could also apply to relay-switching circuits.

No attempt will be made in this book to examine Boole's theories since such theories are of primary interest to philosophers, mathematicians, and logic design engineers. From a technician's standpoint, Boole's theories can be considered as a system of logic based upon two opposite states. Thus any **bistable** device (that is, a device with two opposite stable states) may be used in such a logic system. In digital computers, both flip-flops and gates can be considered to be bistable.

From a logic standpoint, a gate is bistable since the gate is open in one state and closed in the opposite state. (Some computer texts refer to gates as **logical** or **logic gates**.)

The binary number system, too, is bistable. Binary digits can be either 1 or 0, never any other value. Thus Boole's true state may correspond to the open state of the gate or to the 1 digit of the binary number system. The false state, then, would correspond to the closed state of the gate or to the 0 digit of the binary number system.

The heart of the electronic switching, or gating, circuit is some bistable device such as the semiconductor diode, electron tube, or transistor or a combination of them.

As an example, when the anode of the semiconductor diode is positive in relation to its cathode, the diode is conductive (which we may assume to be the true state). With the anode negative in relation to the cathode, the diode is nonconductive (the false state). We may, of course, consider the conductive state to be the false state. Then the nonconductive state must be considered to be the true state.

If we examine the characteristic output current curve of an NPN transistor (see Figure 4-1), we note that if the base is made sufficiently negative (relative to the emitter), the **cutoff point** is reached, and the transistor is nonconductive. If the base is made sufficiently positive, the **saturation point** is reached, and the transistor is fully conductive. If the transistor is to be used as an amplifier (as, for example, in the audio section of a radio receiver), the transistor operates between the two points (in the **active region**). Then a varying input produces a larger, but similarly varying, output.

In a computer, the transistor is generally operated as a switch, that is, as a device having two stable states—conductive and nonconductive. Thus the transistor operates only at the cutoff point or at the saturation point and is able to pass from one point to the other practically instantaneously.

This *on* or *off* condition of the transistor is used because information

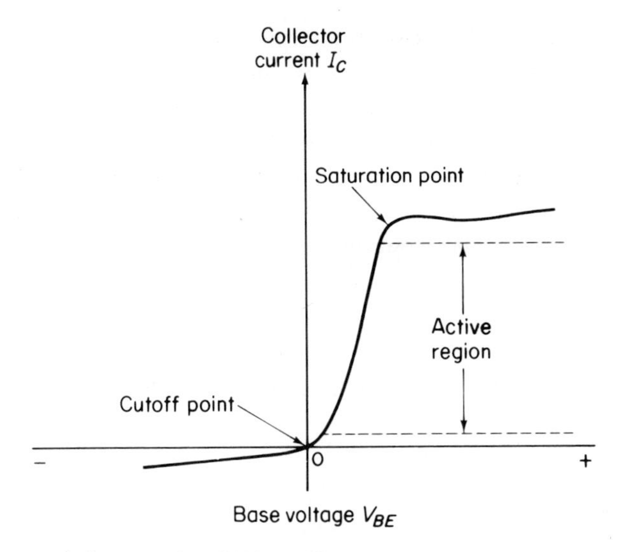

Fig. 4-1. Characteristic curve of an NPN transistor.

within the computer is handled as groups of pulses. Each pulse has two voltage levels. Typically, the levels are +5 V (or −5 V) and 0 V. When a pulse is applied to the base of a transistor, the lower-level voltage keeps the transistor nonconductive (cutoff). The higher-level voltage places the transistor in its fully conductive state (saturation).

Early computer types used electron tubes. Modern computers use semiconductor diodes and transistors because they are smaller, are more rugged and reliable, use less power, and produce less heat. Most of today's computers use a number of integrated circuits. With such ICs, several transistors and/or diodes are contained in a single package and are connected to form a specific circuit or group of circuits (such as four flip-flops in a single package, six gates in a package, and so forth).

With either ICs or discrete components, there are only four basic logic circuits (or digital circuits). There are many variations of each type of basic circuit. No attempt will be made to investigate each variation. Instead, only representative circuits of each type will be considered.

A. PULSES

Before discussing the various basic circuits used in a computer, we shall examine some of the characteristics of the electric pulses with which they operate. (Almost all computer circuits operate with pulses, and usually with groups or *trains* of pulses that appear in a particular sequence to form a binary code.) No matter what sequence is used or what the repetition rate at which the pulses appear is, the pulse voltage changes from one level to another and then returns to the first level.

The characteristics of a typical pulse are shown in Figure 4-2. Note that two voltage levels are required for a pulse. The original voltage level may be some positive or negative (or even zero) value. If the other level is a more positive (or, what amounts to the same thing, less negative) value, the pulse is said to be **positive-going**. If it is a less positive (or more negative) value, the pulse is **negative-going**.

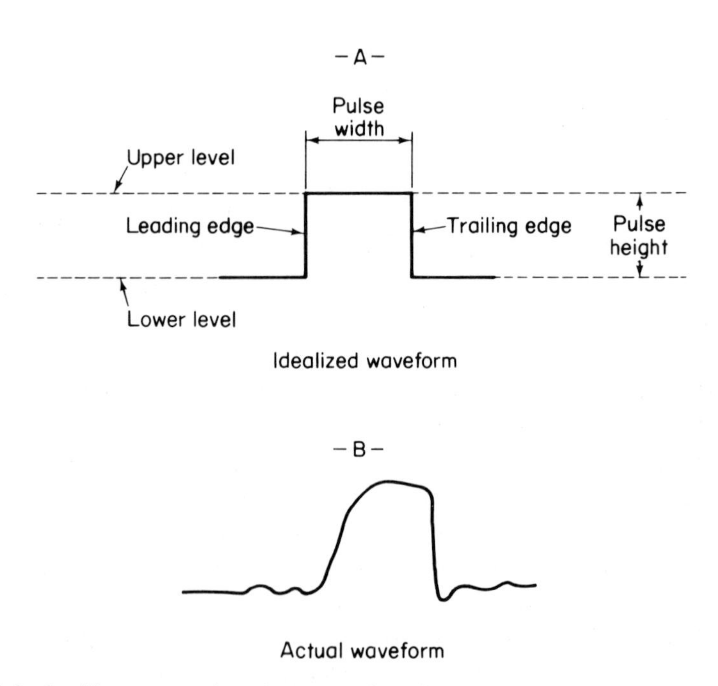

Fig. 4-2. Graphic representation of a rectangular pulse.

In Figure 4-2A, the idealized wave form of a rectangular pulse is shown. (The pulse of Figure 4-2A is positive-going.) The wave form rises instantly from its lower level to its upper level along the **leading edge** of the pulse, maintains this level for the duration of the **pulse width**, and falls instantly back to its lower level along the **trailing edge** of the pulse. The duration of a computer pulse (the pulse width) is generally on the order of 1 microsecond (1 μS), while the repetition rates are usually several thousand pulses per second. Typically, computer pulse amplitudes are less than 5 V.

The rectangular pulse generally does not have the ideal wave form pictured in Figure 4-2A. If examined on the screen of an oscilloscope, the pulses would appear to resemble the wave form shown in Figure 4-2B. The **rise time** (the time required to change from the lower level to the upper level) is not instantaneous and neither is the **fall time** (the time required to change from the upper level to the lower level). Also, the upper level does not remain absolutely constant during the entire pulse width. For most computer work, the actual wave form is close enough for all practical purposes. Should the actual wave form differ materially from the ideal wave form, special pulse-shaping circuits may be used to bring the pulse close to the ideal.

The pulse may also be negative-going. That is, the pulse may fall from its upper level to its lower level along the leading edge and then rise back to the upper level along the trailing edge.

Since the pulse has two voltage levels, it may be considered to be binary in nature. If we indicate one voltage level by binary digit 1 (true) and the other by binary digit 0 (false), the pulse may be used in a binary logic system. If the upper level is taken to indicate binary 1 and the lower level binary 0, we say that the system uses **positive logic**. If the upper level is taken to indicate binary 0 and the lower level binary 1, then **negative logic** is being used.

B. BASIC AND AND OR GATE CIRCUITS

Information in a digital computer consists of groups of pulses flowing from one element to another. One of the basic functions of the logic circuits is to direct the flow of pulses or to stop the pulses, as the occasion requires. This is the job of the **gate circuit**. A gate may be defined as a circuit with a single output and a number of inputs so designed that an output occurs only if a prescribed set of input conditions are met. A gate circuit is discriminatory in nature. That is, the gate will provide an output only under specific input conditions. The two basic gate circuits are the AND gate and the OR gate.

The AND gate may be illustrated by an electrical analogy. See Figure 4-3. In this circuit, the battery, lamp, and switches *A* and *B*

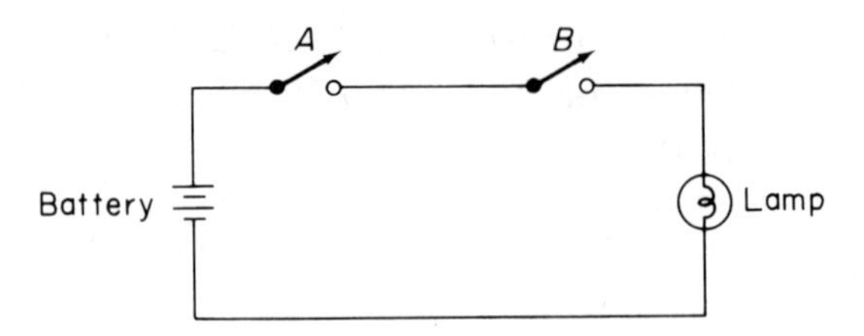

Fig. 4-3. Electrical analogy of the AND gate.

are connected in series. The circuit will be completed and the lamp will be lit only if both switch A *and* switch B are closed. If either or both of these switches are open, the lamp will not light.

To use the AND circuit in a logic system, let us represent the closed state of a switch as true, or binary 1, and the open state as false, or binary 0. Similarly, let us represent the lit lamp as true, or binary 1, and the unlit lamp as false, or binary 0.

Using this system of notation, we may represent all possible conditions for the switches and lamp by the following table:

Switch A	Switch B	Lamp
0	0	0
1	0	0
0	1	0
1	1	1

From this **truth table** we can see that the AND gate will open (lamp lit) if and only if both switches are in the binary-1 position (switch

Fig. 4-4. Electrical analogy of the OR gate.

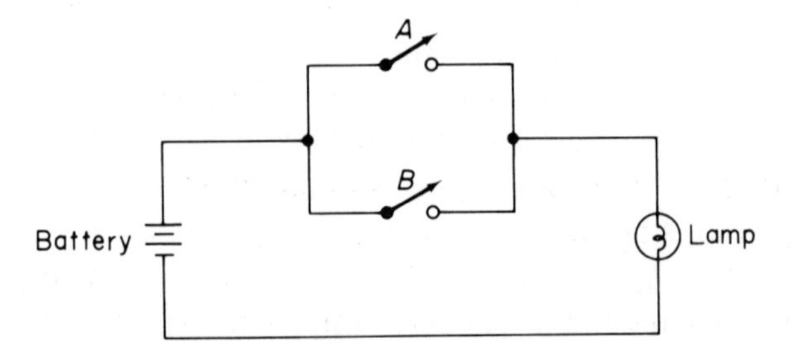

closed). If either or both switches are in the binary-0 position (switch open), the AND gate will be closed (lamp unlit).

Similarly, we may illustrate the OR gate by an electrical analogy. See Figure 4-4. In this circuit, switches *A* and *B* are connected in parallel and in series with the battery and lamp. Using the same system of logic notation, we may obtain the following table:

Switch *A*	Switch *B*	Lamp
0	0	0
1	0	1
0	1	1
1	1	1

From this **truth table** we can see that the gate will be open (lamp lit) if either or both of the switches are in the binary-1 position (switch closed). Only when both switches are in the binary-0 position (switch open) simultaneously will the gate be closed (lamp unlit).

1. Logic Symbols

To facilitate the reading of computer diagrams, it is customary to use symbols somewhat as block diagrams to indicate the various logic circuits. In effect, logic symbols and diagrams are a form of language used in computer circuits. One of the major problems encountered by computer technicians is the fact that each manufacturer speaks a different dialect of the same language. No two major manufacturers use identical symbols in instruction manuals to represent the same circuit element.

This problem was supposedly eliminated when MIL-STD-806 was introduced. However, many manufacturers still do not follow this government standard exactly, some with good reason. For example, the logic symbols used by Hewlett-Packard in their instruction manuals clarify many points left unsaid by MIL-STD-806. Throughout the following discussions, the military standard symbols will be used (where a MIL-STD-806 symbol exists). Manufacturer's modifications will also be given (as an alternative) where they clarify operation of the circuit or symbol function.

Truth table		
A	B	C
0	0	0
0	1	0
1	0	0
1	1	1

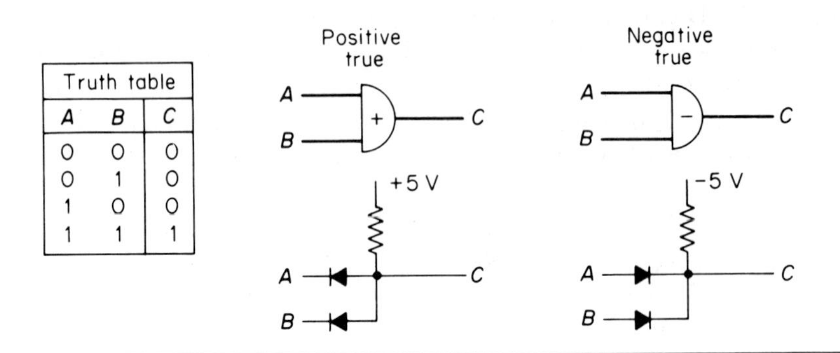

Multiple input

Truth table			
A	B	C	D
0	0	0	0
0	0	1	0
0	1	0	0
0	1	1	0
1	0	0	0
1	1	0	0
1	1	1	1

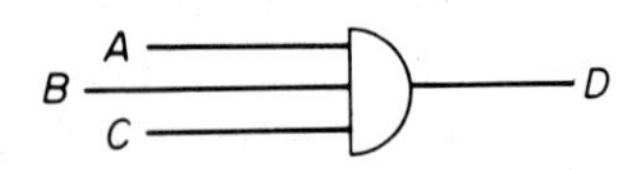

MIL−STD−806

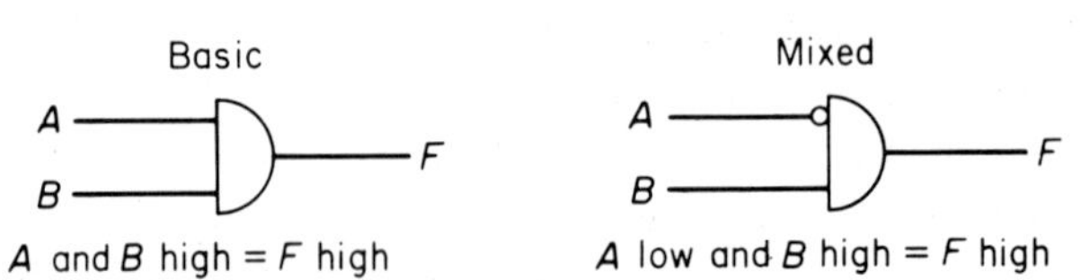

Hewlett−Packard

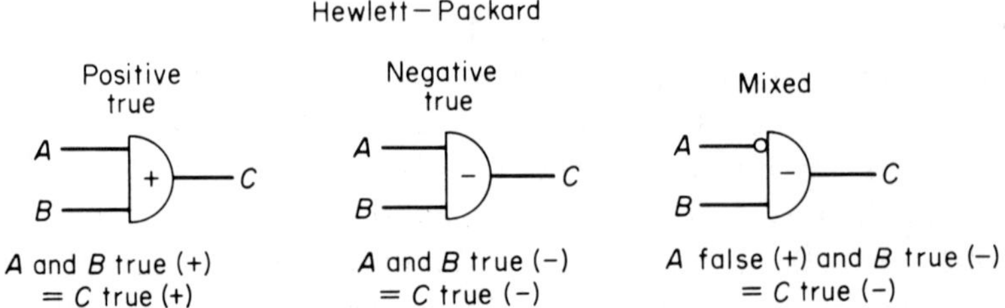

Fig. 4-5. AND gate symbols.

Truth table		
A	*B*	*C*
0	0	0
0	1	1
1	0	1
1	1	1

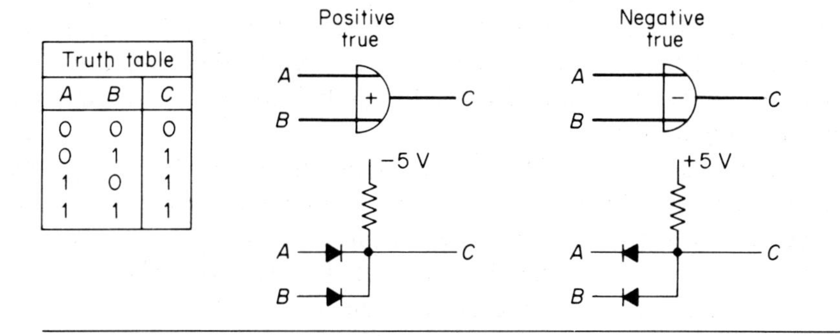

Multiple input

Truth table			
A	*B*	*C*	*D*
0	0	0	0
0	0	1	1
0	1	0	1
0	1	1	1
1	0	0	1
1	0	1	1
1	1	0	1
1	1	1	1

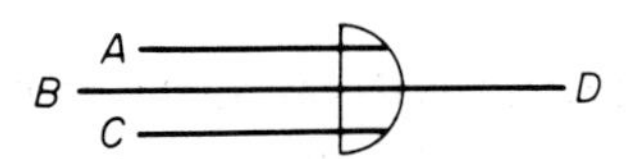

MIL−STD−806

A or *B* high = *F* high

A or *B* low = *F* low

Hewlett − Packard

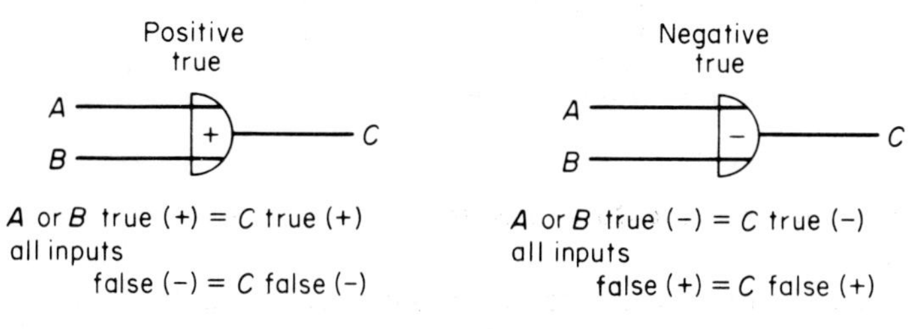

Fig. 4-6. OR gate symbols.

The symbols for the AND gate are shown in Figure 4-5. The two horizontal lines at the left side of the symbols indicate two inputs to the gate. The horizontal line at the right side of the symbols indicates the output. If more than two inputs are applied to the gate, a line for each additional input is added to the symbol, as shown for multiple inputs in Figure 4-5.

The symbols for the OR gate are shown in Figure 4-6. As before, the two horizontal lines at the left of the symbol indicate the two inputs to the gate, while the single horizontal line at the right indicates the output. However, note that the shape of the MIL-STD-806 OR gate symbol is different from the AND gate. (The MIL-STD OR gate symbol is similar to a shield in shape.) The OR gate is also represented by many manufacturers as an AND gate symbol, with the horizontal input lines continuing through the symbol. As with the AND gate, if more than two inputs are applied to the gate, a line for each additional input is added to the symbol, as shown for multiple inputs in Figure 4-6.

With both AND and OR gates, the input lines connect to the flat side of the symbol, and the output lines connect to the curved side. Since inputs and outputs are thus easily identifiable, the symbol can be shown facing left or facing right (or facing up or down), as shown in Figure 4-7.

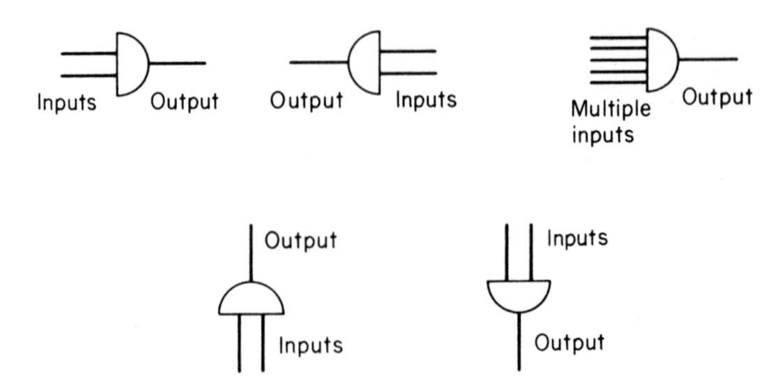

Fig. 4-7. Basic gate symbols (arranged as they may appear on computer logic diagrams).

2. Semiconductor-Diode Gate Circuits

Semiconductor diodes are commonly used in gate circuits similar to that shown in Figure 4-8. In this circuit, the anodes of both diodes

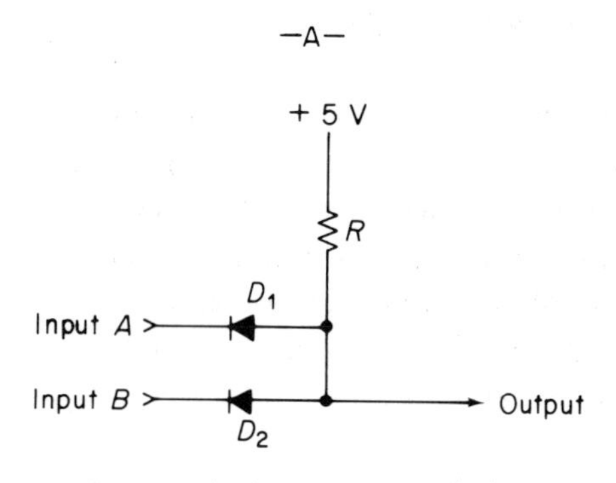

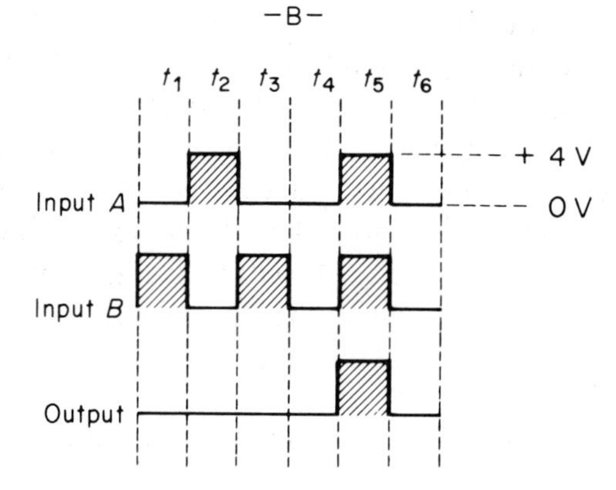

Fig. 4-8. Basic diode AND gate circuit and pulse relationships.

D_1 and D_2 are tied together and are connected to a source of positive voltage (typically 5 V) through resistor *R*. Output is taken from the junction of the two anodes.

Assume that inputs *A* and *B* consist of two sets of pulses, as shown in Figure 4-8B. Assume, further, that the voltage of the upper level of these pulses is more positive than the lower level and less positive than the positive voltage of the source. For example, the voltage source is +5 V, the high level of pulse is +4 V, and the low level of pulse is 0 V.

Let us start with time interval t_1. Input *A* is at the lower level (0 V) and input *B* is at the upper level (+4 V). Initially D_1 and D_2 would both be conductive since their anodes are positive in relation to their cathodes. But since the potential difference between the source (+5 V) and input *A* (0 V) is greater than the potential difference between the source and input B (+4 V), diode D_1 is more heavily conducting and therefore takes charge of the action.

Since D_1 is conductive, the anode assumes the same voltage as the cathode (approximately 0 V). Since the anode of D_1 is connected to the anode of D_2, both anodes assume the lower-level voltage. With the cathode of D_2 at +4 V (input B) and the anode at 0 V, D_2 becomes nonconductive. For all practical purposes, D_2 is removed from the circuit. Thus the circuit will function as if only D_1 is present. As a result the output is the same as input A, that is, the lower-level voltage (or 0 V).

At time interval t_2, we have a similar condition, except that input A is at +4 V and input B is at 0 V. Now, D_1 becomes nonconductive and, again, the output is at the lower-level voltage (or 0 V). At time interval t_3 we have the same conditions as at t_1. At time inverval t_4 both inputs are at the lower level. Since both diodes remain conductive, the output is the same as the input, that is, the lower-level voltage (or 0 V).

At time interval t_5, both inputs are at the upper level (+4 V). The diode anodes are still more positive than the cathodes. Thus both diodes remain conductive and, again, the output is the same as the input. However, this time the output is the upper-level voltage (+4 V). At time interval t_6, we have the same condition as at t_4, and the output drops back to the lower-level voltage.

From an examination of Figure 4-8B, we can summarize the entire action in the following table:

Input A	Input B	Output
Lower level	Lower level	Lower level
Lower level	Upper level	Lower level
Upper level	Lower level	Lower level
Upper level	Upper level	Upper level

From a logic standpoint, we may consider one level of the pulse as representing one binary digit and the other level as representing the opposite binary digit. If we use positive logic, the upper level is considered as binary 1 and the lower level as binary 0. Our table thus becomes

Input A	Input B	Output
0	0	0
0	1	0
1	0	0
1	1	1

Note that the output is binary 1 if and only if both inputs are at binary 1 simultaneously. Thus by this logic we have a **positive** AND gate.

If negative logic is used, we consider the lower level of the pulse as representing binary 1 and the upper level as binary 0. Thus our table becomes

Input A	Input B	Output
1	1	1
1	0	1
0	1	1
0	0	0

Note that the output is binary 1 if either or both inputs are binary 1. Only when both inputs are binary 0 simultaneously does the output become binary 0. This, then, is a **negative** OR gate. Thus the same circuit can be a positive AND gate or a negative OR gate, depending on the logic used, as shown by reference to Figures 4-5 and 4-6.

It should be noted that we are concerned here with two voltage levels applied to each input. It makes no difference where these two voltage levels come from. They may come from a pulse or from any other direct-current (d-c) source. Also, note that the output pulse is a sharp spike (narrow pulse). If rectangular pulses are required, special pulse-shaping circuits may be used to change the spike to a rectangular pulse.

At this point, some questions may arise. Why do we need an OR gate? Why not connect both input circuits directly to the output? However, if both input circuits are tied together, they would affect each other and thus interfere with the levels of the input pulses. Also, there would be interference between the input and output signals. By using an OR gate, both input circuits are isolated from each other. Also, since the output signal cannot flow back through the circuit, there is no interaction between input and output signals. In effect, the OR gate acts as a form of buffer stage.

The circuit of another two-input diode gate circuit is illustrated in Figure 4-9A. Note that this circuit is similar to the one shown in Figure 4-8A. However, the diodes are reversed and the cathodes are connected to the negative voltage source through resistor *R*. Assume that the input pulses resemble those used for Figure 4-8, except that the voltage of the lower level is more negative than the upper level and less negative than the source voltage. For example, the voltage source is −5 V, the high level of pulse is 0 V, and the low level of pulse is −4 V.

With the upper level at input *A* and the lower level at input *B*,

Fig. 4-9. Two-input diode gate using negative-going pulses.

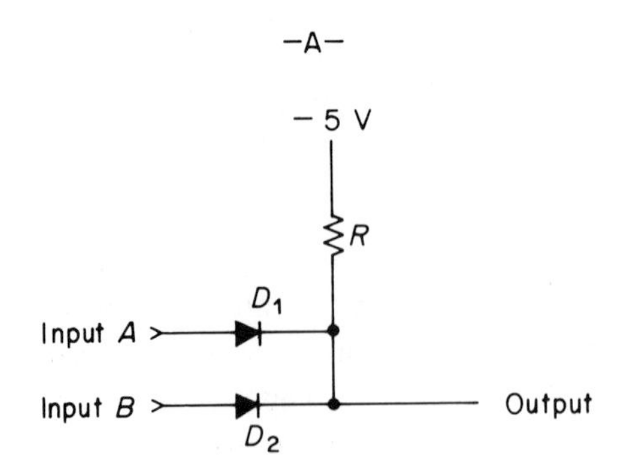

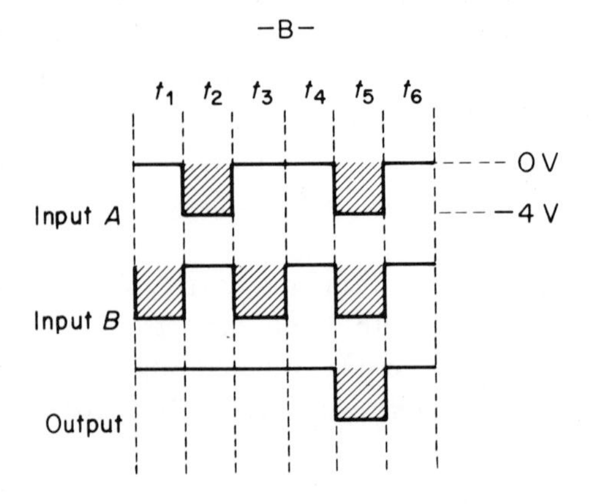

diode D_1 is more conductive. Accordingly, D_2 becomes nonconductive and the output becomes the same as input A (upper level, or 0 V). If input A is at the lower level and input B at the upper level, D_1 becomes nonconductive and the output becomes the same as input B (upper level, or 0 V). With both inputs at the upper level, both diodes are conductive and the output becomes the same as the inputs (upper level, or 0 V). With both inputs at the lower level, both diodes again are conductive. Accordingly, the output again becomes the same as the inputs, or −4 V.

We can summarize the entire action of the gate as follows:

Input A	Input B	Output
Upper level	Upper level	Upper level
Upper level	Lower level	Upper level
Lower level	Upper level	Upper level
Lower level	Lower level	Lower level

If positive logic is used, the upper level of the pulse is represented by binary 1 and the lower level by binary 0. Our table thus becomes

Input A	Input B	Output
1	1	1
1	0	1
0	1	1
0	0	0

You will recognize this as an OR gate, and, using positive logic, the circuit becomes a positive OR gate. If negative logic is used, the lower level of the pulse (−4 V) is represented by binary 1 and the upper level (0 V) by binary 0. The table then becomes

Input A	Input B	Output
0	0	0
0	1	0
1	0	0
1	1	1

You will recognize this as an AND gate. Thus the same circuit may be a positive OR gate or a negative AND gate, depending on the logic used, as shown by reference to Figures 4-5 and 4-6.

Up to now, we have been considering gates with two inputs. It is possible to have such gates with more than two inputs. All we need to do is add another diode, connected in the same configuration as the others (Figures 4-8 and 4-9), for each additional input. Then, for an AND gate, only when all the inputs are at binary 1 simultaneously will a binary-1 output be produced. At all other times, the output will be binary 0. For an OR gate, if any of the inputs is at binary 1, the output will be binary 1. If all the inputs are at binary 0, the output will be at binary 0.

Fig. 4-10. How individual gates may be connected to produce multiple-input gates.

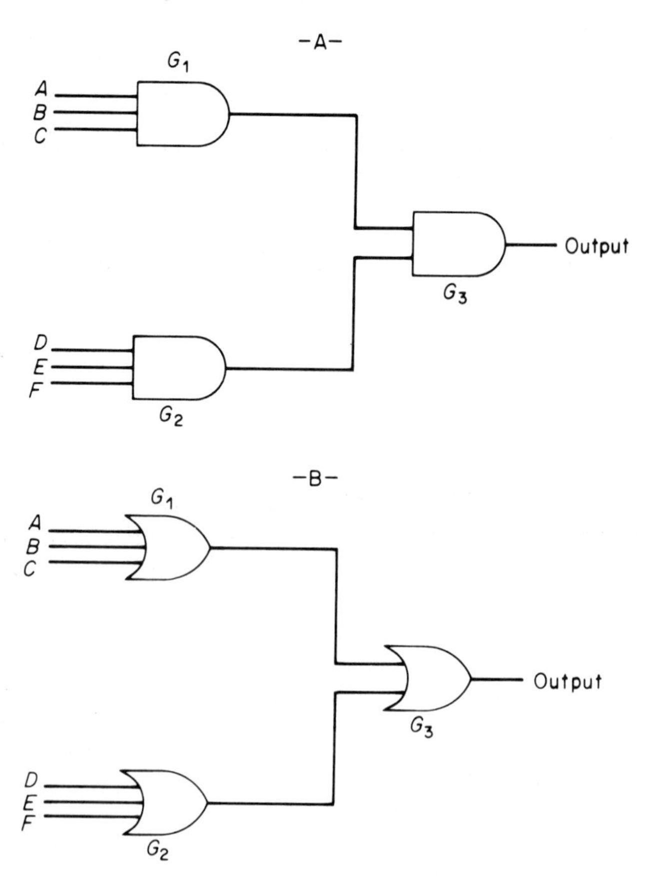

There is a practical limit to the number of inputs a gate circuit can accommodate, because a nonconductive semiconductor diode does not present an infinite resistance but rather some finite resistance. Thus a very small current (termed **reverse current**) will flow through the diode in a nonconductive state. If too many inputs are used by the gate, the reverse current may become large enough to interfere with the pulses.

If more inputs are required than a single gate can accommodate, several similar gates may be paralleled, as shown in Figure 4-10.

In Figure 4-10A, gates G_1 and G_2 are each three-input AND gates. Only if inputs A, B, and C of G_1 are simultaneously at binary 1 will the output from G_1 be binary 1. Similarly, only if inputs D, E, and F are at binary 1 simultaneously will the output from G_2 be at binary 1. The outputs from G_1 and G_2 form the inputs to the two-input AND gate G_3. Only when these inputs are simultaneously at binary 1 will the output of G_3 be at binary 1. Thus the entire circuit forms the equivalent of a six-input AND gate.

As shown in Figure 4-10B, two three-input OR gates may be connected to form the equivalent of a six-input OR gate. If any of inputs A, B, and C is at binary 1, the output of gate G_1 is binary 1. Similarly, if any of inputs D, E, and F is at binary 1, the output of gate G_2 is binary 1. Since the outputs of G_1 and G_2 form the inputs of the two-input OR gate G_3, if any of the six inputs to G_1 and G_2 is at binary 1, the output from G_3 is binary 1.

The gate combinations shown in Figure 4-10 are often contained in a single package (particularly IC packages). Since the packages are sealed, the package can be considered as a multiple-input (six-input, nine-input, and so forth) gate from a troubleshooting standpoint.

The reverse of a multiple-input gate is an ENCODE gate. As shown in Figure 4-11, the ENCODE gate has one input and multiple outputs.

Fig. 4-11. ENCODE gate symbol. (Courtesy of Hewlett-Packard.)

(Positive true shown)

Truth table				
A	*B*	*C*	*D*	*E*
0	Open			
1	1	1	1	1

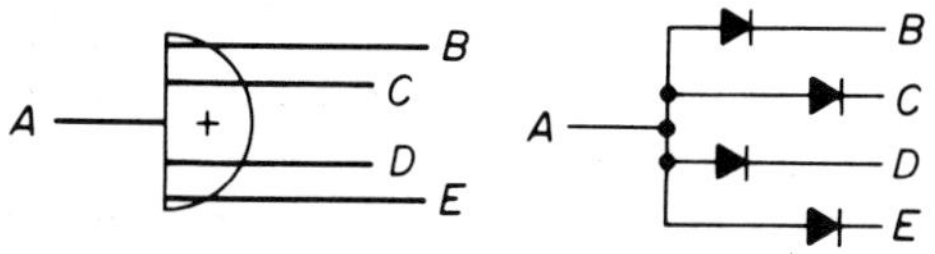

Input *A* true (+) makes all outputs (*B*, *C*, *D*, *E*) true (+)

When the input is true (say at binary 1), all outputs are true (binary 1). When the input is at binary 0, all outputs are at binary 0.

A plus or minus sign is often placed in the symbol to indicate the true state. In the circuit of Figure 4-11, with input *A* positive, all diodes conduct and all outputs are clamped positive. This would be true of binary 1 in a positive-true system. With input *A* negative in the same system, all diodes would be open (nonconducting), producing a false or binary 0.

3. Transistor Gate Circuits

Transistors can be used in gate circuits. Often, transistor gates are preferred to diode gates because of the amplifying ability of the transistor. Thus any reduction of pulse level encountered in passing through the gate is compensated by the amplifying action.

A typical transistor gate circuit is shown in Figure 4-12. This circuit uses two transistors, Q_1 and Q_2, in a parallel common-emitter configuration. Since the transistors are PNP, the emitter-base junction is normally forward-biased by $-V_{BB}$. Because of this bias, Q_1 and Q_2 con-

Fig. 4-12. Basic parallel transistor gate circuit.

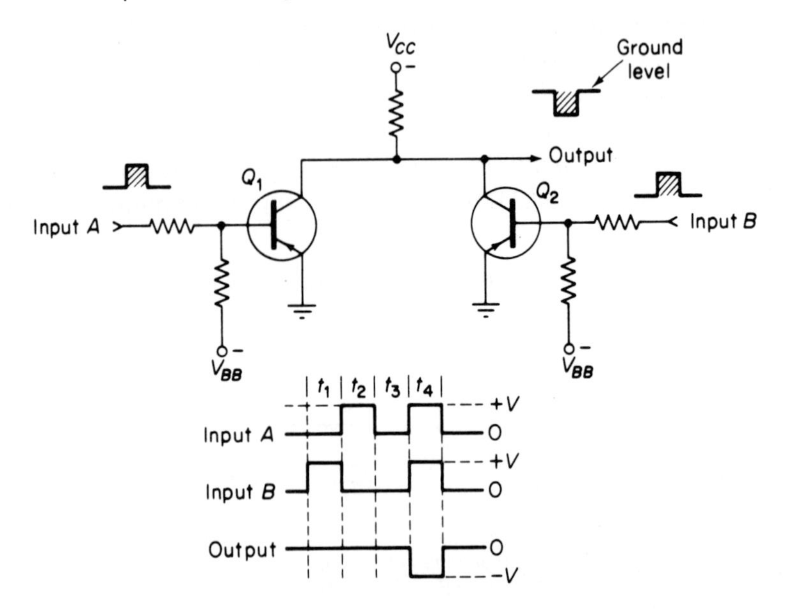

duct heavily (their emitter-to-collector resistances drop to near zero and the collector voltage reaches saturation, V_{CE}(SAT)), and the output drops to near-ground value.

Assume that the input pulses are positive-going with a lower-level voltage that is insufficient to overcome the forward bias presented by $-V_{BB}$ and an upper-level voltage that can overcome the bias. If such a pulse is applied to input A at the lower level, Q_1 remains conductive and the output voltage remains at its near-ground level. At the upper level of the pulse applied to A, the forward bias is overcome, and the emitter-base junction of Q_1 is reverse-biased. As a result, Q_1 is cut off, and the output should change to some value approaching $-V_{CC}$. However, Q_2 is still conductive, so the output voltage remains at its near-ground level.

If a similar pulse is applied to input B, a similar action takes place, but now Q_2 is cut off, Q_1 is conductive, and the output voltage remains at near-ground level.

If two such pulses are applied simultaneously to inputs A and B (with both pulses at their lower levels), both Q_1 and Q_2 remain conductive and the output voltage remains at near-ground level. When both pulses are at their upper levels, both Q_1 and Q_2 are cut off. The output voltage then changes to some value approaching $-V_{CC}$.

We can tabulate the action of this transistor gate as follows:

Input A	Input B	Output
Lower level	Lower level	Upper level
Lower level	Upper level	Upper level
Upper level	Lower level	Upper level
Upper level	Upper level	Lower level

Note with transistor gates that when the input pulses go from the lower levels to the upper levels, the output pulse goes from the upper level to the lower level. This is produced by the common-emitter (or grounded-emitter) configuration of the transistor, which causes such a phase inversion.

If we use positive logic, the upper level of the pulse is considered as binary 1 and the lower level as binary 0. However, for the sake of consistency, because of the phase inversion of the output, we must consider the output lower level as binary 1 and the output upper level as binary 0. (Note that when this is done, the phase inversion does not affect the logic.)

Our table thus becomes

Input A	Input B	Output
0	0	0
0	1	0
1	0	0
1	1	1

If we use NPN transistors instead of PNP types in the circuit of Figure 4-12, both V_{BB} and V_{CC} must be positive values, and the input pulses must be negative-going, with an upper level that is insufficient to overcome the forward bias of $+V_{BB}$ and a lower level that is sufficient to overcome the bias. Because of phase inversion, the output pulse is positive-going with a lower-level voltage near ground and an upper-level voltage that approaches $+V_{CC}$. The action is similar to that of the PNP transistor circuit, except that the logic is reversed. Accordingly, we have a negative AND gate or a positive OR gate.

A series transistor gate circuit is shown in Figure 4-13. Because of the reverse bias produced by $+V_{BB}$, Q_1 and Q_2 are cut off, and the output voltage becomes some value approaching $-V_{CC}$.

Input pulses are negative-going, with upper-level voltages not sufficient to overcome the bias furnished by $+V_{BB}$ but with lower-level voltages sufficient to do so. If the upper level of the pulses is applied to either or both of the transistors, both Q_1 and Q_2 remain in the cutoff condition, and the output voltage remains at some value near $-V_{CC}$. If the lower level of the pulse is applied to either of the two inputs, the corresponding transistor becomes conductive. However, the other transistor remains at cutoff, and since this is a series circuit, the output voltage remains at some value near $-V_{CC}$.

Only when the lower levels of the pulses are applied simultaneously to both inputs do both transistors become conductive at the same time. When this occurs, the output voltage rises to a near-ground level. Note that, again, we have a phase inversion or reversal between the input and output pulses.

Using positive logic and taking into account the phase inversion, we can summarize the action of the series gate as follows:

Input *A*	Input *B*	Output
1	1	1
1	0	1
0	1	1
0	0	0

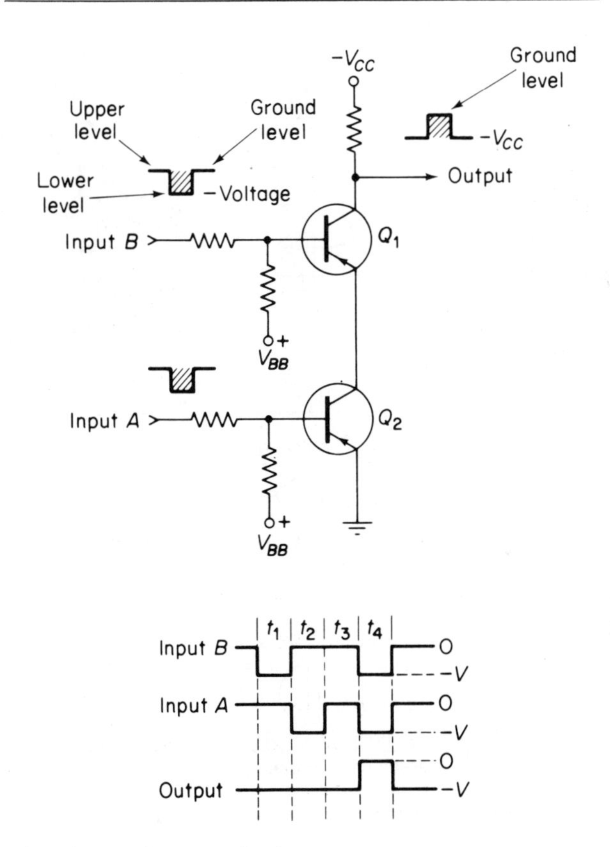

Fig. 4-13. Basic series transistor gate circuit.

Thus we have a positive OR gate or a negative AND gate, whichever logic system is used.

Transistor gates may have more than two inputs by adding a transistor and its associated components in the same configuration (as the others in the gate) for each additional input. As in the case of diode gates, transistor gates should not have too many inputs. However, transistor gates may be paralleled to accommodate additional inputs.

The EXCLUSIVE OR gate is one that usually requires both diodes and transistors. As shown in Figure 4-14, the EXCLUSIVE OR gate has two inputs and an output that will be true if one but not both of the inputs is true. The converse statement is equally accurate: The output will be false if the inputs are both true or both false.

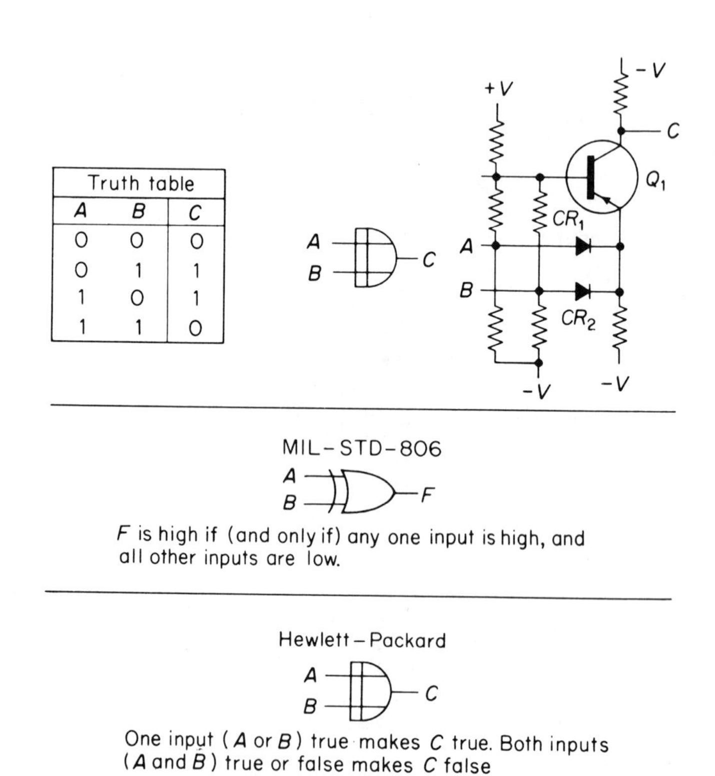

Truth table

A	B	C
0	0	0
0	1	1
1	0	1
1	1	0

A
B
C
+V
-V
Q1
CR1
CR2
-V
-V
MIL-STD-806
A
B
F
F is high if (and only if) any one input is high, and all other inputs are low.
Hewlett-Packard
A
B
C
One input (A or B) true makes C true. Both inputs (A and B) true or false makes C false

Fig. 4-14. EXCLUSIVE OR gate symbol.

It should be noted that when the term OR is used with a gate, an INCLUSIVE OR gate is implied. That is, the output is true if either or both inputs are true. However, in some computer service literature, the gates are identified specifically as INCLUSIVE OR and EXCLUSIVE OR.

The EXCLUSIVE OR gate is independent of polarity and is not generally spoken of as being either positive-true or negative-true.

The operation of the EXCLUSIVE OR gate in Figure 4-14 is as

follows. If either input *A* or *B* is positive, Q_1 will be biased on via CR_1 or CR_2, and the *C* output is positive. If *A* and *B* are both negative, Q_1 is biased on, but the voltage at the Q_1 emitter is negative, and the *C* output is negative. With *A* and *B* both positive, Q_1 is biased off, and the *C* output remains negative. (These results require proper selection of resistor values and operating voltages.)

C. INVERTER, AMPLIFIER, AND PHASE-SPLITTER CIRCUITS

In the digital computer, there are times when it is necessary to invert the polarity of a pulse in order to perform some logical function, or inversion may become necessary to obtain the correct voltage level for some electrical operation. The device used for this purpose is called an **inverter**. The simplest type of inverter is the transformer, where the secondary voltage is 180° out of phase with the primary voltage. In computers, however, phase inversion is generally performed by transistor amplifiers connected in a common-emitter configuration.

When an amplifier is used in any digital work, it is assumed that the output will essentially be the same as the input but in amplified form. That is, a binary-1 input will produce a binary-1 output and vice versa. When inversion occurs, an inversion dot (or possibly an inverted pulse symbol) is placed at the output of the amplifier on the logic diagram. Usually, the element is then termed an inverter rather than an amplifier, even though amplification may occur. (On older logic diagrams, the accepted inverter symbol is a circle with the letter I inside.)

In computer work, an amplifier may be used as a **phase splitter**, that is, one input with dual outputs. One of the dual outputs is in phase with the input, while the other output is out of phase with the input. A similar case exists with **differential amplifiers**, which have dual inputs and dual outputs (although some differential amplifiers have dual inputs and a single output).

Figure 4-15 shows the symbols used on logic diagrams for amplifiers, inverters, and phase splitters. Note that if a plus or minus sign is used in the symbol, this indicates the input polarity required to turn the amplifier on. Also note that one amplifier or inverter symbol may represent any number of amplification stages, or, optionally, separate symbols may be shown for each stage. Logic symbols, by themselves,

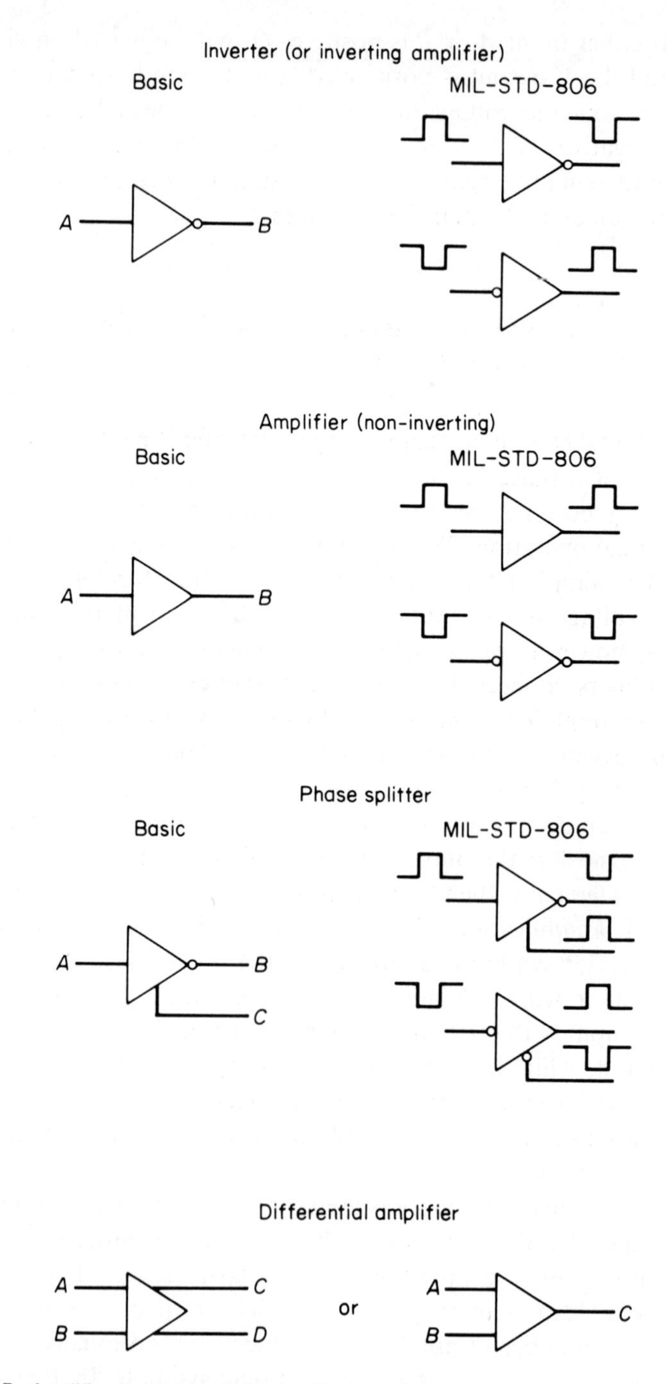

Fig. 4-15. Amplifier, inverter, and phase-splitter symbols.

do not necessarily imply a specific number of components but rather relate to overall logic effect. The rule for inversion dots on phase splitters and (particularly) differential amplifiers is that the dot indicates inversion of an output with respect to the corresponding input (not with respect to the opposite side of the amplifier). For example, if an inversion dot is placed on the *C* output of the differential amplifier shown in Figure 4-15, this will indicate that the *C* output is inverted with respect to the A input.

A transistor version of an inverter circuit is shown in Figure 4-16. Here, an NPN transistor is connected in a common-emitter configuration. The emitter-base junction is reverse-biased by $-V_{BB}$. As a result, the transistor is cut off, and the output voltage is at (or near) the $+V_{CC}$ level.

Assume that the lower level of the input pulse is not sufficient to overcome the negative reverse bias ($-V_{BB}$) but that the upper level of the input pulse can overcome the bias. At the lower level, the transistor remains cut off, and the output voltage remains at the $+V_{CC}$ level. At the upper level, the bias is overcome, and the transistor conducts heavily. As a result, the output drops to near-ground level.

Here we have a phase inversion with the lower level of the input pulse producing the upper level of the output pulse and vice versa. If, in a logic system, we consider the upper level as binary 1 and the lower level as binary 0, a binary 0 at the input produces a binary 1 at the output and vice versa.

A PNP transistor may be substituted for the NPN type in the circuit of Figure 4-16. However, the polarities of the bias voltages and the pulses (both input and output) are reversed.

Fig. 4-16. Basic solid-state inverter circuit.

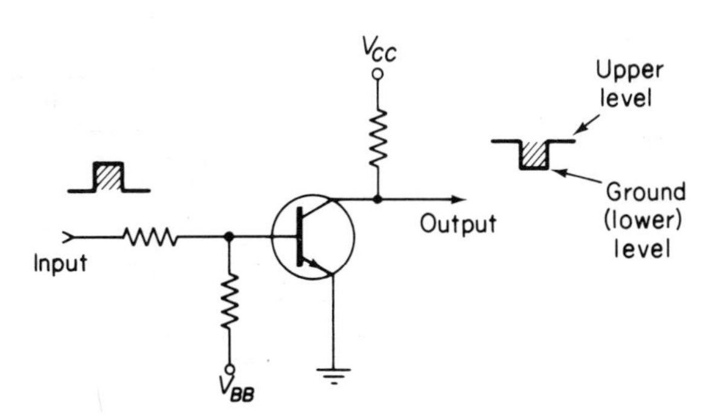

In addition to phase inversion, the inverter circuit of Figure 4-16 acts as an amplifier. As a pulse passes through a diode gate, the voltage levels tend to decrease due to resistance. The gain of the amplifier helps to restore these levels to their normal values. The gain can also provide additional power to drive several other gates.

When used in a logic system, the inverter sometimes is called a NOT circuit, because if a binary 1 is applied to the input, the output is **not** binary 1.

D. NAND AND NOR GATE CIRCUITS

In the logic circuitry of a computer, it often becomes necessary to change the polarity of the output pulse of a gate or, in logic terms, to change a binary-1 output to a binary-0 output and vice versa. This can be done by an inverter following the gate.

The circuit of an AND gate followed by an inverter is shown in Figure 4-17. The AND gate circuit is similar to those discussed in previous sections. If positive-going pulses are applied simultaneously to inputs *A* and *B*, a positive-going pulse appears at the output of the gate. The positive-going pulse is the input to the inverter. The output of the inverter, then, is a negative-going pulse.

Fig. 4-17. Basic NAND gate circuit.

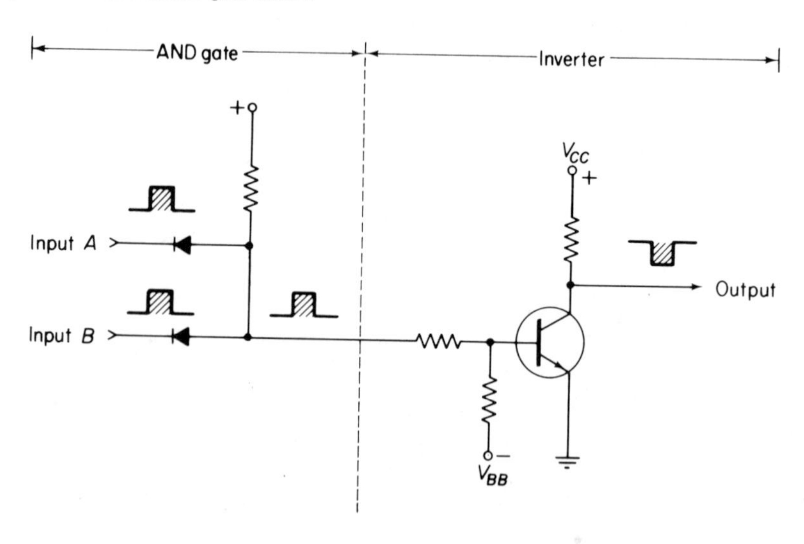

The combination of AND gate and inverter is called a NOT-AND, or NAND, gate. From a binary logic standpoint, if all the inputs are at binary 1 simultaneously, the output from the NAND gate is binary 0. If any input is at binary 0, the output is binary 1. The symbols for the NAND gate are shown in Figure 4-18. The small circle at the output of the symbol (or at both inputs) indicates the NOT or invert function.

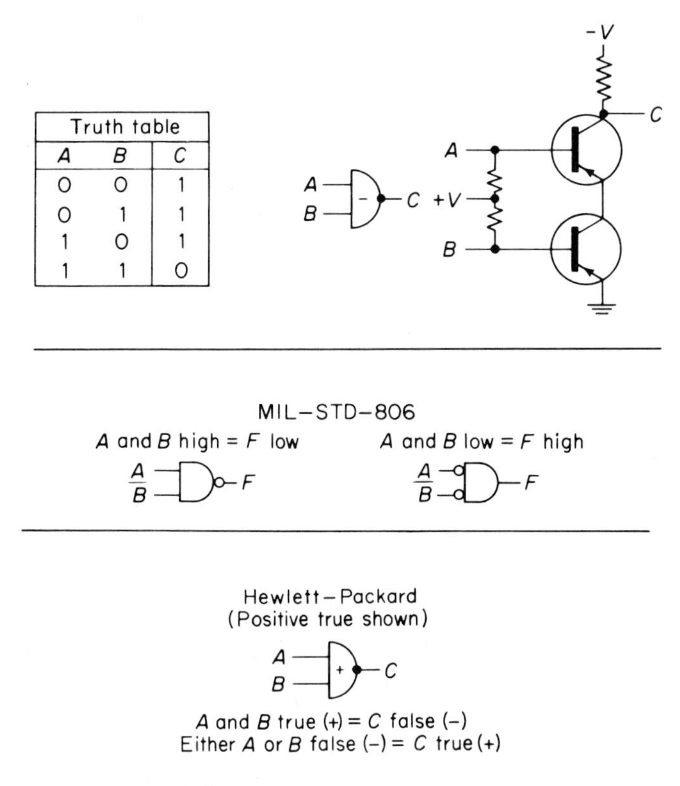

Fig. 4-18. NAND gate symbols.

Similarly, an OR gate may be combined with an inverter to form a NOT-OR, or NOR, gate. If any of the inputs to the OR gate are at binary 1, the output is binary 1. This output becomes the input to the inverter, whose output then becomes binary 0. Thus, if any input to a NOR gate is at binary 1, the output is at binary 0. The symbols for the NOR gate are shown in Figure 4-19. The circuit of Figure 4-19 uses two transistors, thus eliminating the need for an inverter.

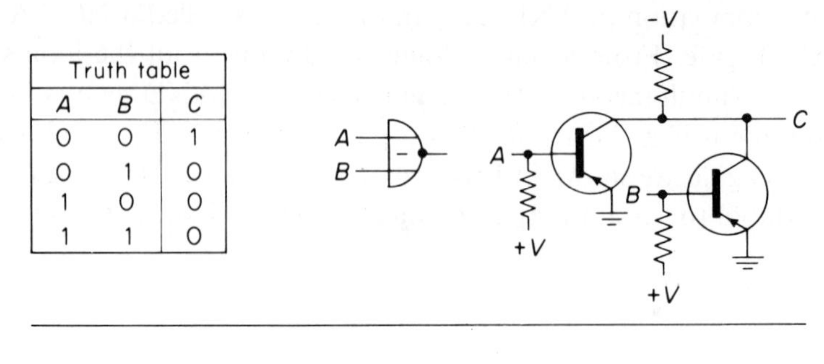

Truth table		
A	B	C
0	0	1
0	1	0
1	0	0
1	1	0

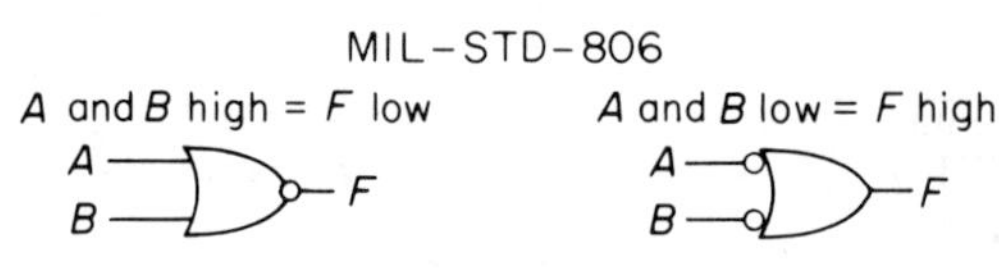

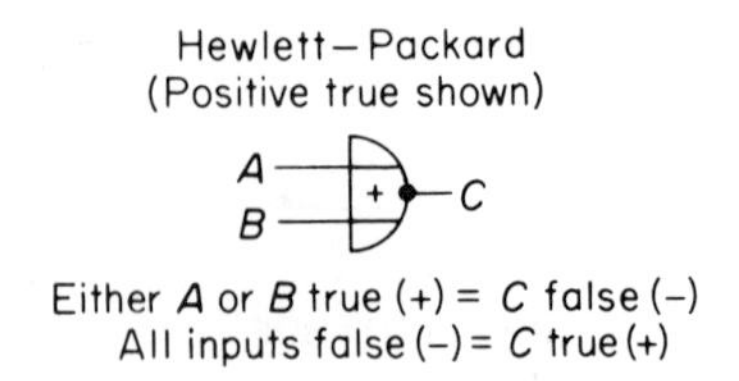

Fig. 4-19. NOR gate symbols.

E. INHIBIT GATE CIRCUIT

The inverter may also be used in the form of a gate to invert the polarity of one or more of the inputs to the gate. Such a circuit is shown in Figure 4-20.

Disregard, for the moment, input *C* to the three-input AND gate. Assume that inputs *A* and *B* are simultaneously at binary 1. The gate then acts as a two-input *open* AND gate, and the output is binary 1. Now assume that input *C* is at binary 1 at the same time. Because of the inverter action, this binary 1 is changed to a binary 0 before it reaches the gate. Accordingly, with binary 1 at two inputs and binary 0 at the other input, the AND gate is *closed* and the output is binary 0.

Thus the presence of a binary-1 signal at the input to the inverter produces a binary-0 signal, which, in turn, inhibits the AND gate. Accordingly, the combination of inverter and gate is called an INHIBIT gate. The symbol for the INHIBIT gate is shown in Figure 4-20. Note

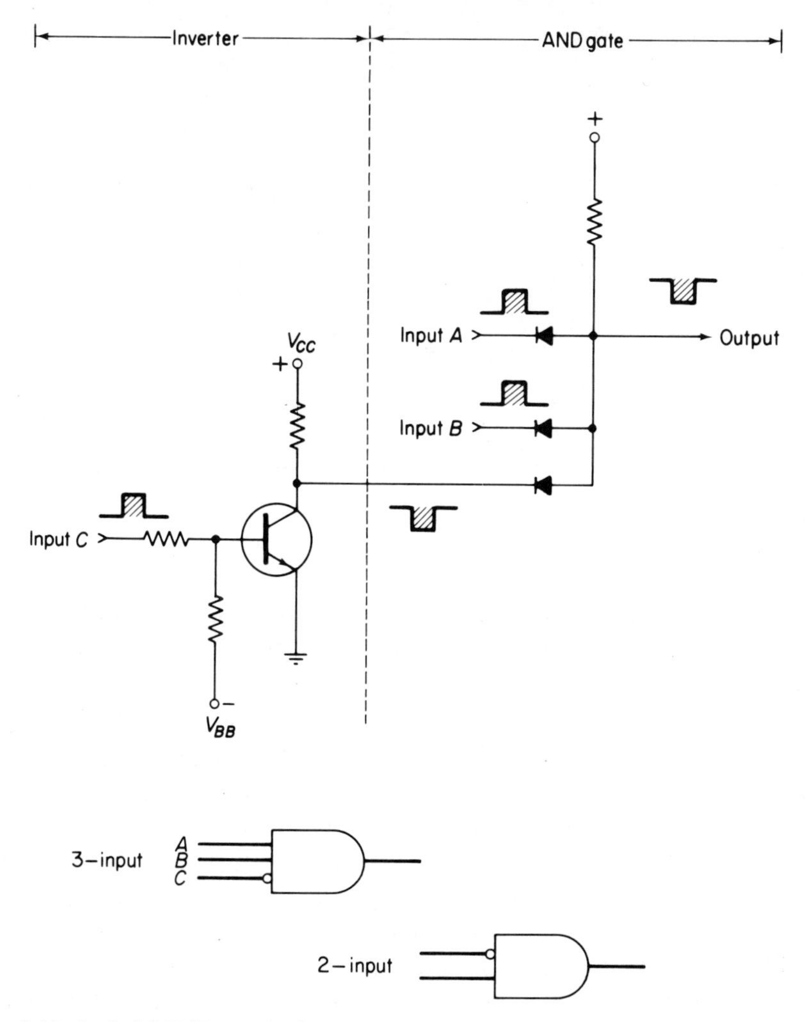

Fig. 4-20. Basic INHIBIT gate circuit.

that an INHIBIT gate can have two or more inputs. The small circle at the input line on the symbol indicates the invert function for that particular input.

F. FLIP-FLOP CIRCUIT

The **bistable multivibrator**, or **flip-flop** (FF), circuit is frequently used in computers. The FF is able to "remember" whether a binary

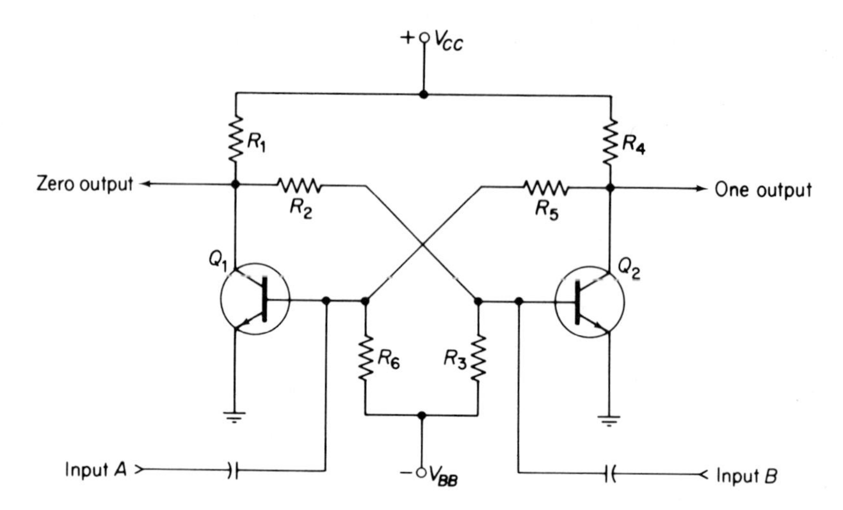

Fig. 4-21. Basic FF circuit.

digit is 1 or 0 and is able to convert one to the other upon application of a triggering pulse. The basic circuit of a FF is illustrated in Figure 4-21.

Note that the circuit consists of two inverters, with the output of one directly coupled to the base of the other through resistors R_2 and R_5. Since $R_1 = R_4$, $R_2 = R_5$, and $R_3 = R_6$, the circuit is balanced electrically. The voltage at the base of Q_1 is the result of the positive voltage of V_{CC} and the negative voltage of V_{BB}, as determined by the voltage divider consisting of R_4, R_5, and R_6. The voltage on the base of Q_2 is the result of the positive and negative voltage sources, as determined by the voltage divider consisting of R_1, R_2, and R_3.

Let us begin by assuming that Q_1 starts to conduct more heavily than Q_2 when the stage is energized. Since the collector current of Q_1 rises, the collector voltage drops because of the increased voltage drop across R_1. This lowered voltage, applied to the base of Q_2 through R_2, reduces the collector current of Q_2. As a result, the collector voltage of Q_2 rises and this increased voltage, applied to the base of Q_1 through R_5, makes Q_1 more conductive. This action is cumulative and quickly results in Q_1 conducting heavily and Q_2 being cut off. This is one of the two stable states of the FF. With no external disturbances, the circuit will remain in the state indefinitely.

Now assume that a negative pulse is applied by input *A* to the base of Q_1. This will cause a reduction of the Q_1 collector current and a rise in the Q_1 collector voltage. The increase in voltage is applied to the base of Q_2 through R_2. If the negative pulse is large enough, the increased voltage on the base of Q_2 will be able to bring Q_2 out of cutoff. As Q_2 starts to conduct, the Q_2 collector voltage drops. This reduction in voltage, applied to the base of Q_1 through R_5, further reduces the Q_1 conduction and increases the Q_1 collector voltage. This action, too, is cumulative and quickly results in Q_2 conducting heavily and Q_1 cutting off. This is the other stable state of the FF. As before, with no external disturbances, the circuit will remain in this state indefinitely.

The circuit can be restored to the first state by applying a similar negative pulse at input B to the base of Q_2. The action is similar to that just described and results in Q_1 conducting heavily and Q_2 being cut off. Thus, by applying the negative pulse to the base of whichever transistor is conducting, the circuit can be flipped to the opposite state. Note that the FF can only be in one of the states or the other at any particular time.

Although the transition time from one state to the other is very short, a certain delay is introduced by capacitances of the transistors and other stray capacitances. To reduce this delay, small capacitors, called commutating or *speedup* capacitors, are sometimes connected across R_2 and R_5. Because these capacitors are in series with the transistor capacitances, the overall capacitance and the delay are reduced.

Now let us examine the voltage levels at the circuit outputs. When a transistor is cut off, the output voltage rises toward V_{CC}. When the transistor is conducting heavily, the output voltage drops to some lower level. Thus with the FF in the state where Q_1 is conducting and Q_2 is cut off, the 0 output is at the lower voltage level, and the 1 output is at the upper voltage level. If the FF is in the opposite state (Q_2 conducting and Q_1 cut off), the 0 output is at the upper level and 1 output is at the lower level.

If, by positive logic, an upper voltage level is considered as binary 1 and a lower voltage level as binary 0, an output can be either binary 1 or binary 0. However, when one output is binary 1 (high), the other is binary 0 (low) and vice versa.

A variation of the basic FF circuit is shown in Figure 4-22. Note that the inputs and outputs are labeled and that diodes are added. Consider the FF to be *at rest* when it is in the state where Q_1 is cut off and Q_2 is conducting. Under such conditions, the 0 output will be at its upper voltage level (binary 1) and the 1 output will be at its lower voltage level (binary 0).

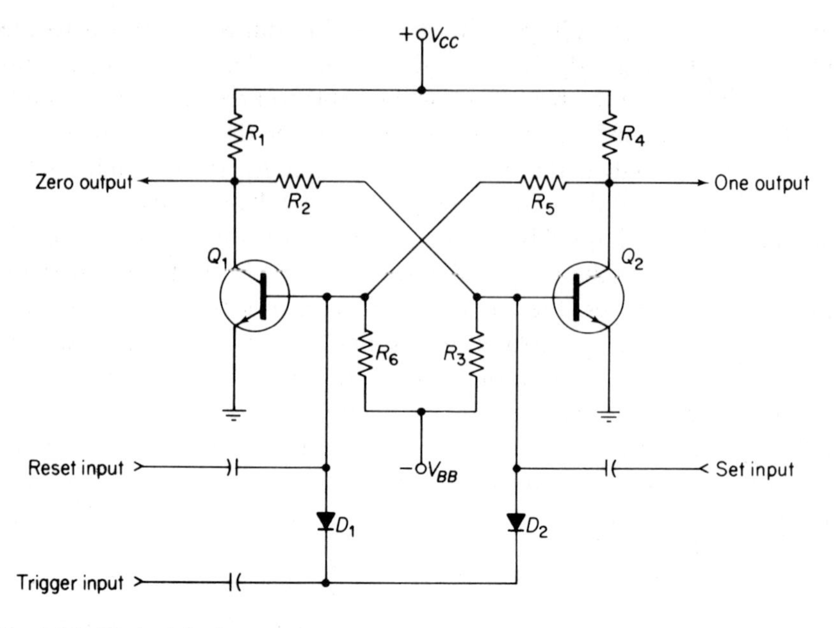

Fig. 4-22. FF circuit with set, reset, and trigger inputs.

If a negative pulse is applied at the *set* input, the circuit will flip to the opposite state, with the 0 output at binary 0 and the 1 output at binary 1. A negative pulse now applied at the *reset* input will restore the FF to the original state, with 0 output at binary 1 and 1 output at binary 0.

To differentiate between the two states of the FF, the state at which the 0 output is at binary 1 and the 1 output at binary 0 is sometimes called the **reset state**. The opposite state, with 0 output at binary 0 and 1 output at binary 1, is called the **set state**.

If a negative pulse is applied at the *trigger* input, the FF will be flipped to its opposite state, regardless of which state the circuit happens to be in at the time. To see how this works, assume that the FF is in the reset state where 0 output is binary 1 and 1 output is binary 0. This means that Q_1 is cut off and Q_2 is conducting.

As the negative pulse is applied at the trigger input, the cathodes of both D_1 and D_2 become negative. Because Q_1 is cut off, the base of Q_1 must be strongly negative, which makes the anode of D_1 negative and prevents the negative trigger pulse from reaching the base of Q_1.

However, since Q_2 is conducting heavily, the base must be at some positive value. With the D_2 anode positive and the cathode negative, D_2 is conductive and so the negative pulse reaches the base of Q_2. As a result, the FF is flipped to the set state with Q_1 conducting, Q_2 cut off, 0 output at binary 0, and 1 output at binary 1.

Diodes D_1 and D_2 are often called **steering diodes** since they steer the trigger pulse to the appropriate transistor.

Assume that a second negative pulse is applied at the trigger input. Now D_2 is nonconductive and D_1 is conductive. Accordingly, the negative pulse gets through to the base of Q_1. The FF is flopped to the reset state, with Q_1 cut off, Q_2 conducting, 0 output at binary 1, and 1 output at binary 0. Thus successive negative pulses applied to the trigger input flip the circuit alternately from one state to the opposite state.

Note that a negative pulse at the trigger input changes an output from binary 1 to binary 0 and vice versa. You will recall that in the binary number system the complement of a binary digit is the opposite digit. (Refer to Chapter 3, subdivision B, 2.) Accordingly, the trigger input sometimes is called the *complementing* input.

1. Types of Flip-flops

There are many types of FF. Those used most frequently in computer circuits are the reset-set (R-S), reset with clock, J-K, toggle, latching, and delay flip-flops.

The basic symbol and rules for applications of FF are shown in Figure 4-23. The following notes provide an explanation of the rules.

The letters FF should appear in either the upper or the lower portion of the symbol, thus identifying the element as a FF (rather than a one-shot multivibrator, Schmitt trigger, and so forth).

A FF is assumed to be the simple R-S type if no other identification is made. When a **clock** input is added, the identifying letter C is placed inside the symbol. A clock input is usually a repetitive pulse (for example, from a time-base generator) and is parallel-connected to both the set and reset side. Clock pulses are transient-operated. That is, they are effective on leading or trailing edges of pulses, somewhat like an alternating-current (a-c) coupled input.

If the clock input has no inversion dot, the input is effective on the true-going edge of the clock pulse. If an inversion dot is shown at the clock input, the clock input is effective on the false-going edge.

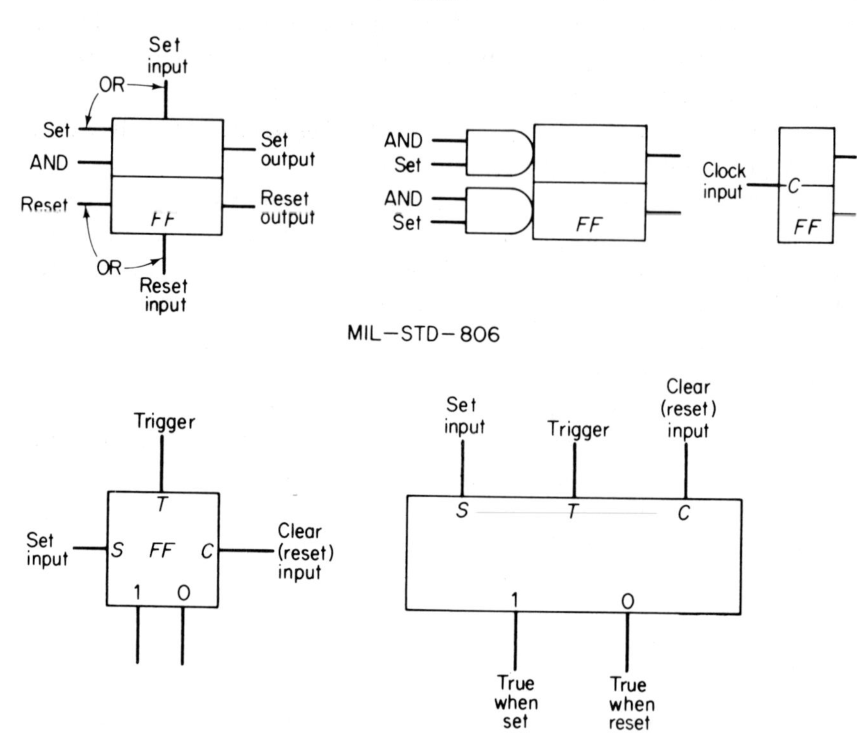

Fig. 4-23. Typical FF symbols.

Multiple inputs on the same side of the FF symbol require the logical AND function (both inputs must be true to set or reset).

Multiple inputs diagonally on the corner of the symbol require the logical OR function (if either input is true, it will set or reset).

In some cases, a gate symbol (AND or OR) will be shown at the set or reset inputs. (This is particularly true where multiple inputs are required.)

2. Reset-Set Flip-flop

The R-S FF has a minimum of two inputs, set and reset (A and B), and usually two outputs, set output and reset output (D and $\bar{D}$), as shown in Figure 4-24.

	Truth table		
A	B	D	$\bar{D}$
1	0	1	0
0	1	0	1
0	0	No change	

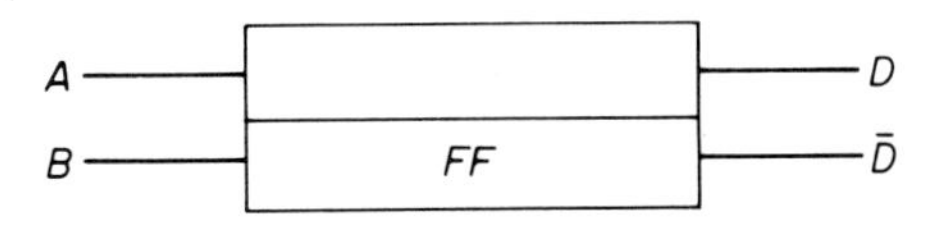

Fig. 4-24. R-S FF symbol and truth table.

The letter $\bar{D}$ indicates that the reset output, whether a 1 or a 0, is always the complement of the set output; that is, when D is true and $\bar{D}$ is false, the FF is defined as being in the set state. With D false and $\bar{D}$ true, the FF is in the reset state.

The FF is set by a true input to A (assuming no inversion dot on the symbol) and is reset by a true input to B. False inputs have no effect on a basic R-S circuit.

Simultaneous true inputs to A and B are forbidden, since some intermediate output state would result. In practice, the FF would try to set and reset simultaneously, probably resulting in an undesired set or reset.

The truth table of Figure 4-24 shows the three allowable input combinations for a basic R-S FF.

If a-c-coupled inputs are used, the FF would be set or reset by true-going transitions at A and B, respectively. If, in addition, input inversion dots are also used, false-going transitions at A or B would set or reset the FF.

3. Reset-Set Flip-flop with Clock Input

An R-S FF with clock (see Figure 4-25) is similar to the basic R-S, except for the addition of the clock input (parallel-connected to both set and reset inputs).

A true input is required to both A and C to set the FF, and a true input to B and C is required for reset.

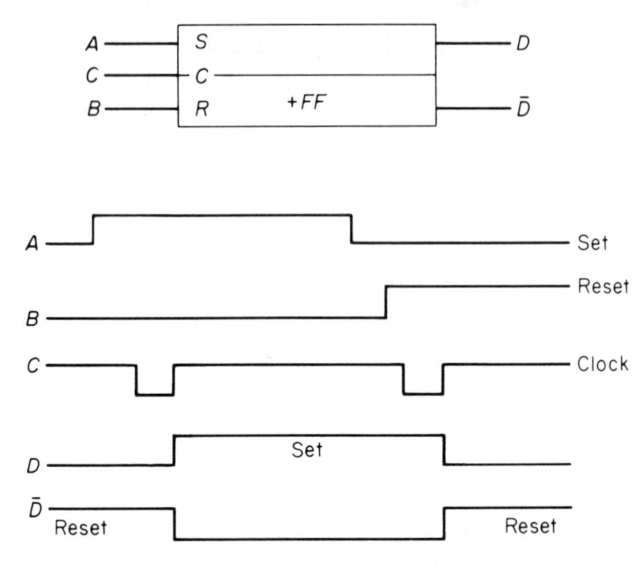

Fig. 4-25. R-S FF with clock input.

Since the clock input operates on a pulse edge, the setting or resetting must be present at *A* or *B* before the clock pulse transition occurs. This time relationship is shown (in positive-true form) in Figure 4-25.

4. J-K Flip-flops

A J-K FF is used (instead of an R-S FF) where there is a possibility of two simultaneous true inputs (which would result in an unpredictable output from an R-S FF).

With a J-K FF, simultaneous true inputs for both set and reset will reverse the existing state of the FF. This requires some method of **storing** two information conditions (the existing output state and the new input state) until the clock pulse time.

Storage can be accomplished by (1) a-c coupling or (2) a dual-rank FF, as shown in Figure 4-26.

The a-c-coupling method uses the *RC* time constant of the capacitive input for short-term storage of the input information.

The dual-rank method combines two FF (input storage and output storage) and several gates as a single logic element. For simplicity of

Truth table					
A	B	Initial state		Resulting state	
		D	$\bar{D}$	D	$\bar{D}$
1	0			1	0
0	1			0	1
1	1	0	1	1	0
1	1	1	0	0	1
0	0			No change	

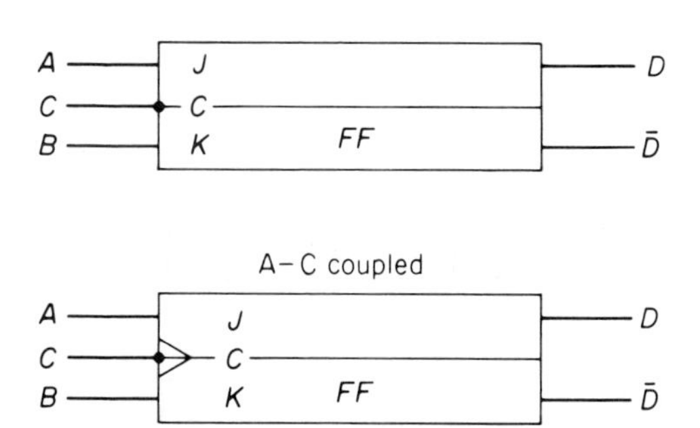

Fig. 4-26. J-K FF symbols and truth table.

representation, the internal dual-rank arrangement of the FF is not usually shown.

Overall operation of a J-K FF (either a-c-coupled or dual-rank) is summarized as follows (and in the truth table of Figure 4-26).

With a true input at *A* only, the leading edge of the clock pulse acknowledges (stores) the input information at *A*; the trailing edge of the clock pulse sets the FF.

With a true input at *B* only, the leading edge of the clock pulse acknowledges (stores) the input information at *B*; the trailing edge of the clock pulse resets the FF.

With true inputs at both *A* and *B*, the leading edge of the clock pulse acknowledges the input information at *A* and *B*; the trailing edge of the clock pulse switches the existing state of the FF.

5. Toggle Flip-flop

The toggle FF has only one input, as shown in Figure 4-27. Each time input A goes true, outputs D and $\bar{D}$ switch states. Since two input pulses or cycles are required to produce one complete cycle of the output, the toggle FF acts as a divide-by-2 element and is commonly used in counting circuits. The letter T inside the symbol identifies the toggle FF.

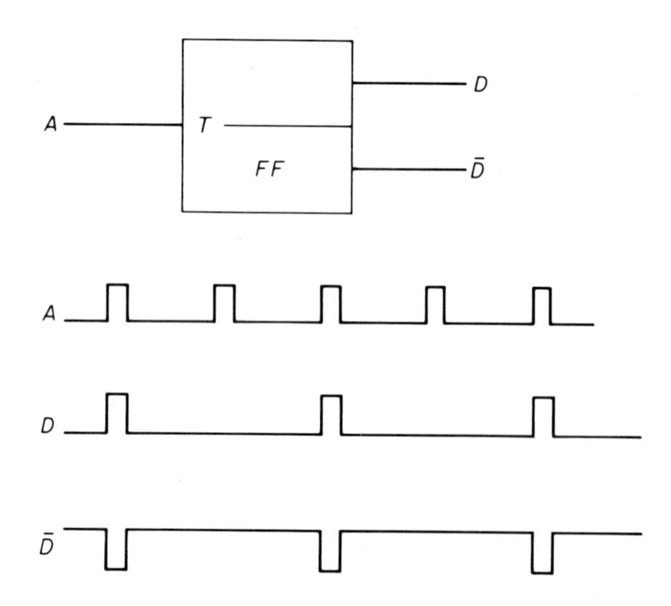

Fig. 4-27. Toggle FF symbol and pulse sequence.

6. Latching Flip-flop

The latching FF has one signal input and a clock. The symbol is identified by the letter L inside the symbol, as shown in Figure 4-28.

The set input responds to a true condition at A, while the reset input responds to a false condition at A. The FF will "latch" into the state existing at A (true-set or false-reset) when the clock pulse at C goes from true to false (usually at the trailing edge of the clock pulse). One unusual feature (not always desirable) is that during the clock pulse duration

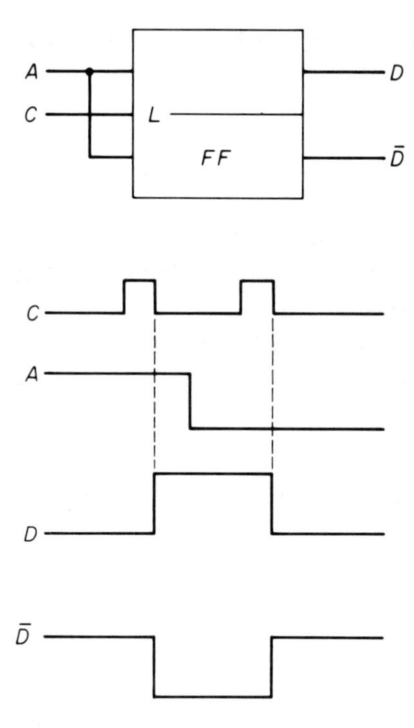

Fig. 4-28. Latching FF symbol and pulse sequence.

the FF is "unlatched," so that if A switches true and false several times during this period, outputs D and $\bar{D}$ will free-switch accordingly.

7. Delay Flip-flop

The delay FF is similar to the latching FF, and its symbol is identified by the letter D, as shown in Figure 4-29. The delay FF will latch into the state existing at A when C goes from true to false. However, unlike the latching FF, the delay FF "delays" any switching of outputs

Fig. 4-29. Delay FF symbol.

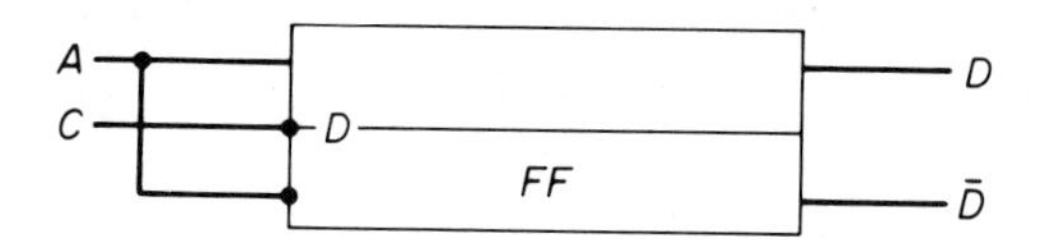

until the trailing edge of the clock pulse occurs. The delay FF does not have an unlatched condition.

G. MULTIVIBRATOR CIRCUIT

In addition to a FF, multivibrators have many uses in digital computers. (As is discussed in a later section of this chapter, multivibrators are often used in delay circuits.)

There are three types of multivibrators in general use with computers: astable, one-shot (or monostable), and Schmitt trigger (bistable).

Fig. 4-30. One-shot (or single-shot) multivibrator symbols.

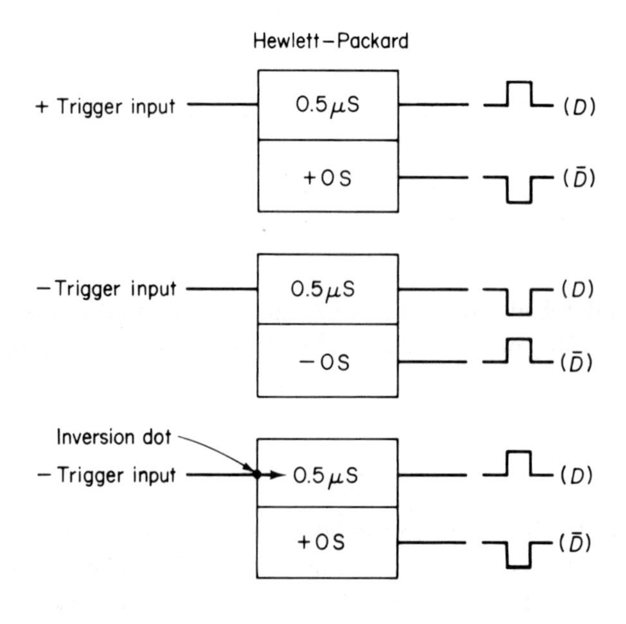

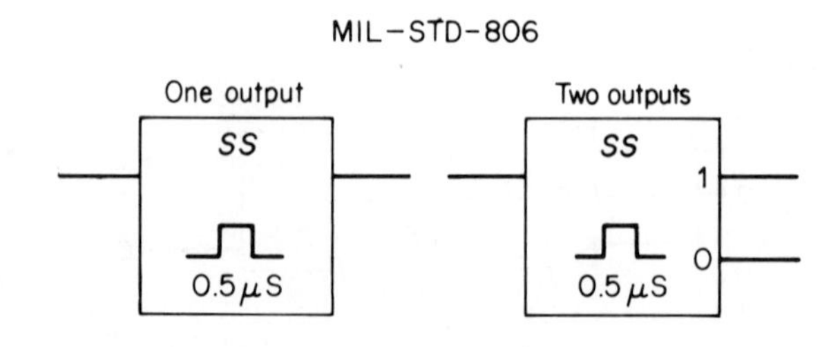

1. One-Shot Multivibrator

The one-shot multivibrator is a monostable switching element, using a multivibrator-type circuit. The one-shot element (sometimes known as a mono) is commonly used as an active delay device and is triggered into its unstable state by an external signal (see Figure 4-30). After an interval determined by circuit constants, the one-shot multivibrator returns automatically to the stable state. Thus a known, fixed delay time is provided.

One-shot inputs are frequently a-c-coupled, and triggering is accomplished when input A goes through a false-to-true transition. The abbreviation OS within the symbol identifies a one-shot multivibrator, and a plus or minus sign may be used to indicate the true state of the D output during the on time.

2. Schmitt Trigger

The Schmitt trigger is a two-state (bistable) element, using a multivibrator-type circuit. The Schmitt trigger is commonly used for level sensing and signal squaring or shaping. When the input voltage is below a reference level, the element is in one state (see Figure 4-31). When the input level goes above the reference level, the element switches to the other state. Switching between states takes place rapidly, making the element useful for squaring signals with poor rise times (converting sine waves to square waves, for example) and for voltage-level restoration.

With input A below the reference level (or false), D is false and $\bar{D}$ is true. When the input is above the reference level, D switches to true and $\bar{D}$ switches to false. (The reference level is established by circuit constants.)

3. Astable Multivibrator

Although all logic switching elements are forms of multivibrators, an astable type is assumed when the term *multivibrator* is used without a modifier (such as one-shot, Schmitt trigger, and so forth). An astable multivibrator will start free-running operation when input A goes true

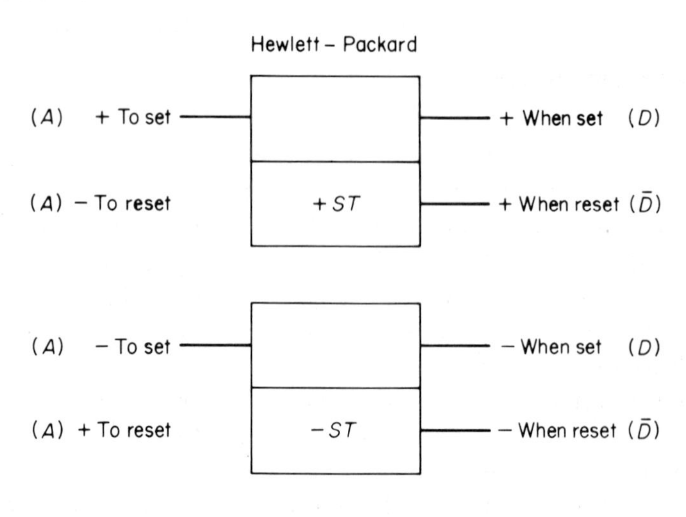

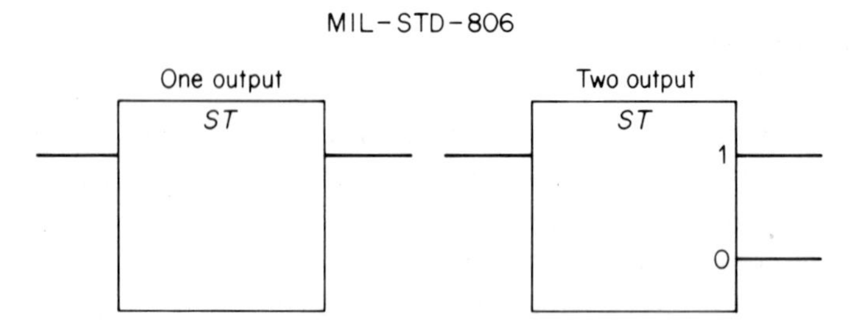

Fig. 4-31. Schmitt trigger (bistable) multivibrator symbols.

and will continue to generate complementary pulse trains at outputs D and $\bar{D}$ until input A goes false, as shown in Figure 4-32. Typical negative-true timing wave forms are shown with the symbol. Note that the minus sign (in front of the letters MV) indicates both the relative level required to start operation and the direction of the first output pulse at D. (The wave forms do not necessarily have to be symmetrical as shown.)

H. DELAY CIRCUITS

In the computer, gates are opened or closed by means of accurately timed pulses. Sometimes it is necessary to increase the width of a pulse

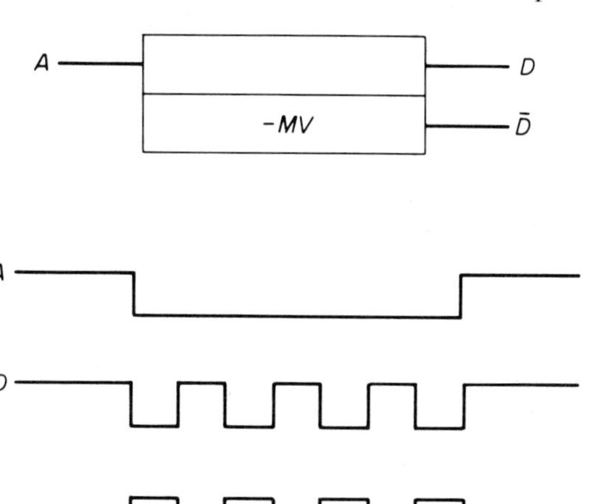

Fig. 4-32. Astable multivibrator symbol and pulse sequence.

to keep a gate open or closed for a longer period of time, or else it may become necessary to increase the time interval between two successive pulses. Delay devices are used for these purposes.

Early computers generally used passive delay devices, such as the **lumped-constant (L-C) delay line**, where sets of L-C components are used to introduce a delay. Some present-day computers also use such passive devices. However, active delay devices are generally preferred. The monostable, or one-shot, multivibrator previously described is typical of the active delay elements found in modern computers.

As discussed, the monostable multivibrator has only one stable state. The other state is only partly stable. That is, the multivibrator can remain in this state only for a definite period of time before it flips itself back to the stable state. This characteristic of a one-shot multivibrator is combined with other circuits to produce a fixed delay.

Figure 4-33 shows the relationship of wave forms within a typical active delay element. Note that the input pulse (a positive-going rectangle) is applied to the multivibrator portion of the delay element. The multivibrator output is a positive-going rectangular pulse, the width of which is determined by the *RC* constants. Next, the output pulse is fed into a differentiating circuit, which produces a positive pulse corresponding to the leading edge of the rectangular pulse and a negative pulse at the trailing edge. The pulses then go to a clipper circuit where the positive pulse is removed, or *clipped*. Finally, the pulse is applied to an inverter, which converts the remaining negative pulse to a positive pulse.

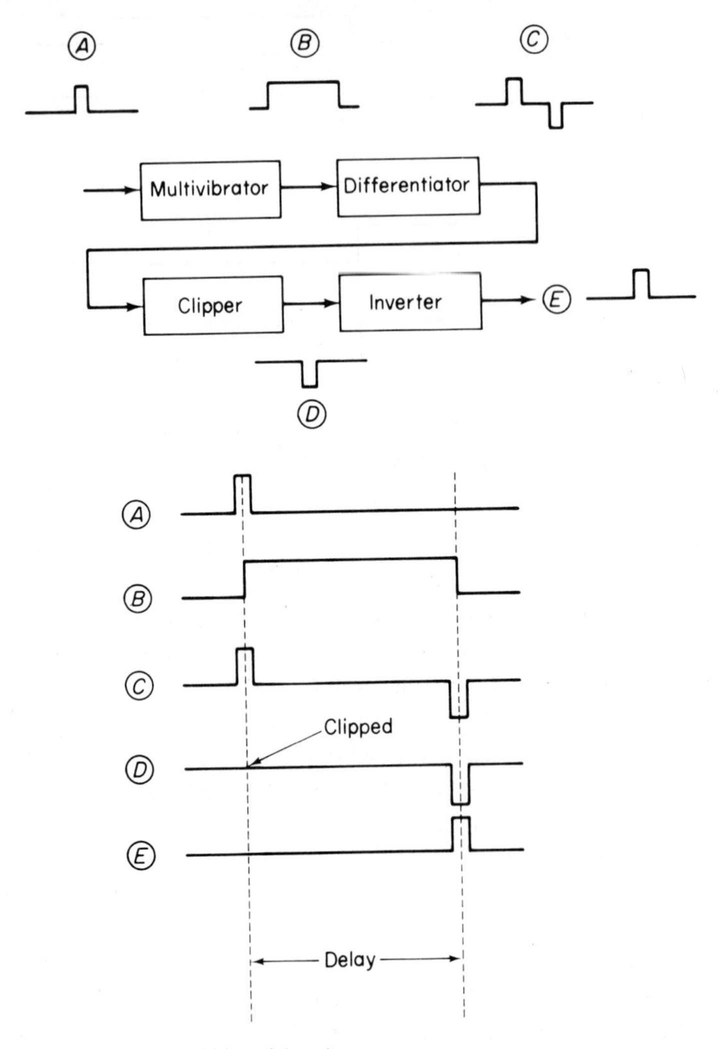

Fig. 4-33. Typical circuits within a delay element.

Note that the final pulse resembles the original input pulse, except that the final pulse has been delayed in time. The length of this delay is determined by the *RC* components of the multivibrator. By selecting the values of these components, the width of the output pulse and thus the time delay can be fixed.

The typical delay symbols, with examples of actual delay time, are shown in Figure 4-34. Typical theoretical wave forms for the elements are shown adjacent to the symbols.

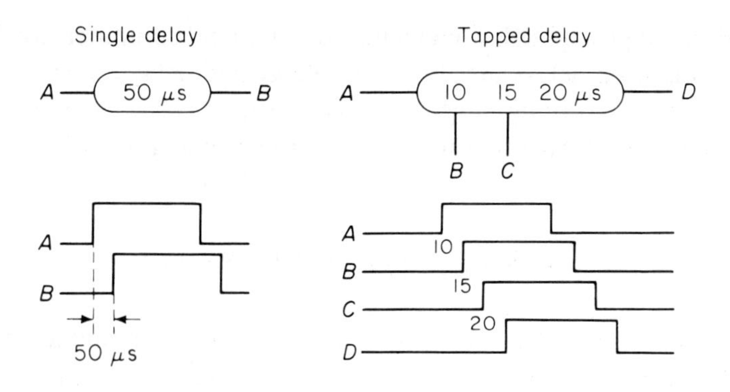

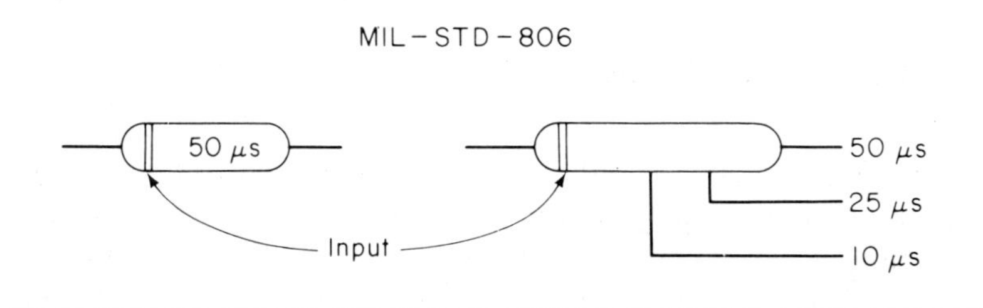

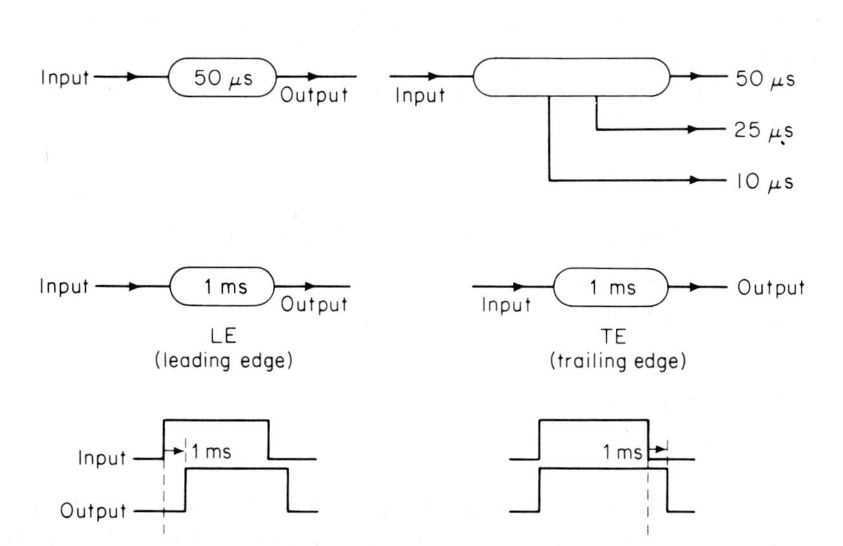

Fig. 4-34. Delay element symbols.

Many types of delay elements are used in computer work. Two frequently used delays are the **tapped delay** and delays effective only on the leading or trailing edges of pulses. Such delay elements, together with the theoretical wave forms, are shown in Figure 4-34.

I. LOGIC-SYMBOL IDENTIFICATION

Logic-symbol identification is one area where manufacturers take off in several directions at once. The following is a summary of the methods of logic-symbol identification in general use.

1. Reference Designations

Most logic diagrams show logic elements as a complete component rather than the many components that make up the element. For example, an amplifier is shown as a triangle rather than as several dozen capacitors, resistors, transistors, and so forth. Therefore the amplifier has a reference designation of its own. On some logic diagrams, the logic element symbols are mixed with symbols of individual resistors, capacitors, and so forth. Either way, the logic element symbol must be identified by a reference designation (to match descriptions in instruction manual texts or as a basis for parts listing).

The following logic-symbol reference designations are in general use:

1. Gates, *G*.
2. Amplifiers and inverters, *A* (sometimes *I* for inverters).
3. Flip-flops, FF.
4. One-shot, OS (sometimes SS for single-shot).
5. Multivibrator, MV.
6. Schmitt trigger, ST.
7. Delay, *D*.

Figure 4-35 shows some examples of how the reference designations are used. Note that the reference designations for switching elements are placed within the symbol. All other designations are (usually)

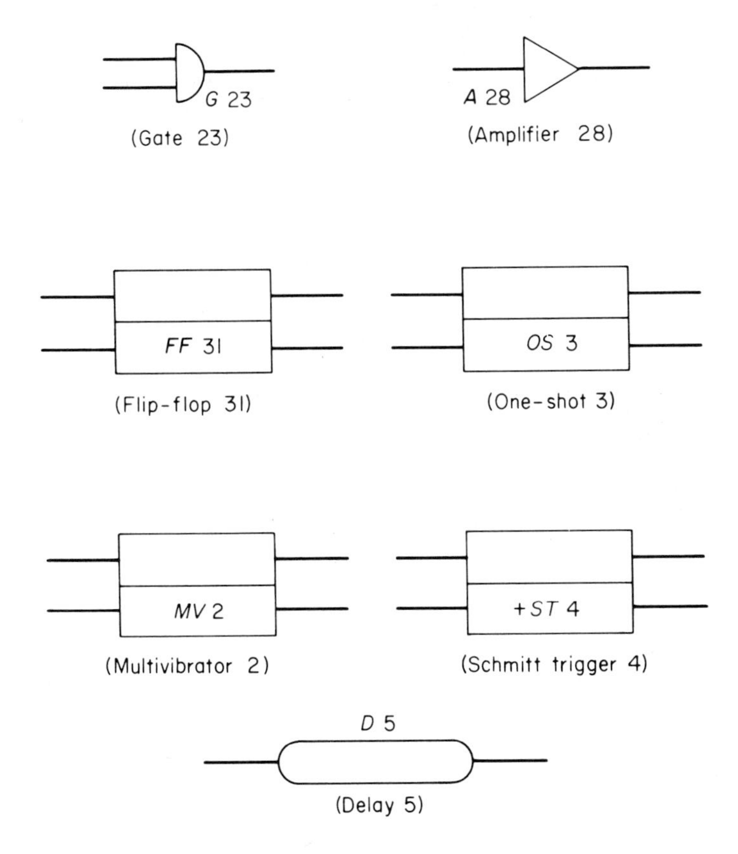

Fig. 4-35. Reference designations for logic symbols.

placed beside the symbol. In the case of switching elements, the true-state sign can be used as a prefix to the designation.

2. Integrated Circuit Reference Designations

When logic elements appear in integrated circuit (or microcircuit) form, the system of reference designations is usually changed. Typical examples of microcircuit logic reference designations are shown in Figure 4-36.

When a microcircuit is used to form one complete logic element, such as an amplifier or gate, the element can assume the microcircuit reference designator, or MC, rather than *G* or *A*.

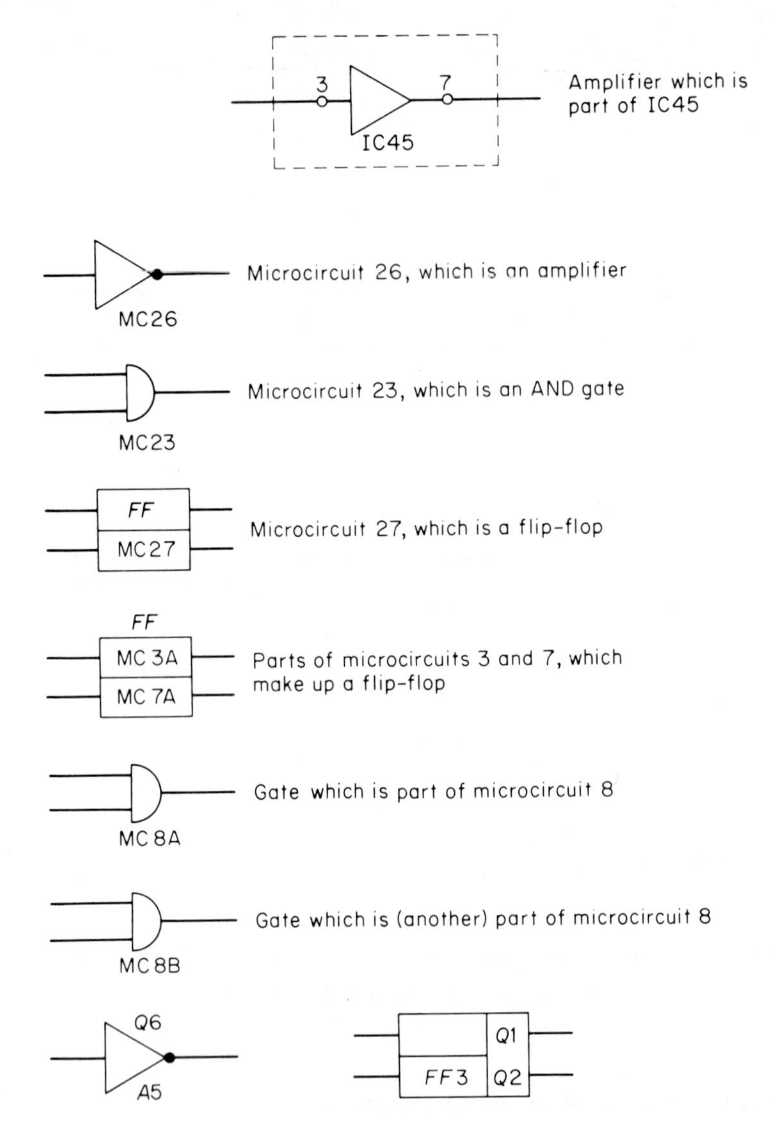

Fig. 4-36. Reference designations for microcircuit (IC) logic symbols.

When a microcircuit is used to form a complete switching circuit, the element can assume the microcircuit designator, MC, but should also include the appropriate abbreviation (such as FF, OS, and so forth) to identify its function.

When a switching element is composed of portions of different microcircuit packages, the designator MC of both packages should be included inside the symbol, and the appropriate abbreviations should be located outside the symbol.

When more than one logic element is included in the microcircuit package, each logic element is identified with a suffix of *A*, *B*, *C*, and so forth.

On some diagrams, the logic element is shown enclosed in dotted lines with the terminals identified. An example of this is shown in Figure 4-36, where an amplifier symbol is enclosed in dotted lines and identified as IC45. This indicates that the amplifier is part of IC45 (integrated circuit number 45), that the input is available at terminal 3, and that the output is available at terminal 7.

On some logic diagrams that correlate to a schematic diagram of the same circuit, the active components of the element may also be designated. For example, in Figure 4-36, Q_6 is the active transistor of amplifier A_5, and Q_1 and Q_2 are the active transistors of FF_3. This system of identification is primarily an aid in troubleshooting.

3. Reference Names

Identification of logic elements by functional name in a diagram is normally done only with switching elements, as shown in Figure 4-37. The upper portion of the symbol can be reserved for this purpose. If the type of switching element (FF, OS, and so forth) is not part of the designation (in the lower portion of the symbol), then the reference name should include the appropriate abbreviation. If designations appear in both the upper and lower portions of the symbol, the name can be placed outside the symbol. For one-shots, it is often convenient to give the time duration as the reference name.

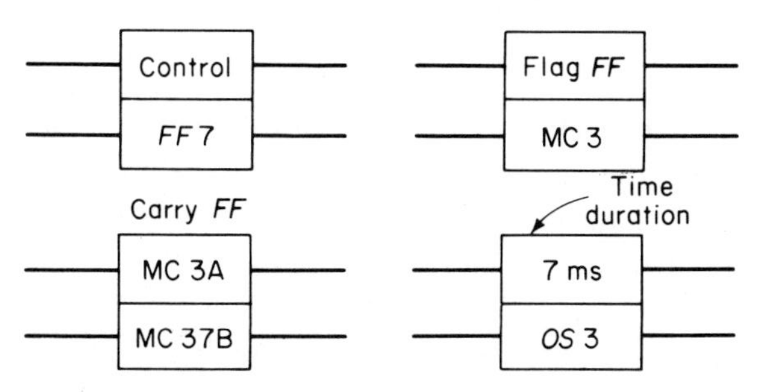

Fig. 4-37. Reference names for logic symbols.

4. Location Information

Logic diagrams are intended to show the combination of logic elements that together form an instrument, a part of an instrument, or a system of instruments. To aid in correlating the diagram with physical locations in instruments, additional information is given (by some manufacturers) with logic symbols, as shown in Figure 4-38. The number in the small triangle is sometimes used to indicate the circuit board on which the element appears. In the example of Figure 4-38, the elements appear on circuit board 2.

If all elements are on the same board, individual identification in this way is unnecessary. Letters and numbers adjacent to inputs and outputs indicate pin numbers of the board (or microcircuit package) where inputs and/or outputs appear (as shown in Figure 4-36).

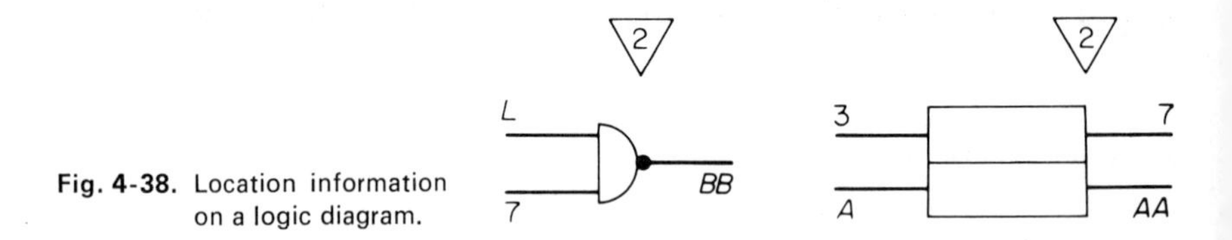

Fig. 4-38. Location information on a logic diagram.

J. MODIFICATION OF LOGIC SYMBOLS

In addition to different systems for identification of logic symbols on computer diagrams, each manufacturer may have its own set of symbol modifiers (in addition to those symbol modifiers used in MIL-STD-806). The following modifiers are in general use.

1. Truth Polarity

Positive (+) or negative (—) indicators may be placed inside a symbol to designate whether the true state for that circuit is positive or negative relative to the false state. This is frequently done with gates and switching elements, as shown in Figure 4-39.

Note that the true voltage level does not have to be absolutely positive (that is, above ground or above an 0-V reference). The two voltage levels at which a logic circuit operates could be —7 and —3 V. A plus sign within the logic symbol representing such a circuit would

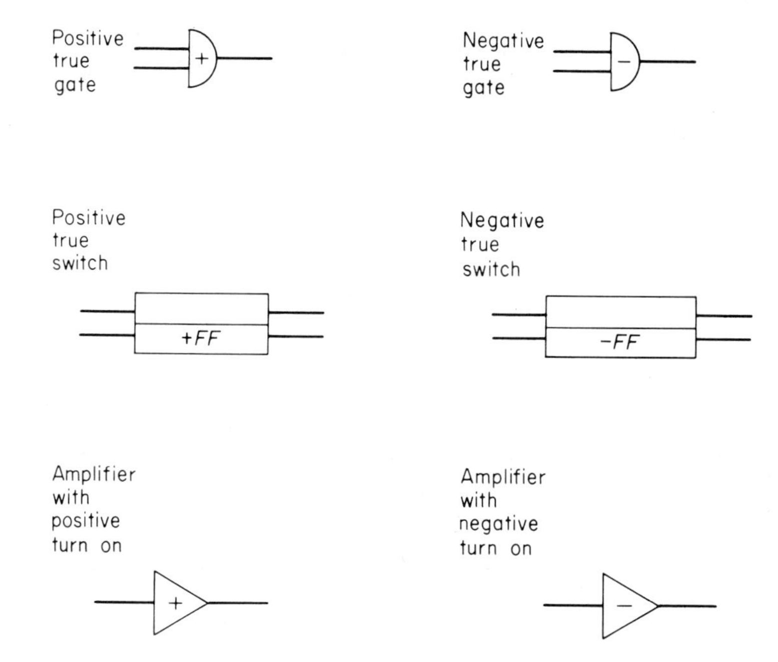

Fig. 4-39. Truth polarity in symbols.

indicate that the −3-V level is true and that the −7-V level is false, because the −3-V level is closer to positive than the −7-V level. A minus sign within the symbol would indicate that the −7-V level is true (since it is more negative) and that the −3-V level is therefore false.

The sign should be used for all logic elements in which true and false levels are meaningful. As an alternative, the logic diagram can state in a note that all logic is positive-true or that all logic is negative-true. (MIL-STD-806 does not distinguish positive-true from negative-true.)

Polarity signs used in amplifier symbols do not have any direct logic significance. Rather, the polarity signs are a troubleshooting aid, indicating the polarity required to turn the amplifier on.

2. Inversion

Generally, logic inversion is indicated by an inversion dot at inputs or outputs. (In some cases, inverted pulses are shown at the inputs and outputs.)

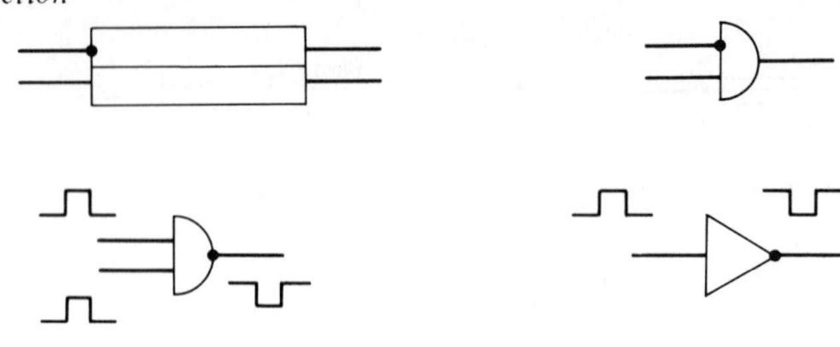
Dots may be solid or open

Fig. 4-40. Methods of indicating inversion in symbols.

When the inversion dot appears on an input (generally only on gates and switching elements), the input will be effective when the input signal is of opposite polarity to that normally required. For example, if the switching element in Figure 4-40 is normally positive-true or is used on a diagram where all logic is positive-true, a negative input at the inversion dot will set the circuit.

When the inversion dot appears at an output (generally only on gates and amplifiers), the output will be of opposite polarity to that normally delivered. For example, if the gate of Figure 4-40 is used in a positive-true logic circuit, the output will be negative. Likewise, the amplifier in Figure 4-40 will produce a positive output if the input is negative and vice versa.

3. Alternating-Current Coupling

Capacitor inputs to logic elements are indicated by an arrow, as shown in Figure 4-41. In the case of gates and switching elements, the

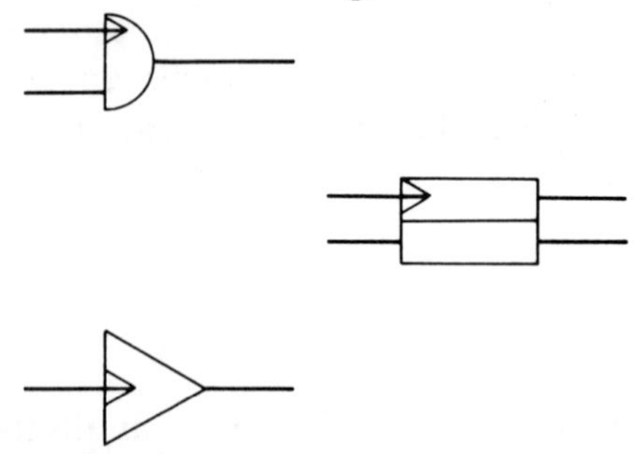

Fig. 4-41. Methods of indicating a-c coupling in symbols.

element responds only to a change of the a-c-coupled input in the true-going direction.

An inversion dot used in conjunction with the coupling arrow indicates that the element responds to a change in the false-going direction.

In the case of an amplifier, a pulse edge of the same polarity as given in the symbol turns the amplifier on briefly and then off as the capacitor discharges. The output is then a pulse of the same width as the amplifier on time. With an inversion dot at the amplifier output, the output pulse is inverted.

K. LOGIC EQUATIONS

Logic equations are sometimes used to aid in the explanation of logic circuits. At one time, some manufacturers presented all logic information (in their instruction manuals) in equation form. Fortunately for technicians, this practice has generally been discontinued. Logic diagrams are used in most computer instruction manuals. These diagrams may or may not be supplemented by the corresponding equations.

When logic equations are used, the familiar algebraic symbols have the following meanings:

1. $+$ means "or."
2. $\cdot$ means "and."
3. $=$ means "equals" (or "is the result of").
4. $-$ means "not" (or "complement of").

For example, the logic equation for a simple two-input AND gate is

$$C = B \cdot A \qquad \text{(or } C \text{ equals } A \text{ and } B\text{)}$$

where A and B are the inputs and C is the output.

The logic equation for the combination of elements shown in Figure 4-42 is

$$E = (\bar{A} + B) \cdot (C + D).$$

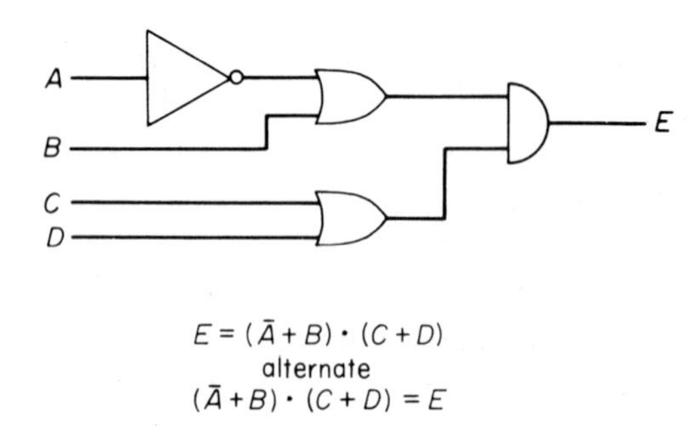

$$E = (\bar{A} + B) \cdot (C + D)$$
alternate
$$(\bar{A} + B) \cdot (C + D) = E$$

Fig. 4-42. Logic diagram and corresponding logic equations.

Sometimes the same equation will be written as

$$(\bar{A} + B)\cdot(C + D) = E.$$

Generally, logic equations are better suited to the design of computers (or other digital equipment) rather than as a tool for troubleshooting.

L. MISCELLANEOUS CIRCUITS

In addition to the circuits described thus far in this chapter, computers contain other electronic circuits such as linear amplifiers, oscillators, limiters, clippers, and differentiators. However, these circuits are generally used for generating, shaping, and otherwise controlling the sizes of the pulses rather than directing their flow through the computer. Since these circuits are conventional, they will not be discussed here.

Fig. 4-43. Summary of truth tables.

A	*B*	AND	NAND	OR	NOR	Exclusive OR	Exclusive NOR
0	0	0	1	0	1	0	1
0	1	0	1	1	0	1	0
1	0	0	1	1	0	1	0
1	1	1	0	1	0	0	1

M. SUMMARY OF TRUTH TABLES

Figure 4-43 summarizes the truth tables for the six basic computer logic circuit elements: AND, OR, NAND, NOR, EXLUSIVE OR, and EXCLUSIVE NOR.

THE SIMCOM DIGITAL COMPUTER

II

Before going on with detailed discussions of the circuits that make up the major units of the computer, let us consider the digital computer and the related equipment as a complete system. The difficulty is that there are many different types of computers. Present-day computers are much more complicated and sophisticated than those of just a few years ago.

Since it would be difficult for a technician not already familiar with computers to immediately grasp the operation of the modern, complex computer, we shall consider a generalized and simplified computer—one that never has nor ever will be built. Nevertheless, this computer will contain the basic principles upon which all digital computers operate. Once the technician understands how this simplified computer operates, he will be in a better position to consider the more sophisticated machines.

Borrowing a technique used by computer manufacturers, we shall call our machine SIMCOM (SIMplified COMputer).

HOW THE DIGITAL COMPUTER OPERATES

5

A. COMPUTER HARDWARE

The digital computer is constructed of a number of interconnected elements—mechanical, magnetic, electrical, and electronic—that are known as the **hardware** of the machine. The computer's **inner memory**, generally consisting of many small magnetic cores or a magnetic drum, is able to store hundreds and even thousands of items of information.

Scattered throughout the machine are a number of elements called **registers**, which are used as temporary storage locations, as the **accumulator** of the arithmetic section where the mathematical operations are performed, and for various other purposes. There also are **counters** used to tally various items of information such as commands (**instructions**) and locations in the memory where the information can be found (**addresses**) and to modify them on command.

There are **decoders**, which translate the instructions to electrical signals for executing these commands and for translating addresses to electrical signals, permitting the computer to locate the required information and transfer it to the appropriate destinations. Interconnecting all these elements is a network of electronic and logic circuits (gates, FF, inverters, delay devices, and so forth) that directs the signals along the appropriate paths.

Also, for direct human-to-machine communication, there is the **supervisory control panel**, or **console**, which contains a number of push-buttons and/or switches such as the START button, which starts the entire computer operation, and the STOP button, which stops all functions of the computer.

The console also contains a series of **readouts**, which inform the operator of the instantaneous values of the information (in number form) stored in the various registers of the computer. These readouts generally consist of small neon lamps that indicate the values in binary (or possibly octal) code. There also may be a readout to show the contents of any address in the memory and a readout to indicate the address of the last instruction being executed when the computer stopped. The latter readout enables the operator to know at what point operation of the computer has been interrupted.

The console may also contain a number of alarm devices (lights, buzzers, and so forth) that alert the operator to the fact that a crucial point in the operation has been reached or warn of some malfunction of the computer or error in the instructions. For example, there is the **overflow** signal, which indicates that the result of some arithmetic operation exceeds the capacity of the register where this result is to be stored.

A manually operated **keyboard** enables the operator to enter information into any location in the memory or to insert extra instructions. On some computers, the keyboard is in the form of a typewriter (similar to a teletype instrument). With this arrangement, the typewriter can both insert information into the computer and read out information from the computer. In this way, the computer may call for additional information or the correct interpretation of some ambiguous item of information. Although the various switches, readouts, alarms, and so forth listed here make up the basic components of most consoles, some computers may also supply additional devices for additional purposes.

B. PERIPHERAL EQUIPMENT

The information fed to the computer falls into two general categories. There are the **data** (consisting of numbers, alphabetic letters, symbols, or combinations of them that are to be processed), and the **instructions** (the commands indicating how the data are to be processed). Since the language of the computer is composed of binary numbers, all information to be used must first be converted to numbers (or combinations of letters and numbers) and these numbers further converted to binary numbers.

The computer is an extremely fast-acting device, performing its operations in microseconds. If we were to attempt to feed in the information by means of some device such as a coding typewriter, which, at its fastest speed, can type only a few hundred characters per minute, most of the computer's time would be wasted waiting for information. To save this time, the information is first entered on cards, punched paper tape, or magnetic tape and then *read in* at an extremely rapid rate, to be stored in the computer's memory, where the data are almost instantly available.

The input equipment associated with the computer falls into two categories: the **on-line** input equipment such as the various **readers**, which read the information contained on the cards, paper tape, or magnetic tape directly into the computer, and the **off-line** input equipment such as the **card punch**, **paper-tape punch**, or **magnetic-tape recorder**, which enter the "raw" information in coded form onto the cards, paper tape, or magnetic tape, respectively, to be used by the readers. Obviously, the off-line equipment can be used at any time and separately from the computer—hence the name.

At the output end of the computer, the results of the operations are generally printed out in the language of the operator on paper sheets or rolls. If a permanant file of these results is required, the computer may enter them on paper cards, paper tapes, or magnetic tapes by operating suitable punches or recorders. These printers, punches, and recorders are known as on-line output equipment. For off-line purposes, the information on cards, paper tape, or magnetic tape may be read by means of suitable readers.

The various input and output devices constitute the peripheral equipment and will be considered further in Chapters 7 and 9.

C. THE PROGRAM

Digital computers solve problems in a step-by-step manner. Since the computer cannot think by itself, a **program** must be prepared that breaks the problem down into a series of sequential, logical, and simple steps. This is the task of the programmer. While an extended discussion of the art of programming is not intended for this book, the technician must have some understanding of the program if he is to learn how the computer operates. (As discussed in later chapters, the first step in troubleshooting is to operate the computer through its normal sequence and to note any abnormalities in operation, sequence, or failure to perform a given step.)

Since there are many variations among computers, a program must be specifically designed for a specific computer. The programmer must know the computer's language and the manner in which the computer operates. The computer program that we shall consider here is for our hypothetical, general-purpose digital computer, the SIMCOM.

1. The Basic Program

As an example of how a program may be prepared for the computer, let us consider a simple scientific problem. In this case, the problem is to determine how far a freely falling body will fall in 5 seconds.

The equation for this problem is $d = gt^2/2$, where d is the distance in feet, t is the time in seconds, and g is the acceleration due to gravity (32 ft/sec for each second of fall).

The programmer analyzes the problem and breaks it down into a sequential series of logical steps. The programmer then draws up a **flow chart**, which diagrams the sequence of the steps to the taken in solving the problem. Such a flow chart is shown in Figure 5-1.

Although the flow chart helps the programmer analyze the problem, the computer cannot use the flow chart as is. The computer has its own language, which is based upon numbers, not alphabetic letters and words. Accordingly, the flow chart must be converted to a program—a sequential set of instructions, in the computer's language, that the computer can follow. This implies, of course, that the programmer must know the capabilities of the computer as well as the language. It would be futile to write an instruction that the computer cannot carry out.

If the computer is to perform the operation indicated by the instruction, the instruction must first be converted to a number, called the **operation code** (or simply **op code**), that the computer can identify. Each type of computer has its own set of operation codes, one for each opera-

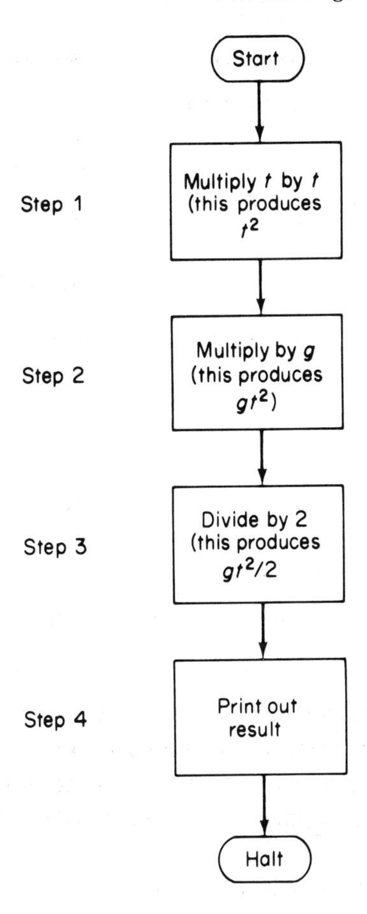

Fig. 5-1. Flow chart for falling-body problem.

tion that the computer is able to perform. Since there are certain types of operations that all computers must perform, there are certain types of operation codes that are common to all computers (although the code numbers may differ from computer to computer).

Thus there must be operation codes for performing the various arithmetic operations, for transferring information from one part of the computer to another, for printing out or otherwise displaying the results obtained, for stopping the computer, and so forth. In addition, there are operation codes that are peculiar to specific computers. Some computers may have more than 100 different operation codes.

Examples of typical operation codes to be used for our SIMCOM computer are shown in Figure 5-2. The alphabetic representation of

Alphabetic (mnemonic) representation	Numerical representation	Meaning of instruction
CAD	10	Clear accumulator and add
ADD	11	Add
SUB	12	Subtract
MUL	13	Multiply
DIV	14	Divide
STO	15	Store
PRT	16	Print
HLT	00	Halt

Fig. 5-2. Examples of typical operation codes for the SIMCOM computer.

the operation code is the abbreviation or mnemonic of the instruction to be used by the programmer in preparing his program. The numeric representation is the operation code that the computer can recognize as instructions. Only the numeric representation of the instruction is fed to the computer.

Both the numbers representing the operation codes of the instructions and the numbers that constitute the data are stored in the memory of the computer (in binary form), but it is not enough merely to store the numbers in the memory. The numbers must be stored where the computer can find them. Accordingly, each number representing the operation code of an instruction or an item of data must be stored at some particular portion of the memory called an address.

Thus the memory section is divided into discrete portions and each portion is given a separate numerical address. Each instruction or item of data is stored at a separate address. The programmer must keep a record of the address of each instruction or item of data. Then, if the programmer wishes the computer to obtain any specific instruction or item of data, he merely supplies the address to the computer (by means of the program). The computer seeks out the specified address and receives the information stored there.

If the data are in numeric form, they are converted to binary numbers. If the data are in alphabetic letters or symbols, alphanumeric codes are used, as described in Chapter 3, subdivision F. Either way, the binary numbers representing the data are stored at specific addresses in the memory.

Note that since both instructions and data are stored in numeric form (using binary numbers), the computer cannot distinguish between instructions and data. Thus, if in searching for an instruction the computer is accidentally directed to the address of an item of data, the computer will attempt to interpret the number found there as the numeric representation of an operation code. Should this "operation code" be meaningless, the computer will halt. The programmer should take care to avoid such errors. Although the use of proper codes is the responsibility of the programmer, the technician must also be aware of problems created by the use of improper codes. Otherwise, the technician may spend hours trying to troubleshoot a properly functioning computer that has been fed an improper code.

There are several methods for arranging the instruction addresses in the memory. Since the instructions follow in sequence, the addresses of the instructions, too, may be in sequential order. Thus instruction 1 may be stored, say, at address 0001. Then instruction 2 would be stored at address 0002, instruction 3 at address 0003, and so forth.

Before the start of operations, the address of instruction 1 (0001) is placed in a **program counter**. Then, as the computer executes instruction 1, a signal is sent to the program counter, advancing the count by 1. The number in the counter now will be 0002, the address of instruction 2. The computer obtains the address of the second instruction from the counter. As the computer executes instruction 2, the signal advances the number in the counter to 0003, the address of instruction 3. This process continues as long as there are instructions to be carried out. The final instruction directs the computer to stop.

There are also several methods for arranging the data in the memory. One method is to store each item of data at any address that is unoccupied and available. Then, when the computer is directed to a certain address for an instruction, it will find both the operation code indicating the instruction and the address of the data required for execution of that instruction.

Note that the program contains not the actual data but the address at which the data are stored. For example, if the programmer wishes the computer to add a certain number, he need only indicate to the computer the operation code for addition and give the address of the number to be added. The computer will then obtain the number at that address and add it to the number in the arithmetic register (accumulator).

As an example, let us program the falling-body problem whose flow chart is shown in Figure 5-1. The data involved are

1. t, the time in seconds that the body is falling.
2. g, the acceleration in feet per second per second of fall, due to gravity.
3. 2, the number by which gt^2 is divided.

As previously indicated, $t = 5$ and $g = 32$.

Fig. 5-3. Program for falling-body problem.

Instruction address	Program stored in computer		Explanation
	Operation code	Data address	
0001	10	1001	CAD (clear and add). Erase any number remaining in the accumulator from a previous operation. Bring the contents of address 1001 (t) to the accumulator.
0002	13	1001	MUL (multiply). Multiply the number in the accumulator by the number at address 1001. (The result is t^2.)
0003	13	1030	MUL (multiply). Multiply the number in the accumulator by the number at address 1030 (g). (The result is gt^2.)
0004	14	1201	DIV (divide). Divide the number in the accumulator by the number at address 1201 (2). (The result is $gt^2/2$.)
0005	15	2001	STO (Store). Store the number in the accumulator at address 2001.
0006	16	2001	PRT (Print). Print out data stored at address 2001.
0007	00		HLT. The computer is directed to halt.

These data may be stored at any unoccupied address in the memory. For example, the data could be stored as 5 (t) at address 1001, 32 (g) at address 1030, and 2 at address 1201. The instructions are to be stored in sequence, starting with address 0001. The program will then appear as shown in Figure 5-3.

The computer will find instruction 1 at address 0001. The instruction (operation code 10) tells the computer to clear the accumulator to zero and then add the number found at address 1001 (5). Meanwhile, the program counter will have been advanced to 0002, the address of instruction 2.

Instruction 2 (operation code 13) tells the computer to multiply the number in the accumulator by the number found at address 1001 (5). The result in the accumulator is now t^2, or 25. As the computer goes to address 0003 (instruction 3), it is told to multiply the number in the accumulator by the number at address 1030 (32). The result in the accumulator is now gt^2, or 800. Instruction 4 (address 0004) tells the computer to divide the number in the accumulator by the number found at address 1201 (2). The result is now $gt^2/2$, or 400, the answer (d) to our problem.

Instruction 5 (address 0005) directs the computer to store the number in the accumulator at address 2001. Instruction 6 (address 0006) directs the computer to point out the result stored at address 2001 so that it may be noted by the operator. Instruction 7 (address 0007) directs the computer to halt.

2. Special Program Instructions

In addition to the routine instructions for our SIMCOM computer, typical examples of which are shown in Figure 5-2, there are a number of instructions that help make the computer the flexible, decision-making machine that it is. These are the **branch** instructions (also known as **jump, skip**, or **transfer** instructions). See Figure 5-4. These instructions

Fig. 5-4. Examples of typical branch operation codes for the SIMCOM computer.

Alphabetic representation	Numerical representatation	Meaning of instruction
BRA	20	Branch, unconditionally
BRN	21	Branch, on negative
BRP	22	Branch, on positive

direct the computer to leave the basic program at some designated point and, under proper conditions, branch or jump to some other designated point of the program.

For example, assume that 200006 appears at a certain point of the program. The first two digits (20) indicate that the computer is to leave the program at this point and branch or jump to the instruction whose address is the last four digits (0006). After carrying out this instruction, the computer is to follow, in sequence, instructions at addresses 0007, 0008, and so forth unless the computer is directed to halt. This is an example of an **unconditional branch** instruction.

The other two branch instructions shown in Figure 5-4, BRN (operation code 21) and BRP (operation code 22), are examples of **conditional branch** instructions. If 210005 appears in the program, it means that if the number in a certain counter or register is negative, the computer must branch to the instruction whose address is 0005, and proceed (in sequence) from there on. If the number is not negative, the computer is to ignore the branch instruction and proceed as if it were not there. The BRP instruction is the same as the BRN, except that branching is to occur if the number is positive. Otherwise, the branch instruction is to be ignored.

3. Example of Branch Instructions

As an example of how the branch instructions are used, let us consider a typical business problem. A sales firm has a large number of items in stock. Since the firm constantly sells these items, the sales manager must know at all times how many of each item are on hand. Also, the manager must know when the stock of each item falls so low as to require replenishing.

The programmer analyzes the problem and breaks it down into a sequential series of logic steps. He then draws up a flow chart that diagrams the sequence of these steps to be taken in solving the problem. See Figure 5-5.

(Note that there may be other, and better, methods for solving the problem. The method shown here is merely for illustrative purposes. Note, too, that in the flow chart of Figure 5-5, instructions are contained in rectangular boxes, questions involving decisions are enclosed in diamond-shaped boxes, and HALT instructions are enclosed in

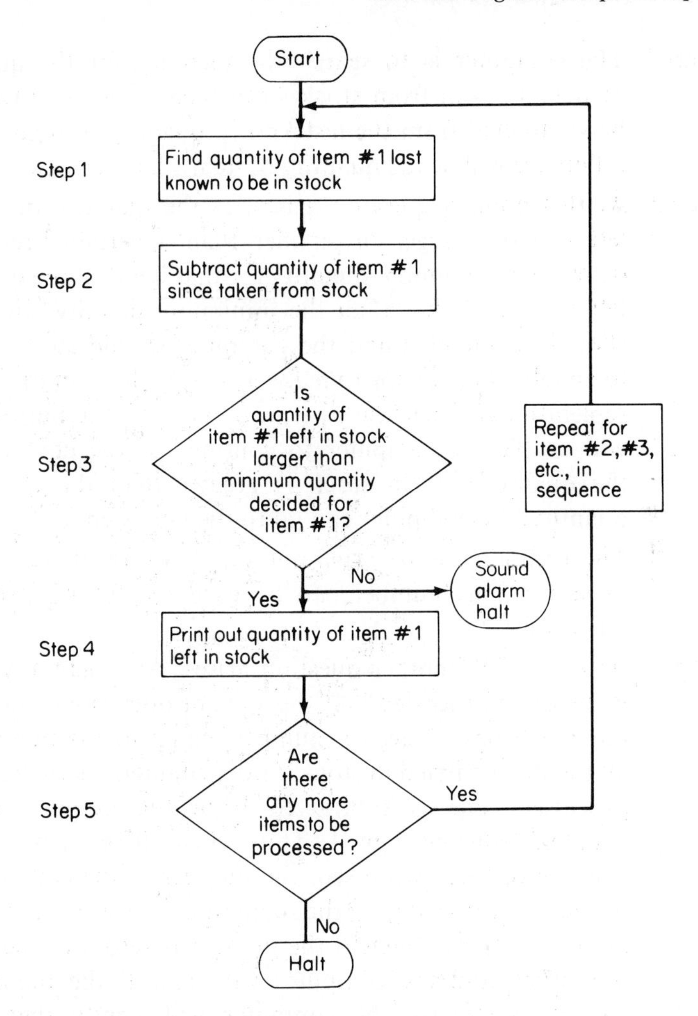

Fig. 5-5. Example of flow chart for inventory control.

elliptical boxes. These differently shaped boxes are for the convenience of the programmer. Unfortunately, each programmer generally uses his own system of designations, despite many efforts at standardization throughout the industry.)

The interpretation of the flow chart in Figure 5-5 as it relates to operation of the computer is as follows:

Step 1. The computer is to search the memory for the quantity of item 1 that last was known to be in stock.

Step 2. The computer is to search the memory for the quantity of item 1 taken from stock since then. This quantity is to be subtracted from the last known quantity of item 1. The difference will be the quantity of item 1 left in stock.

Step 3. At this point a question arises. Is the quantity of item 1 left in stock larger or smaller than a certain previously determined minimum quantity for that item? If the quantity left in stock is less than the minimum quantity, an alarm should be sounded and the computer should stop. This is to enable the operator to make a note of the item that needs replenishing. Then the operator may press a button that will enable the computer to continue to the next step. If the quantity left in stock is greater than the minimum quantity, the computer can go to the next step.

Step 4. The computer is to print out the quantity of item 1 left in stock. This number can be used for future inventory purposes.

Step 5. At this point another question arises. Are there any more items to be processed? At the start of operations, the computer will have placed a number, equal to the number of all the items carried in stock, into a counter. As each item is processed, one is subtracted from the number in the counter, reducing it by 1. Thus when all the items of the stock have been processed, the number in the counter will be zero. Accordingly, the computer must examine the number in the counter. If the number is zero, the operation is finished and the computer will halt. If the number is greater than zero, the computer will signify that there remain other items to be processed. The computer then must subtract 1 from the number in the counter and proceed to repeat the entire process, starting with step 1 and substituting the various quantities associated with item 2. Then the computer must repeat the process for item 3 and so forth, through the entire list.

Note that each time step 5 is reached and there are more items to be processed, a **loop** is made back to step 1. This looping procedure not only saves the programmer's time but, as we shall soon see, a great deal of valuable memory space as well.

At step 3, the BRN (branch, on negative) instruction is used. From the quantity of the item left in stock, the minimum-quantity figure decided for that item is substituted. If the result is a negative number (that is, if the quantity left in stock is less than the minimum-quantity figure), the computer is directed to leave the program at this point and branch to the address of the instruction that causes the computer to sound an alarm and halt. If the result is not a negative number, the BRN instruction is ignored and the computer proceeds to step 4 of the program.

At step 5, the BRP (branch, on positive) instruction is used. At the start of operation, a number (equal to the number of all the items carried in stock) is placed in a counter. As each item is processed, 1 is subtracted from the number in the counter. As long as there are more items to be processed, some positive number will appear in the counter. When all the items have been processed, the number in the counter will be zero. (For our purposes, the number 0 is not considered to be a positive number.)

Accordingly, when the computer reaches step 5, it must examine the number in the counter. If this number is positive, the computer must leave the program at this point and branch back to the address of the instruction for step 1. The computer then proceeds to carry out, in sequence, all the instructions of the loop. If the number in the counter is 0, the computer ignores the branch instructions and proceeds to the next instruction of the program (HLT).

4. External Read-in

A difficulty becomes apparent. Each instruction stored in the memory of the computer contains not only the operation code for that instruction but also the address of the data required to carry out that instruction. Thus, as the computer proceeds through the first loop of the operation, it follows all the instructions of the loop, using the data of item 1. During the next loop, the computer repeats all the instructions of the loop. But now the computer must use the data for item 2. However, the instructions carry the addresses of item 1.

When faced with such a problem, the data for the various items, in sequence are entered on cards, paper tape, or magnetic tape and placed in a reader, which is connected to the computer. Then, before starting to process item 1, the computer directs the reader to read in the data for item 1 and stores these items of data at various designated addresses in the memory.

When item 1 has been processed, the computer directs the reader to read in the data for item 2. The data for item 1 are erased from memory and are replaced by the data for item 2 at these same addresses. Thus, as the instructions of the loop are repeated, the new data are available. This process is repeated each time the computer makes a loop.

5. Subroutines, Libraries, and Automatic Codes

Practically every instruction to the computer involves a routine series of steps. Thus, to add two three-digit numbers, for example, the LSD must be added first. If there is a carry, the carry must be added to the next significant digits. Then these digits must be added. If there is another carry, this carry must also be added to the MSD and then they must be added. Although this series of calculations is complete within itself, the series may only be part of a larger program.

Since the computer can only follow instructions, this routine series of steps should be included in the program. However, to save the programmer's time, this series of steps is programmed by the manufacturer and permanently wired into the computer. Then when the programmer indicates the operation code for an addition, the computer automatically selects the suitable series of steps and follows it.

Frequently, the program may call for special calculations such as square root, logarithmic, and so forth that may not be wired into the computer. Under such conditions, the programmer may include a suitable series of steps within the program. If these types of calculations are repeated throughout the program, the programmer may prepare a special program for each of them, called a **subroutine**, and store it in the memory of the computer. Then, when the programmer calls for such a subroutine, the computer is given the address in the memory and instructed when to insert it into the operation.

The manufacturers of digital computers have sets of basic subroutines, called **libraries**, that are suitable for their machines. They are available to the programmer, and in this way much valuable time is saved and the operational range of the computer is greatly extended.

A large portion of the programmer's task is to translate, or **code**, a program written in human language to the language of the computer. This may be quite tedious because of the great difference between the two languages. Frequently, the computer itself is used to aid in this task. Such use of the computer is called **automatic coding**.

For this purpose, the programmer writes his program in a special intermediate language with which he is familiar. This program is fed to the computer. The computer translates the program into a set of instructions (in the computer language) by means of a special translating program (known as FORTRAN, COBOL, ALGOL, PL/1, BASIC, and so forth) that either had been stored within the computer or is externally available.

D. THE COMPUTER WORD

In the computer, the basic unit of information is the **word**, a group of binary digits stored as a unit at an address in the memory. Depending on the type of computer, the word may contain a fixed or variable number of digits. (In the SIMCOM computer we shall use only words having a fixed number of digits.)

There are two methods for constructing the word. In the **straight binary** (or, simply, **binary**) **computer**, the number representing the information is converted to a corresponding set of binary digits. Thus the decimal number 321, for example, would appear as 101000001. In the **binary-coded decimal** (or simply **decimal**) **computer**, each digit of the number representing the information is converted to its binary equivalent, arranged in proper order, and treated by the computer as a separate character. Thus the decimal number 321 would appear as 0011 0010 0001.

Computers used for scientific work are usually of the binary type, whereas those used for business purposes are generally of the decimal type. Our SIMCOM computer will be of the binary-coded decimal type.

There are also two types of words—the **data word** and the **instruction word**. The data word contains data up to the full number of digits available. Different types of computers may use words of different lengths. Typical word lengths are 35 binary digits (for the binary computers) and 10 binary-coded decimal digits (for the decimal computers). In addition, the data word contains an algebraic sign (plus or minus), usually located at the front of the word. The plus sign is generally indicated by the digit 0 and the minus sign by the digit 1. See Figure 5-6.

The instruction word has the same length as the data word and consists of at least two parts. One of these parts is the **operation code**, which indicates the instruction to be performed. The other part is the address of the **operand** to be used for this instruction. See Figure 5-7.

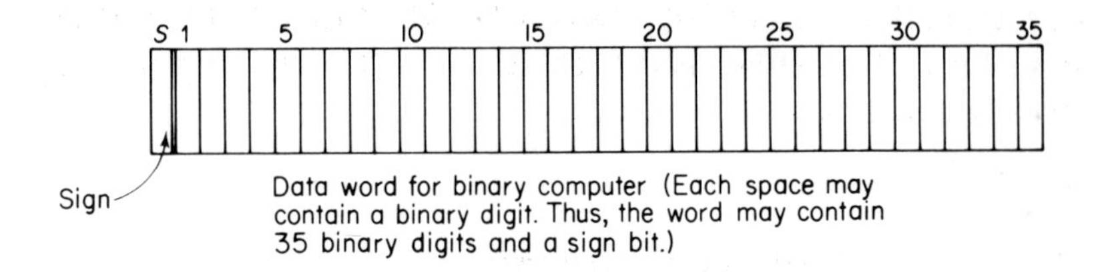

S 1 5 10 15 20 25 30 35
Sign
Data word for binary computer (Each space may contain a binary digit. Thus, the word may contain 35 binary digits and a sign bit.)

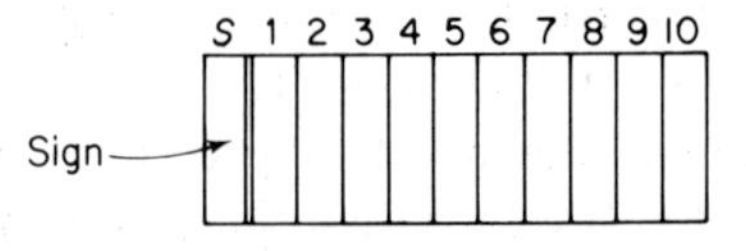

Fig. 5-6. Graphic representation of typical data words.

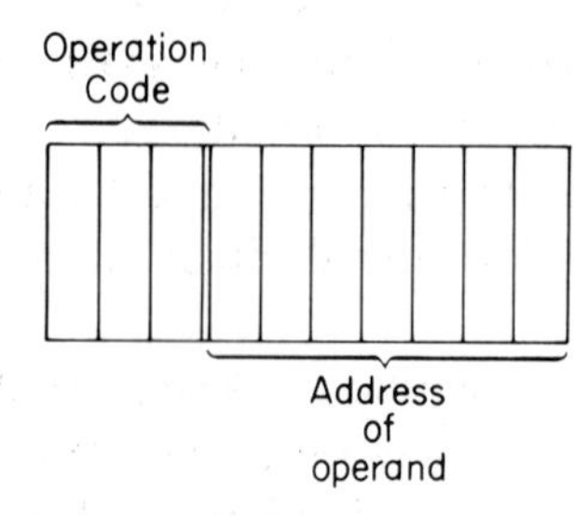

Fig. 5-7. Graphic representation of the instruction word for a single-address computer.

Note that the operand portion may represent different types of information. The operand may be the address of the data required for execution of the instruction or, in the case of a branch instruction, the address of the next instruction to be followed. In a **store** instruction, the operand may be the address where the result is to be stored. In a **print** instruction, the operand may be the address of the data to be printed or the address of the printing device to be actuated. The meaning of the operand is determined by the instruction associated with it. A computer using this type of instruction word is known as a **single-address computer**.

There are computers that use more complicated instruction words. For example, the instruction word may contain not only the operation code and the address of the operand but the address of the next instruction word as well. Or, the instruction word may contain the operation code and the address of the two operands required for executing the instructions. As an example, if the instruction is to add A to B, the instruction word would contain the operation code for addition and the addresses of both A and B.

There are instruction words that contain three addresses—the addresses of the two operands and the address of the next instruction word. In addition to the above, certain words may contain other items of information to be used by the computer. The SIMCOM computer will be the single-address type.

The main memory section of the computer (together with its external storage facilities) is able to store thousands and even millions of words. The registers of the computer generally have storage space for up to one word. Also, whereas the main memory section generally stores its information more or less permanently (at least, for the duration of the program), information is stored only temporarily in the register. Further, the computer must search its memory at a specific address for specific information. The information stored in the register is instantly accessible.

E. THE SIMCOM OPERATION CYCLE

Once the program has been entered (**loaded**) into the memory of the computer, the machine automatically goes through the program in a given cycle. Each cycle has two alternate phases—the **instruction** phase and the **execution** phase. After these two phases have been completed, the cycle is repeated. The "heart beat" of the computer consists of a series of regular, equally spaced electronic pulses produced by an electronic oscillator, called a **clock**, at frequencies as high as 1 MHz.

The duration of each phase of the cycle is determined by a fixed number of pulses. Each phase contains a number of machine operations timed by these clock pulses.

The instruction phase

The instruction words of the program have been stored at consecutive addresses in the memory of the computer. Before the start of operations, the address of the first instruction word has been placed in the program counter. The instruction phase of the cycle starts as this address is transferred to the **address register**. See Figure 5-8.

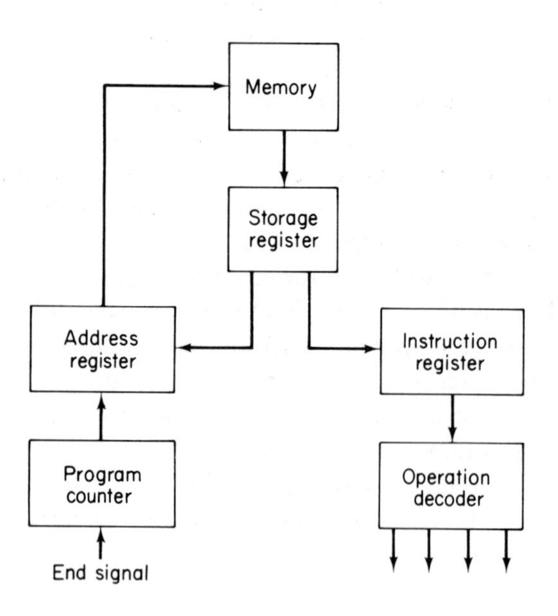

Fig. 5-8. Flow diagram of SIMCOM operation cycle.

(Note that as information is transferred from one storage location to another, the information is not erased from the original location unless specifically so ordered. Thus in our example the address of the first instruction word appears in both the program counter and the address register. On the other hand, when new information is placed in a storage location, any previous information stored at that location is first automatically erased.)

At the address register, the address is decoded, generating the electrical signals that enable the computer to locate the first instruction word stored in the memory. This word is transferred to the **storage register**. The operation code portion of the word is transferred to the **instruction register** and is decoded by the operation decoder into electrical signals that ready the circuits required for execution of the instruction.

The portion of the instruction word that contains the address of the operand is transferred to the address register, first erasing the information previously stored there. This completes the instruction phase of the cycle.

The execution phase

The execution phase starts with the computer locating the operand (at the address indicated by the address register) and transferring it from the memory to the storage register. Then the computer executes the various machine operations indicated by the instruction using the information contained in the operand and activated by the pulses from the operation decoder. When the operation is finished, an **end signal** modifies the address in the program counter by advancing the counter one count. The counter now contains the address of the next instruction.

This completes the execution phase of the cycle. The cycle is repeated over and over again, the instruction phase alternating with the execution phase for each cycle, until the entire program is completed.

In the case of a branch operation appearing in the program, the operation-code portion of the instruction word would be that of the branch instruction, and the operand portion would be the address of the next instruction to be followed if branching is to take place. Under such conditions, this address is placed in the program counter, replacing the address already there. The computer will then operate as previously indicated.

We have just described the complete cycle for the SIMCOM computer. Different computers may have different methods for going through the cycle, but the basic principles of operation are the same for all digital computers.

PRACTICAL COMPUTER CIRCUITS

In previous sections, we discussed number systems and circuits common to most computers, as well as operation of a complete "typical" or theoretical computer. In this section, we shall discuss practical circuits found in actual computers and computer accessories.

The individual components and circuits described thus far can be arranged in various combinations to perform specific functions. For example, **decade counters** using FFs convert a series of pulses into BCD form, such as conversion of a pulse count into an 8421 code. Also, a **decoder** can be used to convert the BCD data into a 10-line or decade readout.

Some other examples using combinations of basic digital components to perform specific functions include analog-to-digital conversion, digital-to-analog conversion, storage registers, shift registers, level comparators, sign or polarity comparators, adders, subtractors, encoders, and a decoder.

The operation of circuits that appear frequently throughout various sections of most computers is discussed in Chapter 6. Chapter 7 covers input/output circuits, while Chapter 8 is devoted to memory or storage circuits and devices.

Chapters 9 and 10 deal with the overall operation of a working computer from both the circuit standpoint (Chapter 9) and the visual readout standpoint (Chapter 10).

As discussed, digital computer circuits can be grouped into five major operational sections. These sections are (1) the input section, which provides interface with all data coming into the computer, as well as circuits that convert the data into a format suitable for processing by the computer; (2) the output section, which provides interface with all data leaving the computer, as well as circuits that convert the processed data into a format suitable for outside equipment; (3) the memory section, which provides temporary (or semipermanent) storage of the data being processed; (4) the arithmetic section, which includes the circuits necessary to process the data; and (5) the control section, which includes the operating controls and readouts necessary to operate and program the computer.

Because the circuits of the input and output sections are often the same or closely related, the discussions for input/output circuits are combined in Chapter 7. Computer accessories (often referred to as the *peripherals*), such as card or tape punches and readers, tape recorders, typewriters, and optical readouts, are considered as part of the input and/or output circuits and are so covered in Chapter 7.

Because of the importance of memory and storage devices, all of Chapter 8 is devoted to memory circuits.

Since there is little standardization in computer control and arithmetic sections, no separate chapters are provided for circuits of these sections. Instead, both the control and arithmetic circuits are discussed throughout Chapters 9 and 10, as applicable.

CIRCUITS COMMON TO ALL COMPUTER SECTIONS

6

The following circuits are "typical" for all sections of most computers. The circuits described can be in discrete form but most often appear as complete IC packages. In the event of failure, such packages must be replaced as a single unit. For this reason, some technicians consider detailed circuit operation of minor importance, preferring to concentrate on the effect of the circuit on the overall system. However, if the technicians thoroughly understand the operation of the circuit package, they will better understand the need for circuit measurements during troubleshooting. (The troubleshooting of computer circuits is discussed in Section IV.)

A. COUNTER/READOUT AND DIVIDER CIRCUIT OPERATION

Most computer counters use **decade counters** that convert the count (series of pulses or events) into a BCD code and **decoders** for conversion of the code into decade form. In applications where the pulses or events must be read out, readout tubes are used to display decade information.

The same basic circuits used for decade counters are used as dividers. Therefore it is necessary to understand the operation of the basic decade before discussing how the decade is used in logic circuits.

1. Decade Circuits

Decade circuits serve two purposes in computer counters. First, the decade will divide frequencies by 10. That is, the decade will produce one output for each ten input pulses or signals. This permits several frequencies to be obtained from one basic frequency. For example, a 1-MHz time base can be divided to 100 kHz by one decade divider, to 10 kHz by two decade dividers, to 1 kHz by three decade dividers, and so forth. When decades are used for division, they are often referred to as **scalers**, although *dividers* is a better term. The second purpose of a decade is to convert a count into a BCD logic code. The division function of a decade is discussed first.

The basic unit of a decade divider is a two-to-one scaler, called a **binary counter**. This unit uses a **bistable multivibrator** or FF. The first input pulse flips the circuit from one state to the other. The second input pulse flops the circuit back to its original state. Each time the circuit is flipped from one state to the other and back again (requiring two input pulses), a single (complete) output pulse is produced.

The output pulses of one FF may be applied to the input of another similar FF for further frequency division. This is called **cascading**. A basic binary counter uses a cascaded chain of four FFs, as shown in Figure 6-1. The count of this chain is 16 (2^4).

Assume that all four FFs are in their 0 state, that a positive-going input is required to change FF states, and that the FF outputs are positive-going only when they shift from a 1 state to a 0 state.

Pulse 1 causes FF_1 to move from the 0 to the 1 state. The output of FF_1 is then negative-going and has no effect on FF_2. Pulse 2 causes FF_1 to move from the 1 to the 0 state. The output of FF_1 is then positive-going and moves FF_2 from the 0 to the 1 state. Pulse 3 causes FF_1 to move from the 0 to the 1 state (negative output with no effect on FF_2). Pulse 4 causes FF_1 to go from 1 to 0. This moves FF_2 from 1 back to 0. Thus four counts are required for FF_2 to go through a complete cycle. This process is repeated, requiring 16 pulses, before FF_4 goes through a complete cycle.

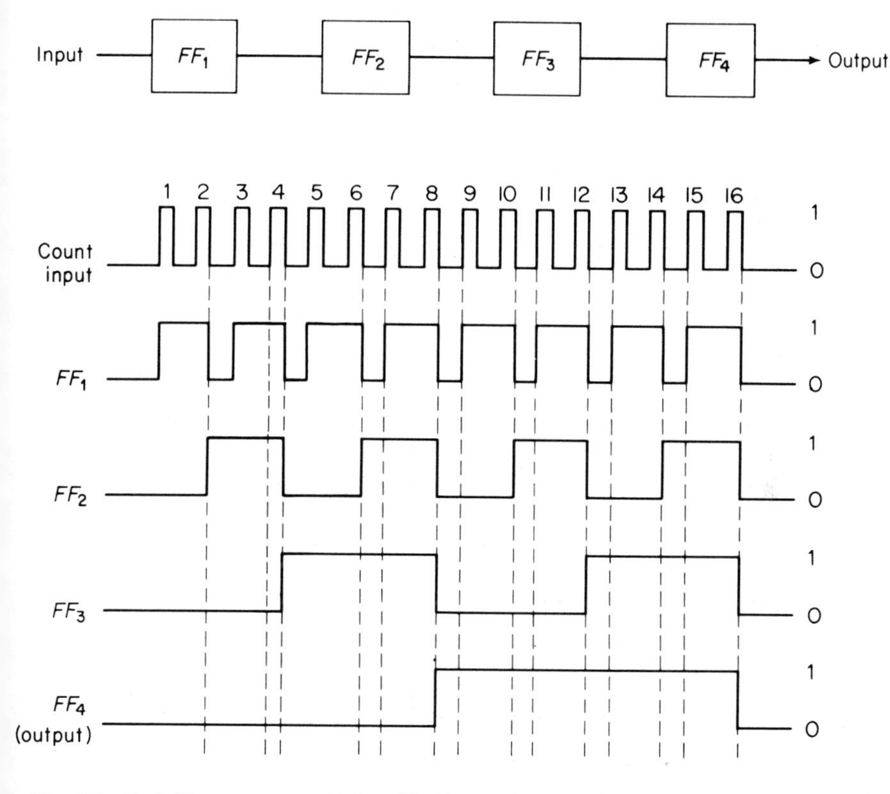

Fig. 6-1. Basic binary counter with four FFs in cascade.

A **binary decade counter** uses feedback of the pulses to produce one output for each ten input pulses. In effect, a binary decade counter is a divide-by-10 counter. There are many circuits for converting a pure binary count to a decade count. All such circuits involve the feedback of pulses. The circuit shown in Figure 6-2 is typical of the many feedback systems. The timing diagram shown in Figure 6-2 illustrates the count sequence. Note that the output of FF_4 (which is the output of the complete decade circuit) shifts from 1 to 0 only after the tenth pulse.

2. Decade-to-BCD Conversion

Figure 6-3 shows a decade circuit capable of converting a series of pulses into an 8421 binary code. One FF is used for each of the digits.

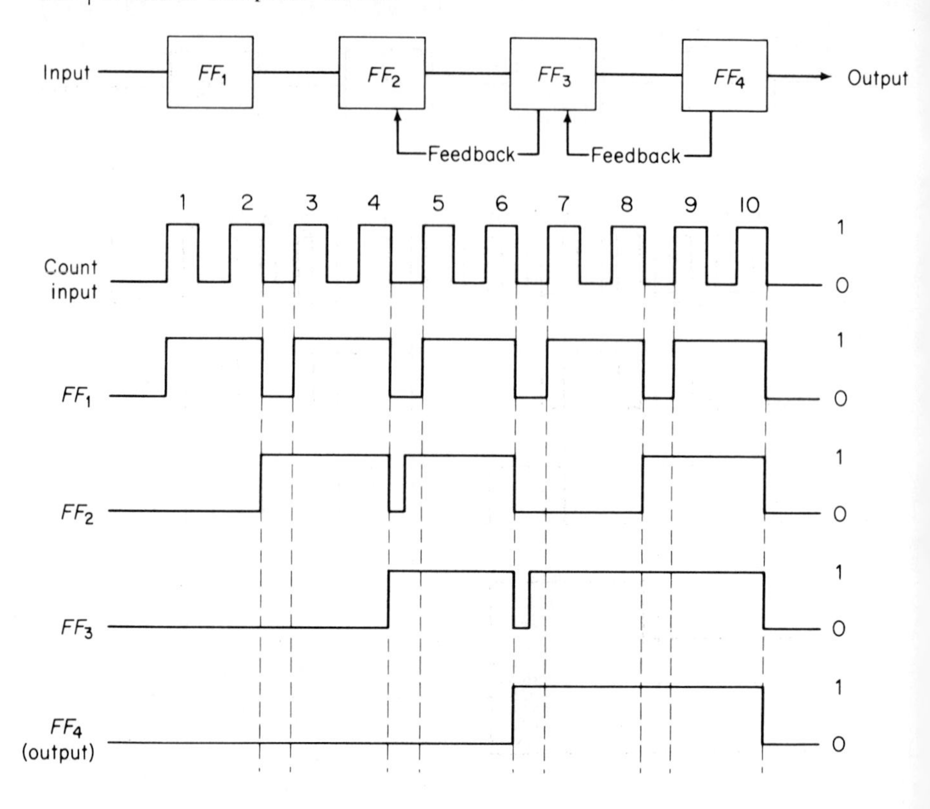

Fig. 6-2. Binary decade counter with four FFs in cascade.

Input pulses are fed into the FF_1. FF_2, FF_4, and FF_8 are cascaded and receive pulses after the FF_1.

For each state of an FF, one of the collectors is more positive than the opposite collector. When the states change, the polarities reverse. Some logic systems are positive-true, while others use negative-true. In the following discussions it is assumed that positive-true is used for all circuits. That is, when an input or output is positive, that input or output is true. In the case of an FF, when one output or collector is true, the opposite collector is false.

For the FFs shown in Figure 6-3, when the 8421 lines are positive, the 8421 lines are true. With the FFs in the same state, the $\overline{8421}$ lines are negative (false). When the FFs change states, the 8421 lines are negative (false) and the $\overline{8421}$ lines are true.

At the beginning of a count, the 8421 lines are negative (false). This is represented by a 0. The $\overline{8421}$ lines are positive (true). This is repre-

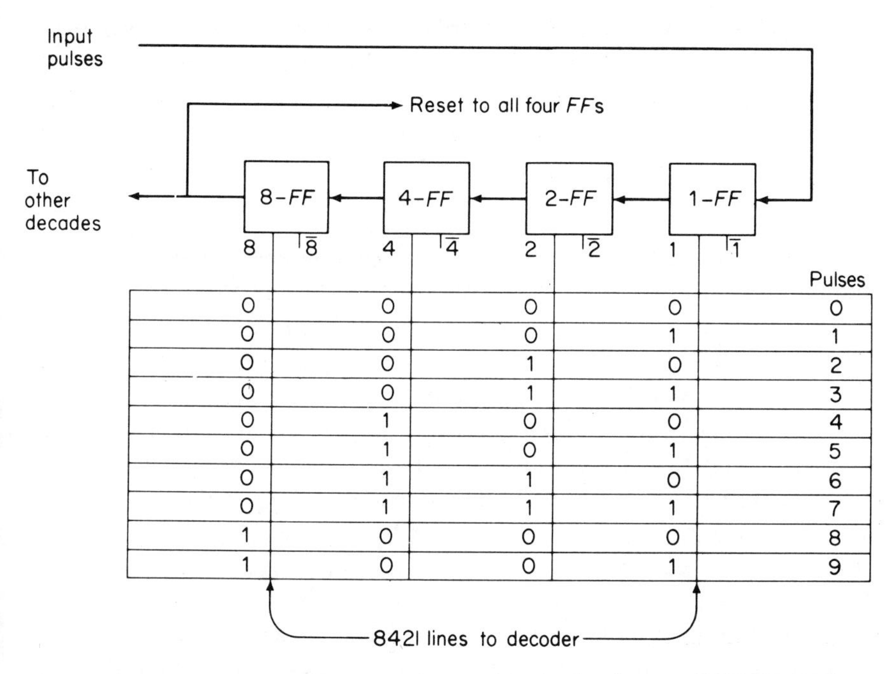

8	4	2	1	Pulses
0	0	0	0	0
0	0	0	1	1
0	0	1	0	2
0	0	1	1	3
0	1	0	0	4
0	1	0	1	5
0	1	1	0	6
0	1	1	1	7
1	0	0	0	8
1	0	0	1	9

Fig. 6-3. Binary decade circuit for converting a series of pulses into an 8421 binary code.

sented by a 1. In a practical decade circuit the decades are set (or reset) to this condition by the application of a voltage or pulse. Typically, the pulses are supplied by a time base at the end of a 10 count.

When the first pulse in the count is applied, the FF_1 changes states. The 1 line becomes positive, represented by a 1, and the $\overline{1}$ line goes negative. (Note that the $\overline{8421}$ lines will always be at the opposite of the 8421 lines. The $\overline{8421}$ 0 and 1 states are omitted from Figure 6-3 for clarity.)

When the second pulse is applied, the FF_1 changes states. The 1 line goes false (0) and the 2 line goes true (1). With the third pulse applied, the FF_1 goes true (1) but the FF_2 remains true. [Remember that the FF_2 will change states for each complete cycle of the FF_1. When the fourth pulse is applied, the FF_1 goes to 0, as does the FF_2. This causes the FF_4 to change states (the 4 line goes to positive or 1).]

This process is repeated until a 9 count is reached. At that point, the FF_8 moves from 1 to 0 and produces an output. This output is returned to the reset line and serves to reset all the FFs to the false state (the 8421 lines at 0). The output from the FF_8 can also be applied to the FF_1 of another decade. Any number of decades can be so connected. In a readout device, one decade is required for each readout tube.

3. BCD-to-Readout Conversion

Figure 6-4 shows the output of a decade connected to a decoder that converts the BCD code into 10-line form. Each of the ten outputs (0–9) is connected to the corresponding cathodes of a readout tube. This is the basic circuit arrangement for a typical electronic counter used in computers. One readout tube (together with one decoder and one decade) is required for each digit of the counter. In a practical computer circuit, a **register** and/or **storage** circuit is connected between the decades and their corresponding decoders. These registers hold the BCD count data until they are cleared by the operator or will sample the count at some given rate. The operation of registers is discussed in later paragraphs of this chapter.

Note that the decoder is essentially a group of AND gates connected to provide nine inputs (8421, $\overline{8421}$, and an **enable** input) and ten outputs (0–9). As discussed, an AND gate requires that all inputs be true (positive in this case) to produce an output. All the AND gates in Figure 6-4 have three inputs, which must be true before they will produce an output.

The output of gates 0–9 are connected to the cathodes of a readout tube. The readout tubes are visible through the computer control panel. Each readout tube consists of ten cold cathodes and a common anode, all enclosed in a gas-filled envelope. These cathodes are shaped as numbers 0–9 and are stacked one above the other. When one of the decoder gates (0–9) produces an output, the corresponding cathode circuit is completed. The gas between that particular number-shaped cathode and the common anode is ionized, causing the cathode to glow, thereby revealing its number at the computer control panel. One decoder gate produces an output at any given time. Thus the remaining cathodes are nonionized and remain unlit (not visible from the computer control panel).

Assume that the circuit of Figure 6-4 is part of an electronic counter used in a computer and that the counter's gate is held open for a count of seven input pulses. Under these conditions, the $\overline{8}$, 4, 2, and 1 lines will be true (1). Likewise, the 8, $\overline{4}$, $\overline{2}$, and $\overline{1}$ lines will be false (0). The B AND

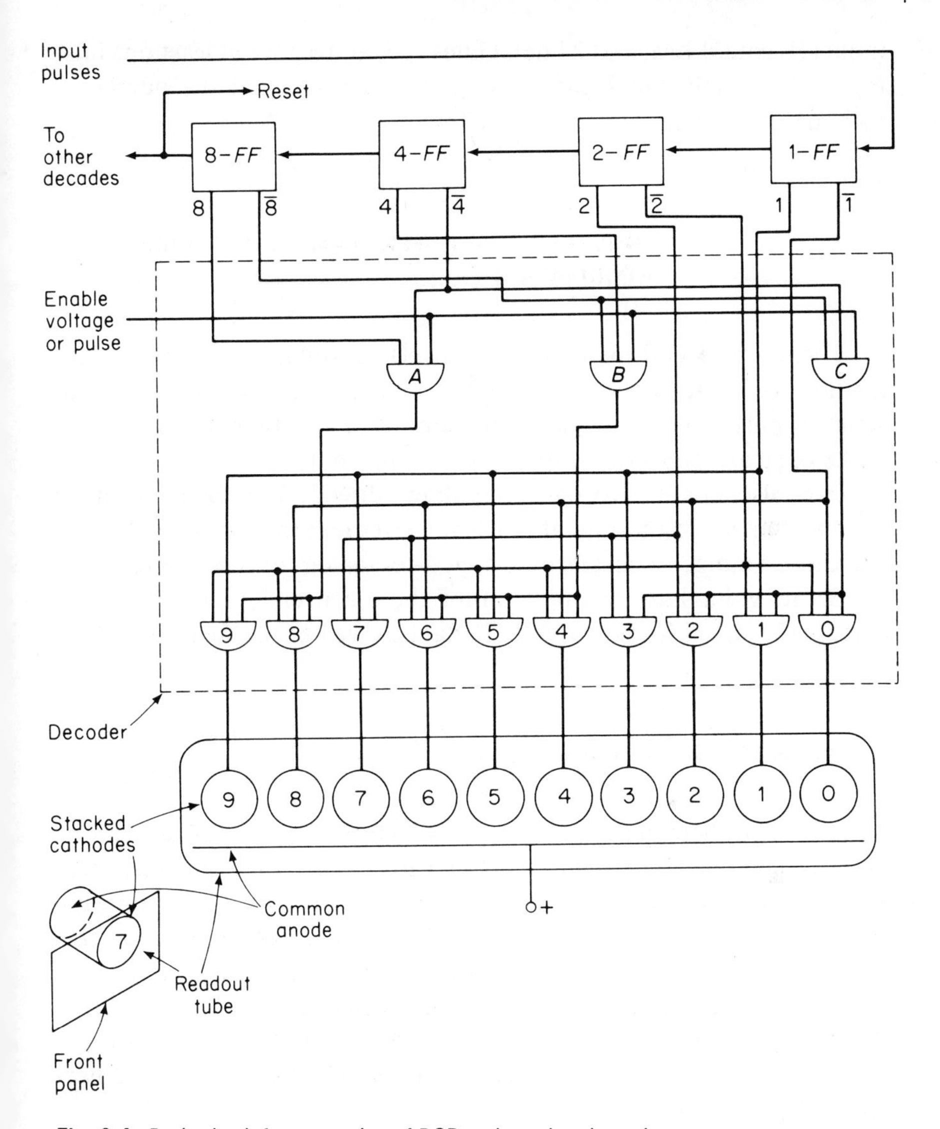

Fig. 6-4. Basic circuit for conversion of BCD code to decade readout.

gate of the decoder will have three true inputs ($\overline{8}$, 4, and enable). The enable pulse or voltage is always true and is applied (manually or by a timing pulse from the computer's control section) whenever a readout is desired.

Both the A and C gates will have at least one false input. Thus only the 4, 5, 6, or 7 gates can produce an output. The 7 gate has three true inputs (B gate, 1 line, and 2 line). Gates 4, 5, and 6 have at least one false input. Thus only the 7 gate produces an output, and the number 7 cathode of the readout tube will glow.

B. CONVERSION BETWEEN ANALOG AND DIGITAL INFORMATION

There are several methods for converting voltage (or current) into digital form. One method is to convert the voltage into a frequency or series of pulses. Then the pulses are converted into BCD form, and the BCD data are converted into a decade readout.

It is also possible to convert voltage directly into BCD form by means of an analog-to-digital (a/d) converter and to convert BCD data back into voltage by means of a digital-to-analog (d/a) converter.

Before going into the operation of these conversion circuits, let us discuss the signal formats for BCD data as well as the **four-bit system.**

1. Typical BCD Signal Formats

Although there are many ways in which pulsed wave forms can be used to represent the 1 and 0 digits of a BCD code, there are only three ways in common use. These are the NRZL (non-return-to-zero-level), the NRZM (non-return-to-zero-mark), and the RZ (return-to-zero) formats. Figure 6-5 shows the relation of the three formats.

In the NRZL format, a 1 bit is one signal level, while a 0 bit is another signal level. These levels can be 5 V, 10 V, 0 V, −5 V, or any other selected values, provided that the 1 and 0 levels are entirely different and predetermined.

In the RZ format, a 1 bit is represented by a pulse of some definite width (usually a $\frac{1}{2}$-bit width) that returns to the zero signal level, while a 0 bit is represented by a zero-level signal.

In the NRZM format, the level of the wave form has no meaning. A 1 bit is represented by a change in level (either higher or lower), while a 0 bit is represented by no change in level. [Generally, NRZM is not used in computer work. One exception is where computers must feed into (or accept data from) an existing NRZM system.]

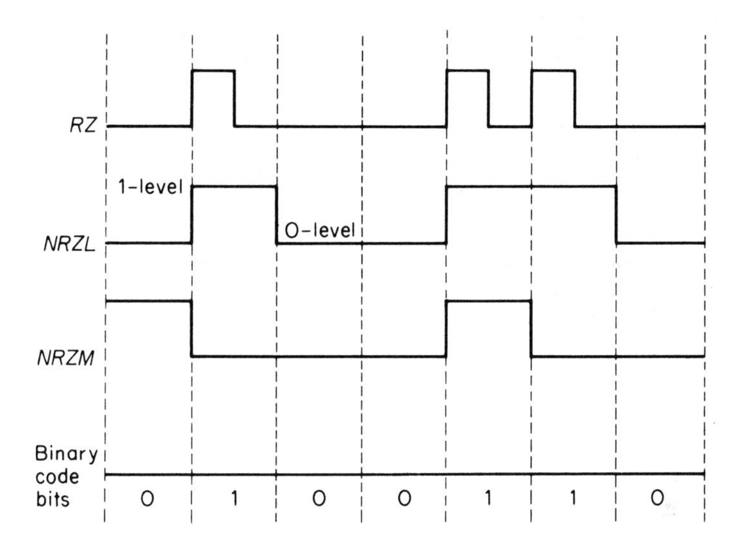

Fig. 6-5. Typical BCD signal formats.

2. The Four-Bit System

As the name implies, a four-bit system is one that is capable of handling four information bits. Any fractional part (in sixteenths) can be stated by using only four binary digits. As discussed, the number 15 is represented by 1111 in the binary system. (Zero is then represented by 0000.) Thus any number between 0 and 15 requires only four binary digits. For example, the number 1101 is 13, the number 0011 is 3, and so forth. Although not all BCD codes use the four-bit system, it is common and does provide a high degree of accuracy for conversion between analog and digital data.

In practice, a four-bit a/d converter (also known as a binary encoder in some computer service literature) samples the voltage level to be converted and compares the voltage to $\frac{1}{2}$ scale, $\frac{1}{4}$ scale, $\frac{1}{8}$ scale and $\frac{1}{16}$ scale (in that order) of some given full-scale voltage. The encoder then produces four bits in sequence, with the decision made on the most significant (or $\frac{1}{2}$ scale) first.

Figure 6-6 shows the relation among three voltage levels to be encoded (or converted) and the corresponding binary code (in NRZL form). As shown, each of three voltage levels is divided into four equal time increments. The first time increment is used to represent the $\frac{1}{2}$-scale

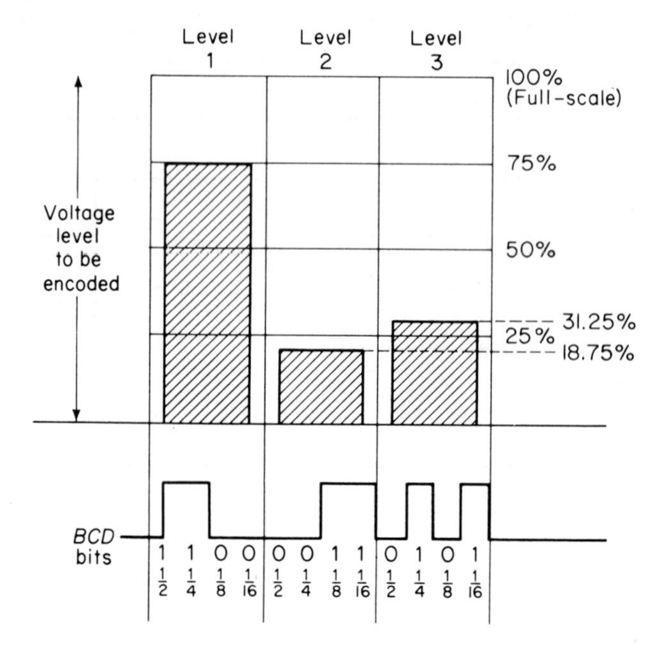

Fig. 6-6. Relationship among three voltage levels to be encoded and the corresponding BCD code (using the four-bit system).

bit, the second increment is used for the $\frac{1}{4}$-scale bit, the third increment for the $\frac{1}{8}$-scale bit, and the fourth increment for the $\frac{1}{16}$-scale bit.

In level 1, the first two time increments are at a binary 1, while the second two increments are at a binary 0. This would be represented as 1100, or 12. Twelve is three-fourths of 16. Thus level 1 is 75 percent of full scale. For example, if full scale is 100 V, level 1 is 75 V.

In level 2, the first two time increments are at a binary 0, while the second two increments are at a binary 1. This is represented as 0011, or 3. Thus level 2 is three-sixteenths of full scale (or 18.75 V).

This can be expressed in another way. In the first or half-scale increment, the encoder produces a binary 0, because the voltage (18.75) is less than half-scale (50). The same is true of the second, or quarter-scale, increment (18.75 V is less than 25 V). In the third or one-eighth-scale increment, the encoder produces a binary 1, as it does in the fourth or one-sixteenth-scale increment, because the voltage being compared is greater than one-eighth of full scale (18.75 is greater than 12.5) and greater than one-sixteenth of full scale (18.75 is greater than 6.25).

Thus the half and quarter increments are at zero or off, while the one-eighth and one-sixteenth-scale increments are on. Also $\frac{1}{8} + \frac{1}{16} = \frac{3}{16}$, or 18.75 percent.

In level 3, the first time increment is 0, the second is 1, the third is 0, while the fourth is 1. This is a binary 0101, or 5, and represents five-sixteenths of full scale (31.25 V).

3. Analog-to-Digital Conversion

One of the most common methods of direct analog-to-digital conversion involves the use of an encoder that uses a sequence of half-split, trial-and-error steps. This produces code bits in serial (all on one line, one after another) form.

The heart of an encoder is a **conversion ladder** (a form of digital-to-analog converter), which is shown in Figure 6-7. The ladder provides a means of implementing a four-bit binary coding system and produces

Fig. 6-7. Binary conversion ladder used in the four-bit system.

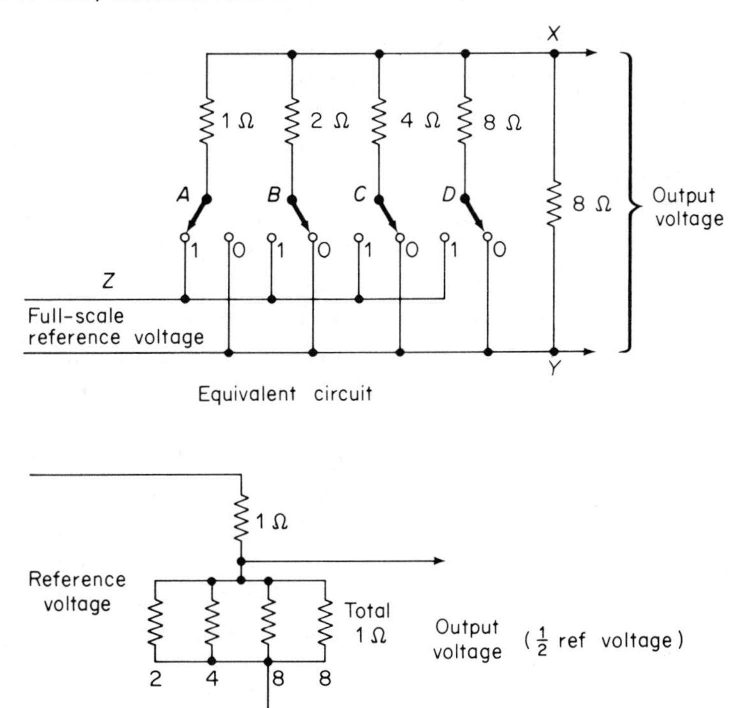

an output voltage that is equivalent to the switch positions. The switches can be moved to either a 1 or 0 position, which corresponds to a four-place binary number. The output voltage describes a percentage of the full-scale reference voltage, depending on the binary switch positions.

For example, if all the switches are in the 0 position, there is no output voltage. This produces a binary 0000, represented by 0 V.

If switch *A* is in the 1 position and the remaining switches are in the 0 position, this produces a binary 1000 (decimal 8). Since the total in a four-bit system is 16, 8 represents one-half of full scale. Thus the output voltage is one-half of the full-scale reference voltage. This is accomplished as follows.

The 2-, 4-, and 8-ohm (Ω) switch resistors and the 8-Ω output resistor are connected in parallel. This produces a value of 1 Ω across points *X* and *Y*. The reference voltage is applied across the 1-Ω switch resistor (across points Z and *X*) and the 1-Ω combination of resistors (across points *X* and *Y*). In effect, this is the same as two 1-Ω resistors in series. Since the full-scale reference voltage is applied across both resistors in series and the output is measured across only one of the resistors, the output voltage will be one-half of the reference voltage.

In a practical encoder circuit, the same basic ladder is used to supply a comparison voltage to a **comparison circuit**, which compares the voltage to be encoded against the binary-coded voltage from the ladder. The resultant output of the comparison circuit is a binary code representing the voltage to be encoded.

The mechanical switches shown in Figure 6-7 are replaced by electronic switches, usually FFs. When the FF is in one state (the on state), the corresponding ladder resistor is connected to the reference voltage. In the off state, the resistor is disconnected from the reference voltage. The switches are triggered by four pulses (representing each of the four binary bits) from the computer's time base. An enable pulse is used to turn the comparison circuit on and off, so that as each switch is operated, a comparison can be made for each of the four bits.

Figure 6-8 is a simplified block diagram of such an encoder. Here, the reference voltage is applied to the ladder through the electronic switches. The ladder output (comparison voltage) is controlled by switch positions, which, in turn, are controlled by pulses from the time base. The sequence of these pulses is also shown in Figure 6-8.

The following paragraphs outline the sequence of events necessary to produce a series of four binary bits that describe the input voltage

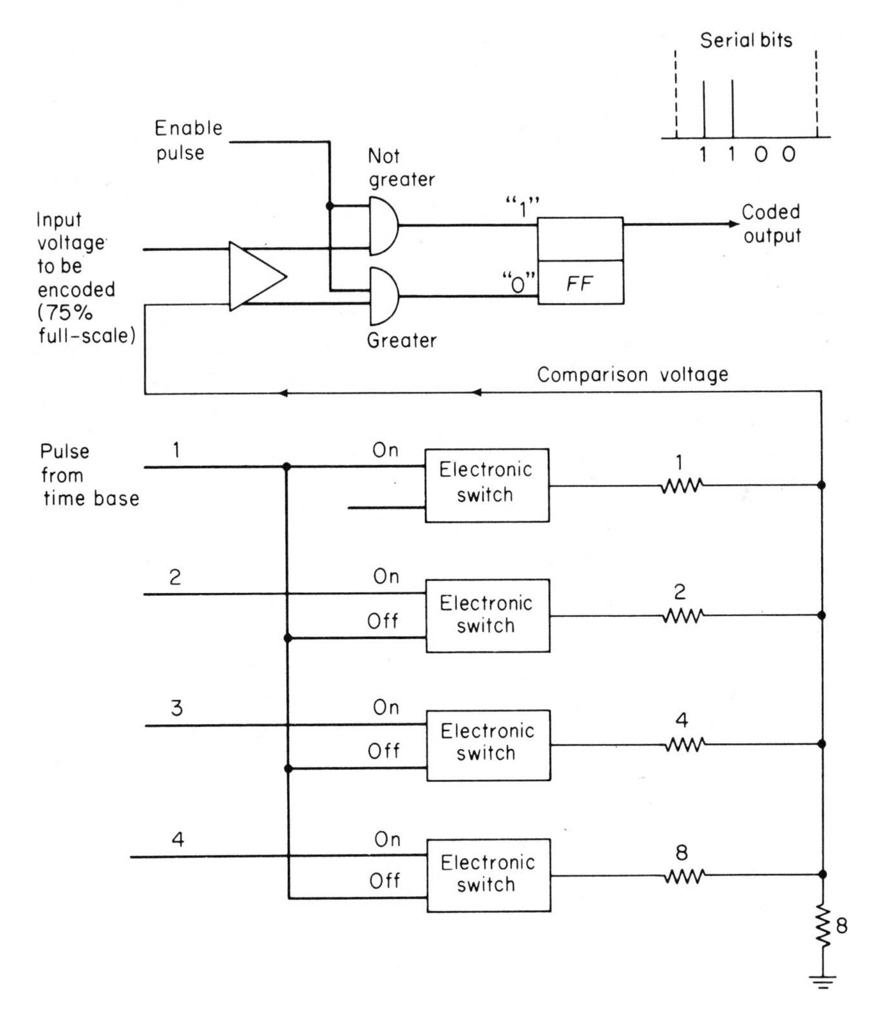

Fig. 6-8. Analog-to-digital converter (binary encoder) using the four-bit system.

as a percentage of full scale (in one-sixteenth increments). Assume that the input voltage is three-fourths of full scale (or 75 percent).

When pulse 1 arrives, switch 1 is turned on and the remaining switches are turned off. The ladder output is a 50-percent voltage that is applied to the differential amplifier. The balance of this amplifier is set so that its output will be sufficient to turn on one AND gate and turn off the other AND gate if the ladder voltage is greater than the input voltage. Likewise, the differential amplifier will reverse the AND gates if the ladder voltage is not greater than the input voltage. Both AND gates are enabled by the pulse from the time base.

In our example (75 percent of full scale), the ladder output is less than the input voltage when pulse 1 is applied to the ladder. As a result, the *not greater* AND gate turns on, and the output FF is set to the 1 position. Thus, for the first of the four bits, the FF output is a 1.

When pulse 2 arrives, switch 2 is turned on and switch 1 remains on. Both switches 3 and 4 remain off. The ladder output is now 75 percent of full-scale voltage. Thus the ladder voltage equals the input voltage. However, the ladder output is still not greater than the input voltage. Consequently, when the AND gates are enabled, the AND gates remain in the same condition. Thus the output FF remains at a 1.

When pulse 3 arrives, switch 3 is turned on. Switches 1 and 2 remain on, while switch 4 is off. The ladder output is now 87.5 percent of full-scale voltage and is thus greater than the input voltage. As a result, when the AND gates are enabled, they reverse. The not greater AND gate turns off, and the *greater* AND gate turns on. The output FF then sets to the 0 position.

When pulse 4 arrives, switch 4 is turned on. All switches are now on. The ladder output is now maximum (full-scale) and thus is greater than the input voltage. As a result, when the AND gates are enabled, they remain in the same condition. Likewise, the output FF remains at a 0.

The four binary bits from the output are 1, 1, 0, and 0, or 1100. This is a binary 12, which is 75 percent of 16.

In a practical encoder, when the fourth pulse has passed, all the switches are reset to the off position. This places them in a condition to spell out the next four-bit binary word.

4. Digital-to-Analog Conversion

A digital-to-analog converter performs the opposite function of the analog-to-digital converter just described. A d/a converter produces an output voltage (usually dc) that corresponds to the binary code. Information to be converted is usually applied to the d/a input in serial form. However, some d/a converters receive 4-line data (also known as parallel form).

As shown in Figure 6-9, a conversion ladder is also used in the d/a

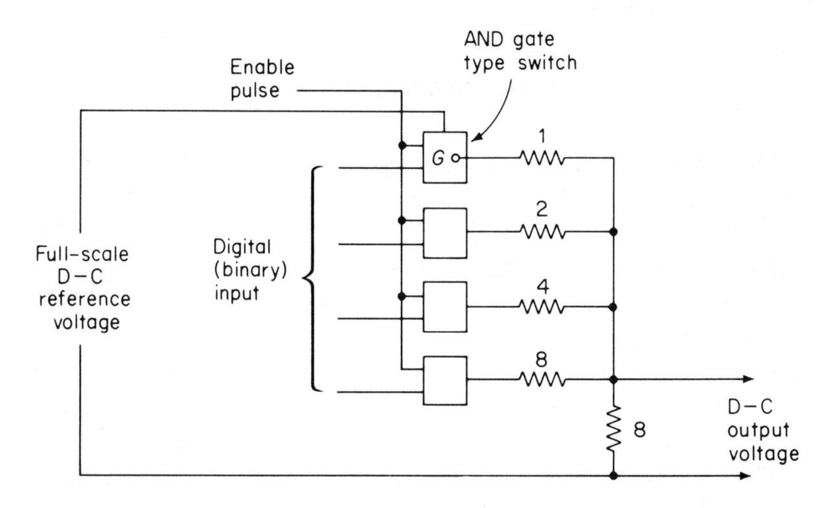

Fig. 6-9. Digital-to-analog converter using the four-bit system.

converter. The output of the conversion ladder is a dc voltage that represents a percentage of the full-scale reference voltage. The output percentage depends on the switch positions. In turn, the switches are set to on or off by corresponding binary pulses. If the information is applied to the switches in 4-line form, each line can be connected to the corresponding switch. If the data are in serial form, the data must be converted to parallel (4-line in this case) form by a shift register and/or storage register (described in later paragraphs of this chapter).

The switches in a d/a converter are essentially a form of AND gate. Each gate completes the circuit from the reference voltage to the corresponding ladder resistor when both the enable pulse and the binary pulse coincide.

Assume that the digital number to be converted is 1000 (a binary 8). When the first pulse is applied to the ladder switches, switch *A* is enabled and the reference voltage is applied to the 1-Ω resistor. When switches *B*, *C*, and *D* receive their enable pulses, there are no binary pulses (or, the pulses are in the low-level 0 condition, depending on the binary pulse format used). Thus switches *B*, *C*, and *D* do not complete the circuits to the 2-, 4-, and 8-Ω ladder resistors. These resistors combine with the 8-Ω output resistor to produce a 1-Ω resistance in series with the 1-Ω ladder resistance. This divides the reference voltage in half to produce 50 percent of full-scale output. Since 8 is one-half of 16, the 50-percent output voltage represents a digital 8.

C. STORAGE REGISTERS

The storage register is a combination of gates and FFs used to store binary information. A typical storage register is illustrated in Figure 6-10. This register can store four bits of binary information applied to inputs *A*, *B*, *C*, and *D*. The inputs must be positive-true.

Assume that *A* and *C* are at positive levels (true) and that *B* and *C* are negative (false).

Before the information is stored, all four FFs are reset by the leading edge of the reset/store command pulse (from the computer's time base). This clears the register of any previously stored data.

The trailing (positive-going) edge of the reset/store command pulse is coupled into the four positive-true input AND gates. Inputs that are true (*A* and *C*) enable a true output from the corresponding gates,

Fig. 6-10. Typical storage register.

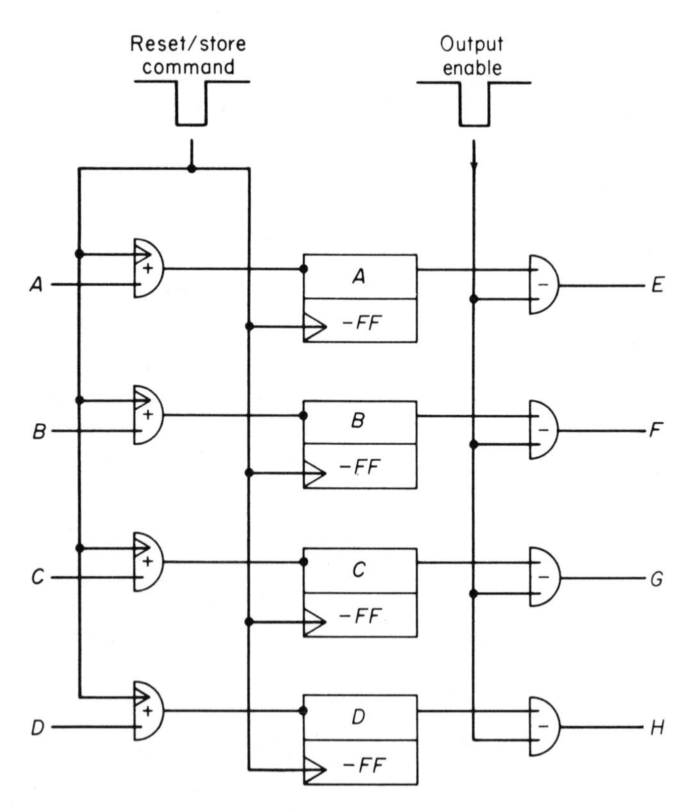

which, in turn, set FFs *A* and *C*. The other two FFs (*B* and *D*) remain in the reset state. The information at *A*, *B*, *C*, and *D* is now stored in the four FFs.

When the stored information is required, the output enable line is made negative (by a pulse from the computer's time base), and output lines *E* and *G* from the set FFs are true (negative-true, now). Outputs *F* and *H* are false (positive). (If positive-true outputs are required from the FFs, then the complementary output of the FFs can be used.)

Fig. 6-11. Typical storage register symbols. (Courtesy of Hewlett-Packard.)

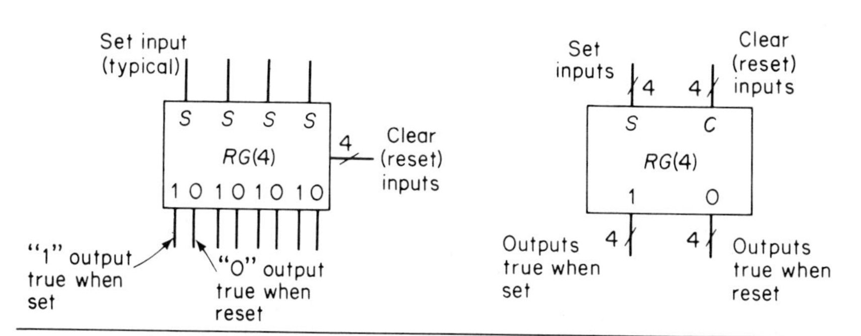

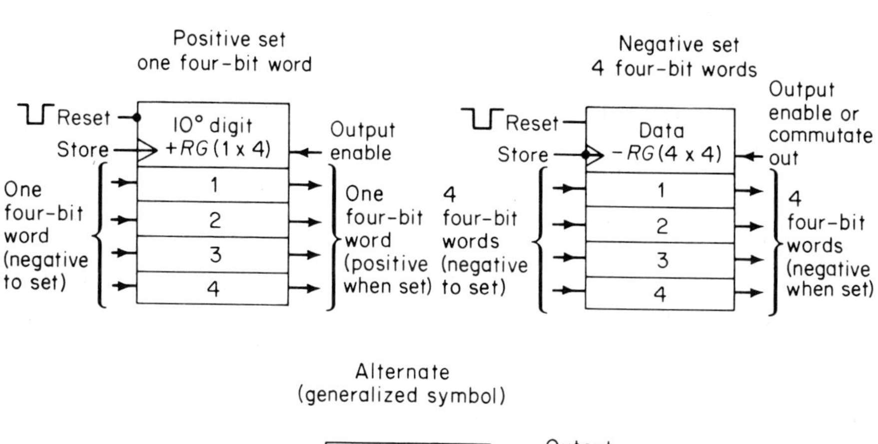

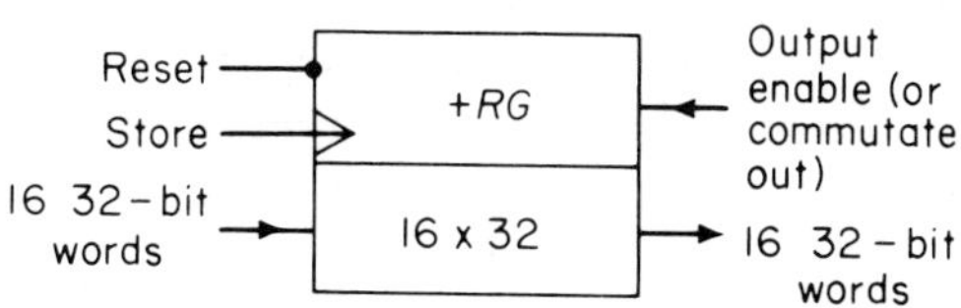

The storage register of Figure 6-10 is called a 4 × 1 register. The 4 denotes the number of bits per word or character. The 1 indicates the number of characters or words. The storage capacity is expanded by adding 4 × 1 registers, one for each added character. The expanded register is then called a 4 × 2, 4 × 3, and so forth register. If the characters require more than four bits, the register is increased by 5 × 1, 5 × 2, and so forth by adding storage FFs and associated gates (see Figure 6-11).

By using one stored pulse, parallel data (all four binary pulses occurring simultaneously) are stored. Then by successively enabling the register for each character, parallel-to-serial conversion is obtained (corresponding bits of each register are OR-gated together.) The process of successively enabling a multicharacter storage register is sometimes called **commutation.**

D. SHIFT REGISTERS

Shift registers have many functions. A shift register is sometimes used to perform arithmetic functions of multiplication and division. When a number is multiplied by 10, it is shifted to the left and a 0 is added. For example, the number 377 × 10 is 3770 (377 shifted to the left and a 0 added). Division, the opposite of multiplication, requires a right shift. A shift register is also used for serial-to-parallel converion of binary pulses.

As shown in Figure 6-12, one form of shift register is made up of FFs and delay elements. The FFs are connected together so that each one transfers its existing data to the next FF when the reset input is applied. (The reset input pulse applied simultaneously to all FFs is often known as the *advance* input when referring to a shift register.) One FF is required for each bit to be converted. Thus four FFs are shown for four binary bits. This is similar but not identical to the decade discussed previously.

When the advance (reset) line is pulsed, as it is between every binary pulse bit, the FFs in the set (1) state switch to 0, and those in the reset (0) state remain in the 0 state. The output signal from each FF is shaped and delayed in the delay circuits before the signal is directed to the 1 input of the next FF to complete the shift operation. Serial data can be inserted into the first FF between each shift.

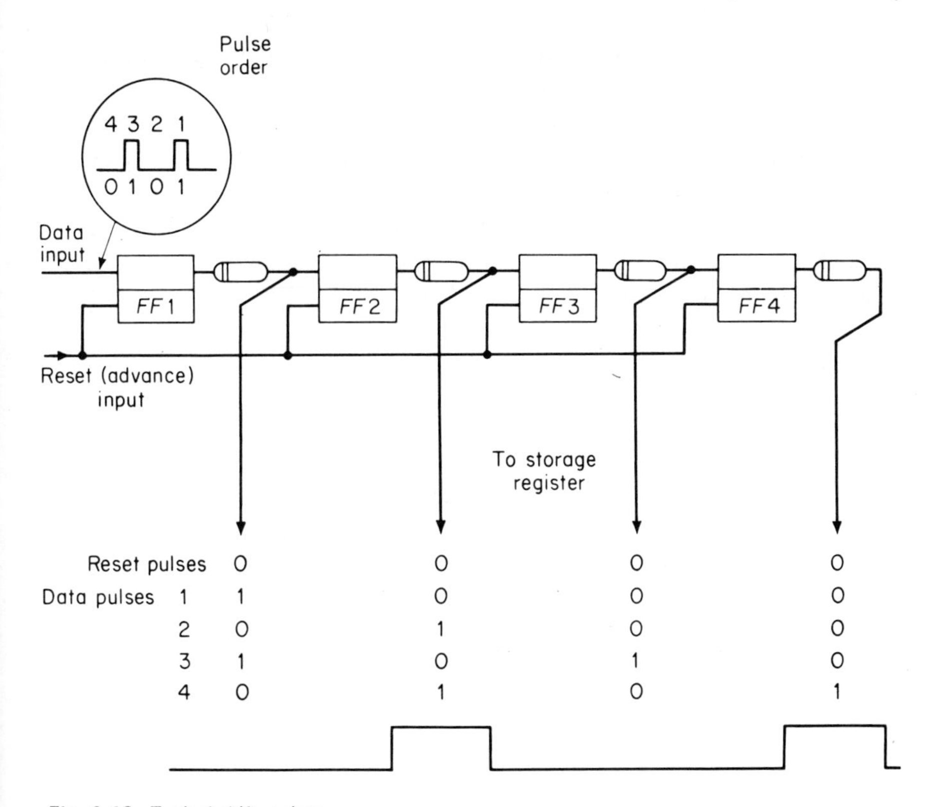

Fig. 6-12. Typical shift register.

Assume that four binary bits in serial form are applied to the input of the register in Figure 6-12 and that the pulses appear as 0101 (binary 5), as shown. All the FFs are in the 0 state before each binary pulse. At pulse 1, FF_1 goes to the 1 state, and the remaining FFs stay in the 0 state. Between pulses 1 and 2, all FFs go to 0, but the 1 condition of FF_1 is delayed and applied to FF_2.

At pulse 2, FF_1 stays in the 0 condition (since the second bit is 0), but FF_2 moves to a 1 state, since it received the delayed pulse from FF_1. At pulse 3, FF_1 goes to the 1 state, FF_2 goes to 0, and FF_3 now goes to 1, since it received the delayed pulse from FF_2. At pulse 4, FF_1 remains in the 0 state, FF_2 moves to the 1 state (pulse from FF_1), FF_3 goes to 0 (since it receives a 0 from FF_2), and FF_4 (thus far unaffected) moves to a 1 state (received from FF_3).

At the end of the four bits, before all FFs are reset to 0, the existing states (0101) are fed into a storage register. Then the output of the storage register can be used as needed, for example, to operate the electronic switches of a d/a converter.

The circuit of Figure 6-13 shows another form of shift register. Here, each of the FFs can be set individually to a given state by external pulses. This FF function is known as *preset* or *direct set*. In addition, the FFs are set synchronously to the corresponding state each time a clock pulse is present. The output of each FF assumes the state at its input when the clock pulse is applied.

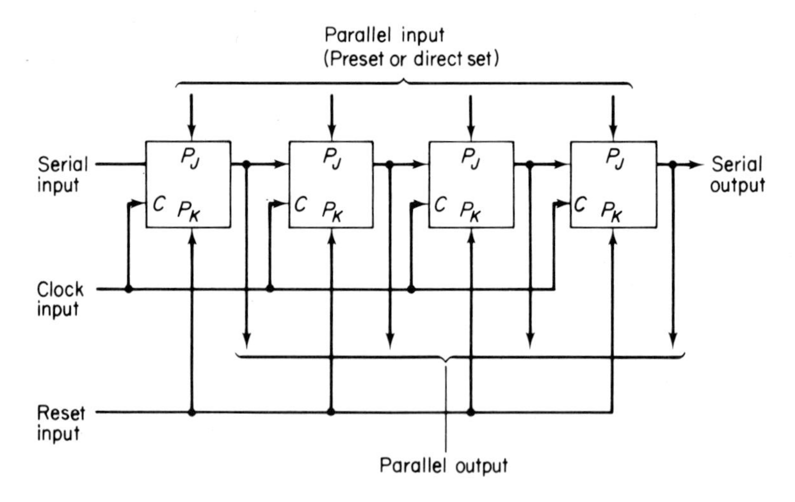

Fig. 6-13. Shift register with both parallel and serial input/output capability.

The combination of direct set and synchronous clock set permits the register to be used either for parallel or serial operation or combinations of both.

Serial-in/serial-out operation of the register is similar to that described for the circuit in Figure 6-12. Each time the clock pulse is applied to all FFs simultaneously, each FF moves to the state determined by the output of the previous FF. Thus serial data entered at the serial input are passed (shifted) from FF to FF. The serial output is taken (or shifted) from the last FF. However, the most significant bit of data is taken first.

Parallel-in/parallel-out operation is essentially a transfer function since no shifting is involved. Each FF is set to the corresponding state (1 or 0) by external *preset* or *direct-set* pulses. The output state of each FF is then applied to the external circuits.

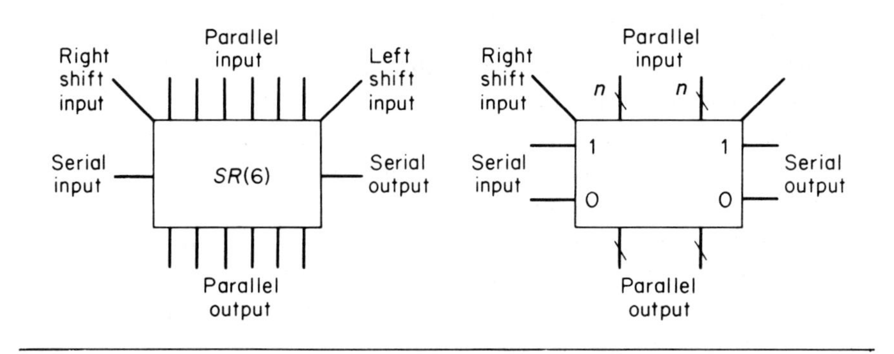

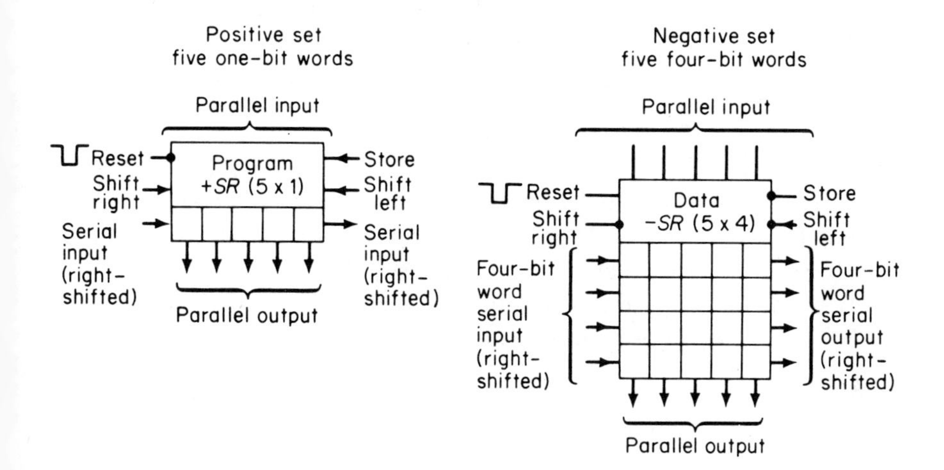

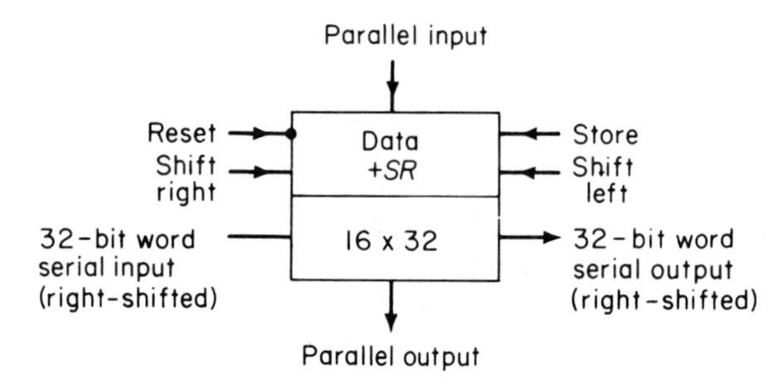

Fig. 6-14. Typical shift register symbols. (Courtesy of Hewlett-Packard.)

Serial-in/parallel-out operation is also similar to the operation of the basic shift register. Serial data are entered at the first FF and are shifted through each FF stage by the clock pulse. At the end of each word (after four bits in this case), the state of each FF (1 or 0) represents the corresponding binary number. The output of each FF is then applied to an external circuit, typically a storage register, for futher use.

Parallel-in/serial-out operation (or parallel-to-serial conversion) involves both the shift and transfer functions. Each FF is set to the corresponding state (1 or 0) by external preset or direct-set pulses. These states are then shifted through each FF stage by the clock pulse. The serial output is taken (or shifted) from the last FF. Again, the most significant bit of data is taken first.

As shown in Figure 6-14, all types of shift registers are usually presented in symbol form on computer logic diagrams.

E. SIGN COMPARATORS

Sign comparators have many uses in computers. Typically, a sign comparator is used to determine the sign of numbers (plus or minus) or to compare the polarity of d-c voltages.

As shown in Figure 6-15, a typical sign comparator consists of two FFs, four AND gates, and two OR gates. The two FFs, each indicating

Fig. 6-15. Typical sign (or polarity) comparator.

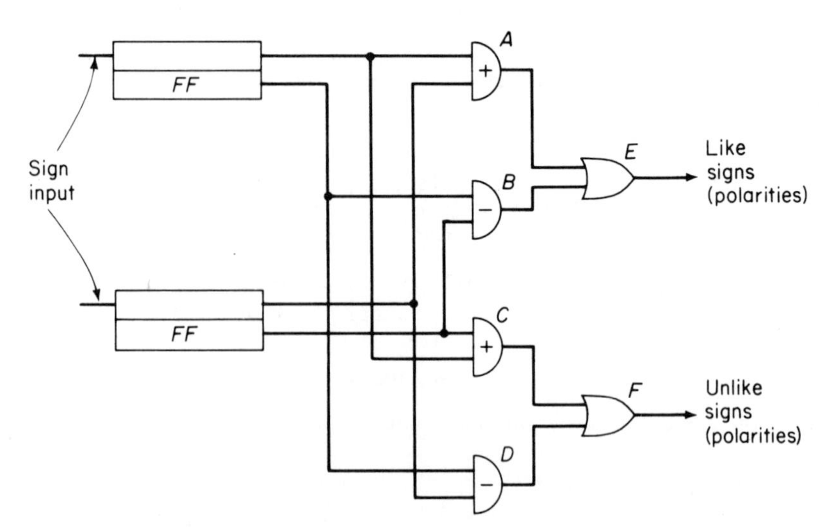

the polarity of an applied voltage, can produce four possible combinations, two for like polarities and two for unlike polarities.

If the FFs have the same output, one of the AND gates (*A* for positive or *B* for negative) will have an output, and OR gate *E* will provide an output signal. That is, there is an output indicating like polarities whether both FFs have a positive or negative output. One of the two AND gates will provide an output signal, and since an OR gate requires only one input to produce an output, OR gate *E* will provide a like-polarity output.

If the two polarities are opposites (one positive and one negative), there are only two possible combinations. For either combination, one of two AND gates (*C* or *D*) will provide an output to OR gate *F*, indicating an unlike-polarity output.

F. ADDERS

Adders (half-adders and full adders) are used primarily in computer circuits to perform mathematical functions. However, adders can also be used as some form of comparison circuit.

1. Half-adder

When only two binary digits are to be added, a half-adder can be used. The output is a sum ($1 + 0 = 1$, $0 + 1 = 1$) or a carry ($1 + 1 = 10$, which is a 0 sum and a carry 1, or a binary 2). The two digits to be added have only four possibilities, as shown in Figure 6-16. The digit to be added (*A*) is the *addend* and the other digit (*B*) is the *augend.*

If both *A* and *B* digits are 0 (or false), there is no output from the OR gate. Likewise, there is no output from AND gate *A* and hence no carry. That is, the output from AND gate *A* is 0 (false).

Note that this same carry output is also applied to AND gate *B* through an inversion. Thus, if the carry output is 0, the inverted input to AND gate *B* is 1. With a 0 from the OR gate and a 1 from the inverted input, there can be no output from AND gate *B*. Thus we have 0 sum and 0 carry.

If either *A* or *B* digits equal 1, there is an output from the OR gate to AND gate *B*, but the AND gate *A* output remains 0. This 0 output is

Addend (digit *A*)	Augend (digit *B*)	Sum	Carry
0	0	0	0
0	1	1	0
1	0	1	0
1	1	0	1

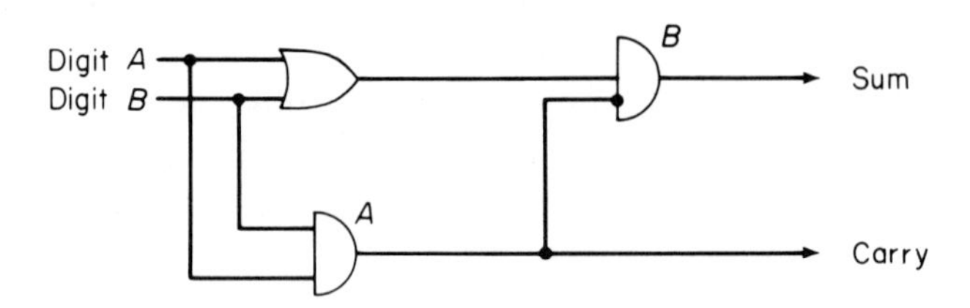

Fig. 6-16. Typical half-adder.

inverted to a 1 and is applied to AND gate *B*. Now, a 1 from the OR gate and a 1 from the inversion result in a sum output of 1 and a 0 carry output.

If both *A* and *B* digits equal 1, they will pass through the OR gate to produce a 1 and also through AND gate *A* to produce a carry output of 1. This carry 1 is inverted to AND gate *B*, so a 1 and a 0 are applied to AND gate *B*, and there is no sum output. Thus the sum is 0, and the carry is 1.

2. Full Adder

A full adder is shown in Figure 6-17. This circuit makes it possible to add two three-digit numbers. As shown, there are eight possible combinations. However, aside from all zeros, there are only three different cases, depending on the number of 1s (trues).

For a single 1, there are three possibilities: $1 + 0 + 0$, $0 + 1 + 0$, and $0 + 0 + 1$. Thus there is always a sum but never a carry.

For any two 1s ($1 + 1 + 0$, $1 + 0 + 1$, $0 + 1 + 1$) there is a carry but never a sum.

For three 1s ($1 + 1 + 1$), there are both a sum and a carry.

Where every digit is 0 ($0 + 0 + 0$), there is neither a sum nor a carry.

	A Addend	B Augend	C Carry (in)	Sum	Carry (out)
1	1	0	0	1	0
2	0	1	0	1	0
3	0	0	1	1	0
4	1	1	0	0	1
5	1	0	1	0	1
6	0	1	1	0	1
7	1	1	1	1	1
8	0	0	0	0	0

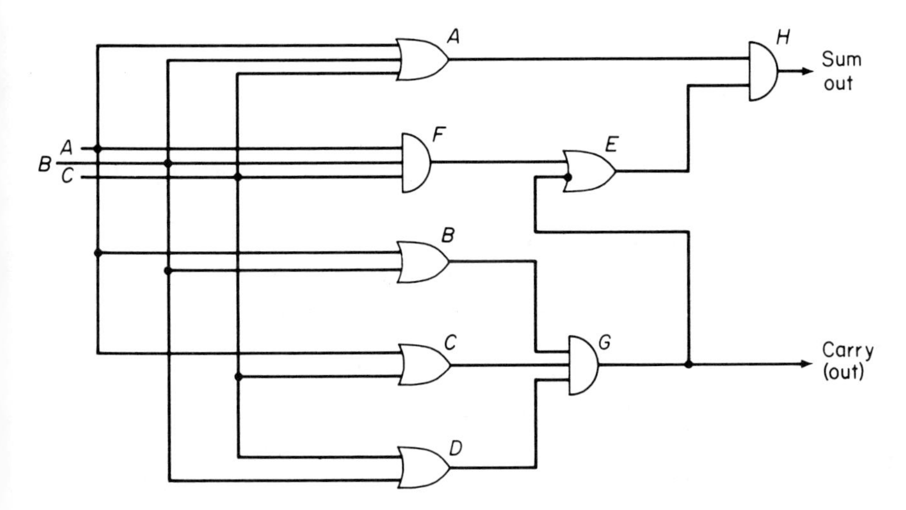

Fig. 6-17. Typical full adder.

If all digits are 1s, the three OR gates *B*, *C*, and *D* each have two 1s, and so there is a 1 from each, resulting in three 1s in AND gate *G*. This provides a carry, which is inverted and appears as a 0 at OR gate *E*. But the three 1s into AND gate *F* provide a 1 input to OR gate *E*; hence OR gate *E* has an output. OR gate *A* has three 1s, so there are two 1s input at AND gate *H*. This produces both a sum and a carry output ($1 + 1 + 1 = 11$, a binary 3).

If two digits are 1s, the three OR gates *B*, *C*, and *D* will each have at least one 1. AND gate *G* will have three 1s, providing a carry output. AND gate *F* will have two 1s and no output (0 output). AND gate *G* will have an output (the carry output), but it is inverted to a 0 at the input of OR gate *E*. Thus both inputs to OR gate *E* are 0, as is its output to AND gate *H*. This produces a carry but no sum $(1 + 1 + 0 = 10,\ 1 + 0 + 1 = 10,\ 0 + 1 + 1 = 10$, a binary 2).

If only one digit is a 1, there cannot be three inputs to AND gate *G* and hence no carry. The inversion changes this carry 0 to a 1, which OR gate *E* passes to AND gate *H*. Another input from OR gate *A* is applied to AND gate *H*, producing a sum output. This results in a sum but no carry $(1 + 0 + 0 = 1, 0 + 1 + 0 = 1, 0 + 0 + 1 = 1)$.

If all digits are zero, there is no input to AND gate *G* and hence no carry. There is no output for OR gate *A* and hence no output from AND gate *H* and no sum $(0 + 0 + 0)$.

3. Parallel and Serial Adders

Binary numbers can be added in parallel form or serial form. Both methods are used in computer circuits.

The parallel adder is generally simpler to implement than the serial adder. Parallel addition is an **asynchronous** operation, independent of a clock timing signal. A basic four-bit parallel adder is shown in Figure 6-18. Note that the circuit is composed of three full adders and one half-adder. Here, two four-bit binary numbers (*A* and *B*) are applied to the inputs simultaneously. A preliminary sum is formed simultaneously at all four stages. However, when a carry is generated, it appears at the input of the next higher-order stage or to overflow if there is no additional stages. In a practical circuit, the input binary number is

Fig. 6-18. Four-bit parallel adder.

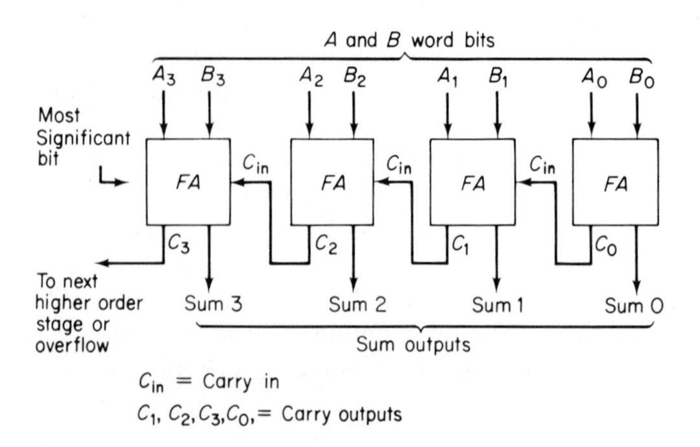

stored in a register and then gated into the adder. At a predetermined time, the sum number is gated out (to another register).

Binary serial addition is a time-sequential (**synchronous**) operation, performed one bit at a time. The basic serial-adder concept is illustrated in Figure 6-19. The circuit is composed of three registers, a full adder, and a carry storage element (usually a FF).

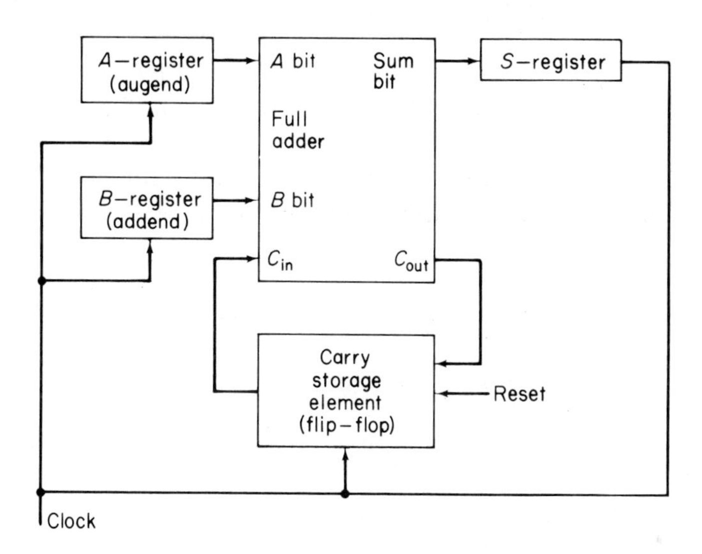

Fig. 6-19. Basic binary serial adder. (Courtesy of Motorola.)

The *A* register contains the augend number and the *B* register contains the addend number. The *S* register receives the sum number bits serially as they are generated from the full adder. The carry storage element (FF) provides temporary storage for C_{out} until C_{out} is used in the next addition, and the next C_{out} is placed in the storage element. The carry storage element must be clocked by the same timing pulse that is applied to the registers.

In operation, the two least significant bits are added first, forming a least significant sum bit and a carry bit. The least significant carry bit is then added to the two next highest-order bits, and the sum and carry bits are formed, and so forth. The two numbers to be added are each stored in the corresponding *A* and *B* registers. The two numbers are fed serially into the full adder, and the sum bits are fed serially into the *S* register.

After the final two bits from *A* and *B* are added, the carry storage element contains the final C_{out}, which can represent an overflow-alarm bit if desired. (Register circuits often include an overflow-alarm network to indicate that the register is full and can accept no further inputs.) If the *A* and *B* registers are large enough such that the most significant bit positions in both registers are 0 before the two numbers are added, no overflow condition will occur.

The *A*, *B*, and *S* registers operate in a shift-right mode. The augend and addend numbers are loaded into the *A* and *B* registers in either a serial or parallel mode.

The *S* register of Figure 6-19 can be eliminated by feeding the sum bits back into the *A* register. This concept is shown in Figure 6-20. Under these conditions, the *A* register is known as an **accumulator register**.

In the circuit of Figure 6-20, the number in the *B* register is added to the number in the *A* register, and the sum appears back in the *A* register.

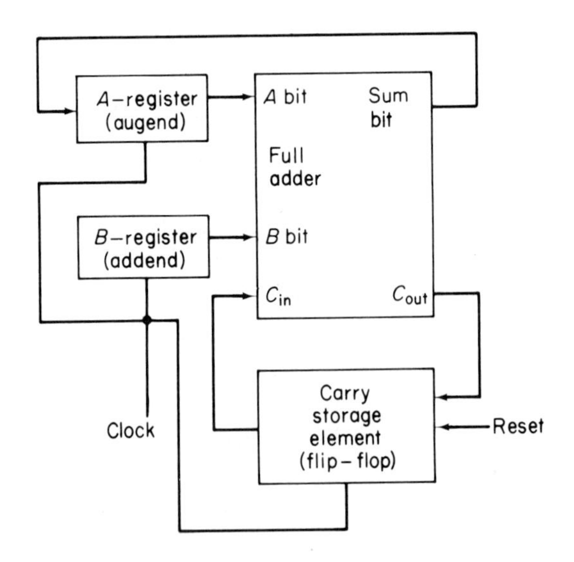

Fig. 6-20. Binary serial adder with the S register eliminated. (Courtesy of Motorola.)

G. COMPARISON CIRCUIT

The half-adder can be used as a comparison circuit for detecting errors. If two unlike digits are fed into the half-adder, the output is a sum. If the digits are alike (0 and 0 or 1 and 1), there is no sum output (even though there may be a carry output). Thus the half-adder is a detector of equality or inequality.

Figure 6-21 shows how a half-adder is used to compare the contents of two registers. The binary count in register *A* is transferred to register *B*, and the half-adder must make sure that both registers contain the same count. The half-adder compares the contents of the *A* and *B* registers, digit by digit. As long as the half-adder has no sum output, the digit in *A* is the same as its respective digit in *B*. If there is a sum output, the digit in *A* is unlike the digit in *B*.

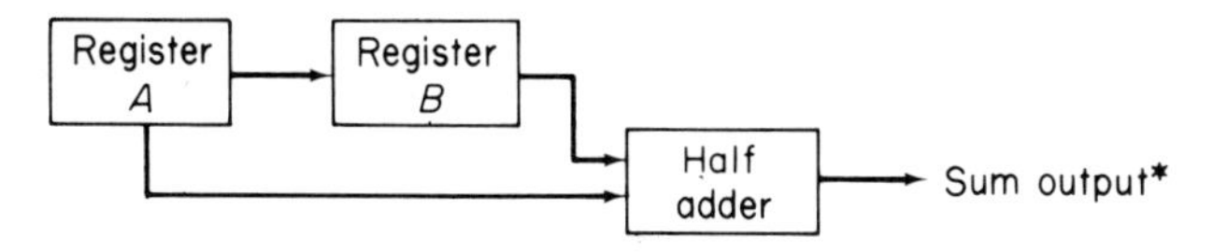
Register
A
Register
B
Half
adder
Sum output*
*Digits are alike if there is no sum output.
Digits are unlike if there is a sum output.

Fig. 6-21. Half-adder used as comparison circuit (equality detector).

H. SUBTRACTORS

The operation of a binary number subtractor circuit is essentially the same as that for an adder circuit. However, the carry in is replaced by a *borrow in*, the carry out is replaced by a *borrow out*, and the sum is replaced by a *difference*.

The circuit of Figure 6-22 is a universal adder/subtractor in that the circuit performs either addition or subtraction depending on the state of the "control" input. If the control input is low (0), the sum and carry appear as outputs, and the circuit operates as a full adder. If the control input is high (1), the difference and borrow outputs are used, and the circuit functions as a full subtractor. The circuit of Figure 6-22 uses both EXCLUSIVE OR and NAND gates.

A full-subtractor circuit using only NAND gates is shown in Figure 6-23. Here, input *B* is subtracted from *A*, and the borrow input is also subtracted from input *A*. When the circuit of Figure 6-23 is used in a computer system, the borrow output is connected to the borrow input of the next higher position.

I. PARITY CIRCUITS

In computers, there are several special codes that have been specifically designed for detecting errors that might occur with digital

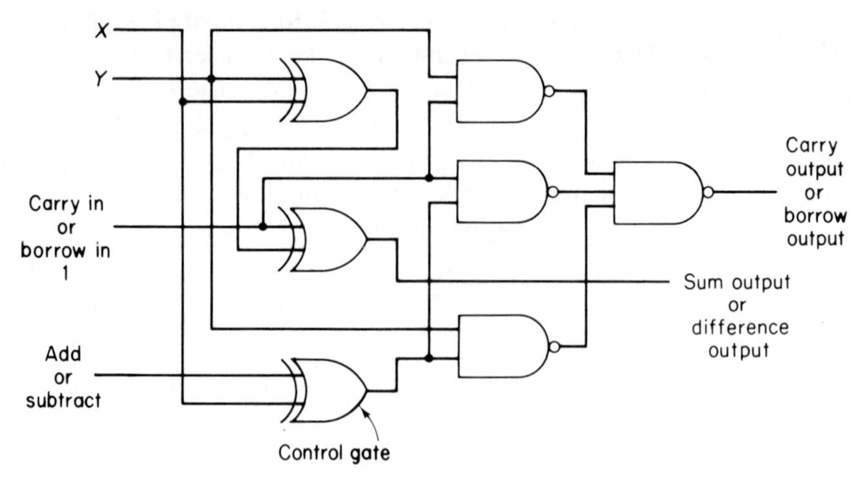

Fig. 6-22. Universal adder/subtractor. (Courtesy of Motorola.)

Fig. 6-23. NAND gate full subtractor. (Courtesy of Cambridge Thermionic Corporation.)

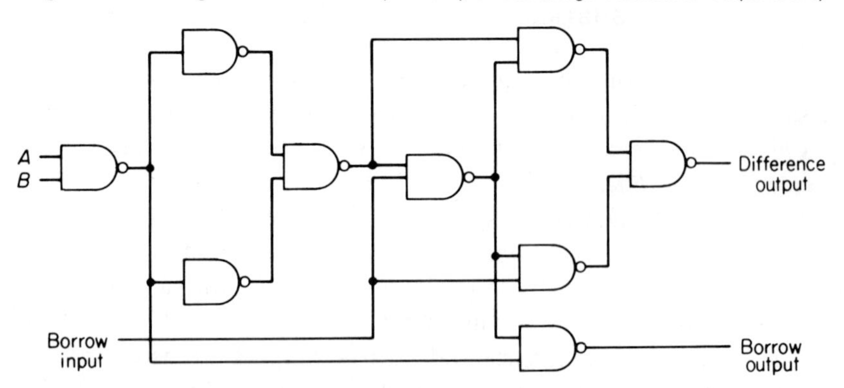

Difference

A	*B*	Borrow input	Output
0	0	0	0
0	0	1	1
0	1	0	1
0	1	1	0
1	0	0	1
1	0	1	0
1	1	0	0
1	1	1	1

Borrow

A	*B*	Borrow input	Output
0	0	0	0
0	0	1	1
0	1	0	1
0	1	1	1
1	0	0	0
1	0	1	0
1	1	0	0
1	1	1	1

counting. Any logic network that operates on a binary counting system is subject to counting errors due to circuit failure, noise in the circuit, or some similar occurrence. For example, a defective amplifier can reduce the amplitude of a pulse (representing a binary 1) so that it appears as a binary 0 at the following circuit. Likewise, noise in a circuit could be equal in amplitude to a normal binary 1 pulse. If such noise occurs at a time when a particular circuit is supposed to receive a binary 0, the circuit can react as if a binary 1 were present.

1. Parity Systems

One method for detecting errors is know as **parity check**. Parity refers to the quality of being equal, and a parity check is actually an equality-checking code. The coding consists of a parity digit added to the digits of a given binary number. The additional digit is known as a parity digit or parity bit and may be either a 0 or a 1. The parity bit is chosen to make the number of all bits in the binary group even or odd. If the system is chosen where the bits in the binary number plus the parity bit are even, the system is known as *even parity*. If not, the system is referred to as *odd parity*.

As an example, the decimal number 7 in binary-coded decimal (0111) with even parity will require a 1 in the parity bit place. Thus in the total of five bits (four binary bits plus the one parity bit) there is an even number of 1s. With odd parity, the parity bit is 0 for decimal 7, since there must be an odd number of 1s in odd parity.

The following table illustrates the use of **odd parity check**.

Decimal number	8421 binary number	Parity bit	Number with parity bit included
0	0000	1	00001
1	0001	0	00010
2	0010	0	00100
3	0011	1	00111
4	0100	0	01000
5	0101	1	01011
6	0110	1	01101
7	0111	0	01110
8	1000	0	10000
9	1001	1	10011

2. Fundamental Parity Generators and Checkers

Computer error detection circuits based upon the parity system use both parity generators and parity detectors (or checkers).

The function of a parity generator is to examine the computer word (group of binary bits) and calculate the information required for the added parity bit. For example, if there are three 1s in the binary group and the even parity system is used, a 1 must be used for the parity bit to make an even number in the complete parity word. Once the parity bit has been included, the parity word (binary bits plus parity bit) can be examined after any series of operations or at any point in the computer to determine if a failure or error has occurred.

A parity detection circuit (or parity checker) examines the parity word to see if the desired odd or even parity still exists (for example, after passing through several hundred logic gates). If an error has occurred, the computer control can be informed that the computer is not functioning properly (by means of a control panel lamp or alarm).

The fundamental operation required in parity generation and detection circuits, that of comparing inputs to determine the presence of an odd or even number of 1s, can be effectively performed by EXCLUSIVE OR logic gates. A basic EXCLUSIVE OR gate performing the function $\overline{A}B + A\overline{B}$ serves to calculate parity over inputs A and B. EXCLUSIVE OR (and EXCLUSIVE NOR) gates can be interconnected to form **parity trees** and thus perform parity calculations for computer words of greater length.

The parity scheme described thus far (known as **simple parity**) detects the presence of a single error in a word (or group of binary bits). If two errors occur, the output does not indicate that an error has occurred. Thus simple parity will detect an odd number of errors but will fail if an even number of errors occurs.

3. Advanced Parity Schemes

Advanced parity schemes have been devised to recognize that an error has occurred and to detect which bit is in error. Several extra bits must be added to the system word to accomplish these parity checks. One such scheme is referred to as Hamming parity single-error detection and correction (after R. W. Hamming). Using this scheme, a four-bit binary word requires that three additional bits (Hamming parity bits) be added.

4. Simple Parity Checking with Parity Trees

The circuit of Figure 6-24 consists of seven EXCLUSIVE NOR gates connected to form an eight-bit parity tree. Each gate has a 0 logic output if and only if one of its two inputs is at a 1 logic level. Thus the output of the three-stage parity tree will be in the 0 state if there is an odd number of 1s over the eight inputs.

The circuit of Figure 6-25 is a four-bit parity tree, providing a 0 output state if an odd number of 1s exist over the respective inputs.

The circuits of Figures 6-24 and 6-25 form the basic "building blocks" for a 20-bit-word simple parity generator and detector scheme.

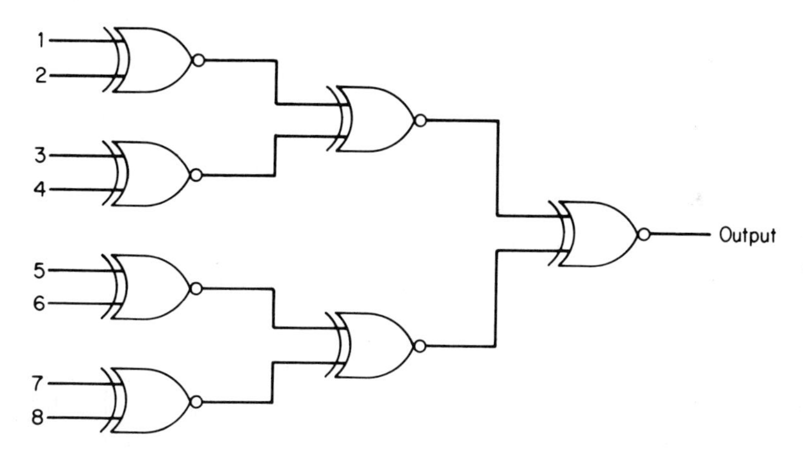

Fig. 6-24. Eight-bit parity tree. (Courtesy of Motorola.)

Fig. 6-25. Four-bit parity tree. (Courtesy of Motorola.)

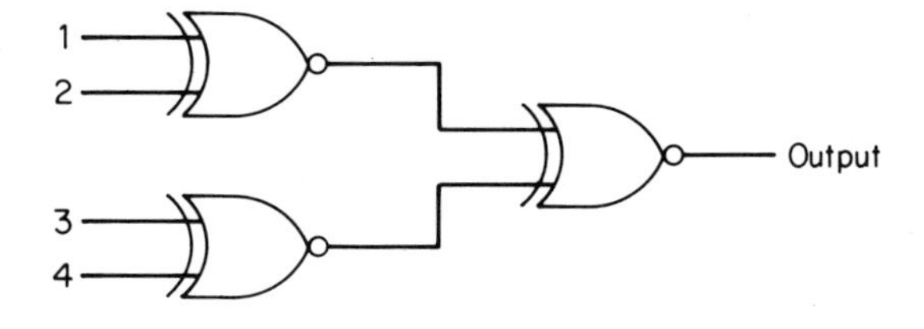

The 20-bit-word parity generator is shown in Figure 6-26. If a parity word containing odd parity is required (the 20-bit-word plus the parity bit are to contain an odd number of 1s), then the direct readout from the parity tree (output *A*) is used as the parity bit. If even parity is required, an inverter (or gate) is used, as shown at output *B*.

The 20-bit-word parity detector is shown in Figure 6-27. The original 20-bit-word is connected to a two-stage parity tree almost identical to that used for the 20-bit parity generator. However, for the detection circuit, the output of the tree is compared with the input parity bit.

The parity bit can serve as the input to the second stage of the tree. For odd parity detection, output *A* is in the 1 state if there is no error.

Fig. 6-26. Twenty-bit-word parity generator. (Courtesy of Motorola.)

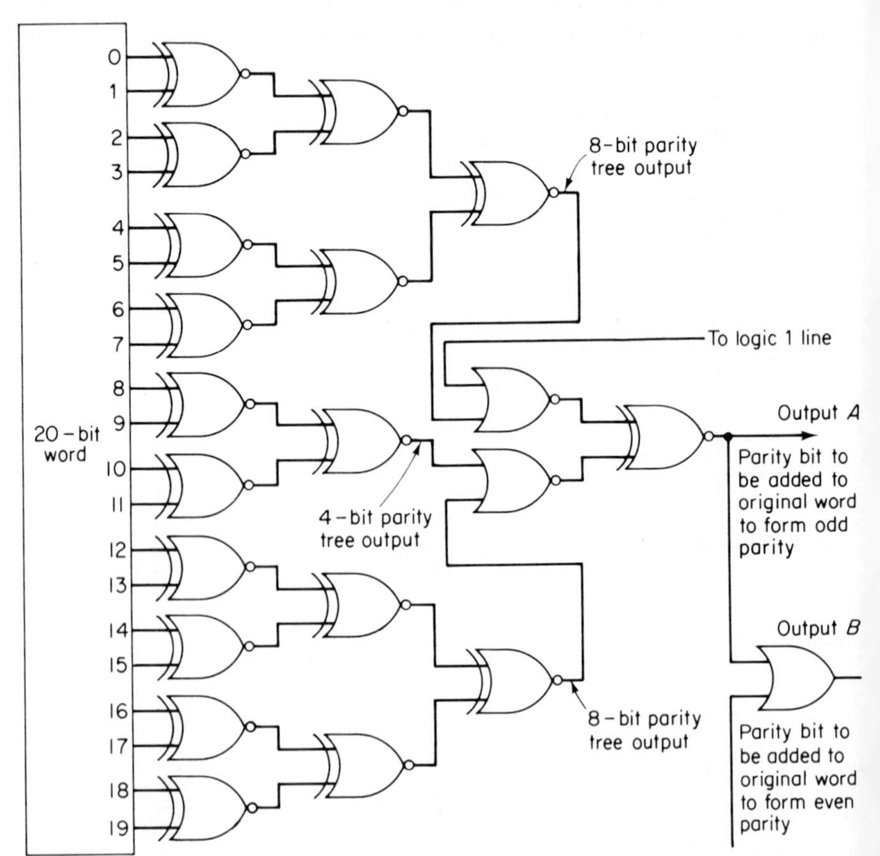

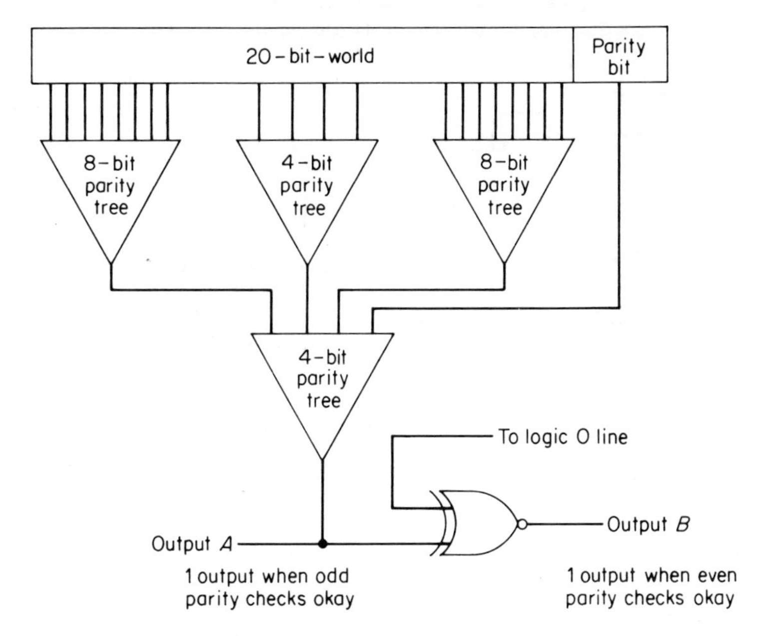

Fig. 6-27. Twenty-bit-word parity detector or checker. (Courtesy of Motorola.)

An even parity detection results in a 1 output (for output *B*) if no error is introduced.

The circuits of Figures 6-26 and 6-27 can be expanded as necessary to accommodate words of greater length. However, additional parity trees are required.

The circuit of Figure 6-28 consists of six EXCLUSIVE OR gates and one EXCLUSIVE NOR gate connected to form an eight-bit parity tree. Note that the EXCLUSIVE NOR gate must also have an OR output. Output *A* is in the 1 state when an even number of 1s exist over the eight inputs. Output *B* is in the 1 state when an odd number of 1s exist over the eight inputs. The circuit of Figure 6-28 forms the basic building block for a 44-bit-word simple parity generator and detector system.

The 44-bit-word parity generator is shown in Figure 6-29. If odd parity is required, output *A* is used. Output *B* is used for even parity. Note that any unused inputs are connected to a logic 0 line, as shown.

The 44-bit-word parity detector is shown in Figure 6-30. In this circuit, the input parity bit is connected as an input of the first stage of comparison. An odd parity condition causes output *A* to be in the

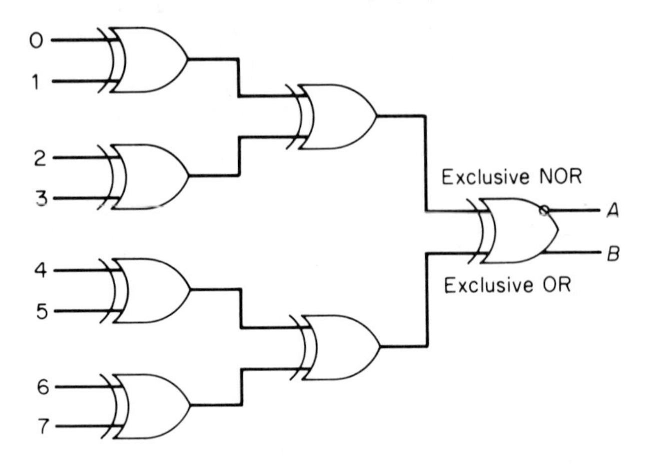

B = 0, A = 1 whenever an even number of inputs are true
B = 1, A = 0 whenever an odd number of inputs are true
0
1
2
3
4
5
6
7
Exclusive NOR
Exclusive OR
A
B

Partial truth table

0	1	2	3	4	5	6	7	Outputs A	Outputs B
0	0	0	0	0	0	0	0	1	0
0	1	1	0	0	1	1	1	0	1
1	1	0	1	1	1	0	1	1	0
1	0	1	1	1	0	1	0	0	1

Fig. 6-28. Eight-bit parity checker/generator. (Courtesy of Motorola.) $B = 0$ and $A = 1$ whenever an even number of inputs are true; $B = 1$ and $A = 0$ whenever an odd number of inputs are true.

0 state if no errors are present. For even parity, output *B* is in the 0 state if no errors are introduced.

5. Hamming Parity Code Detection and Correction

Advanced parity schemes (often known as single-error correction) require that redundant information be added to the word so that the *bit number in error* can be identified. The Hamming parity code is a system for adding the required redundant bits of information, and the redundant bits are called Hamming parity bits.

A block diagram of a Hamming code system is shown in Figure 6-31. This system is for a 16-bit message word and requires five Ham-

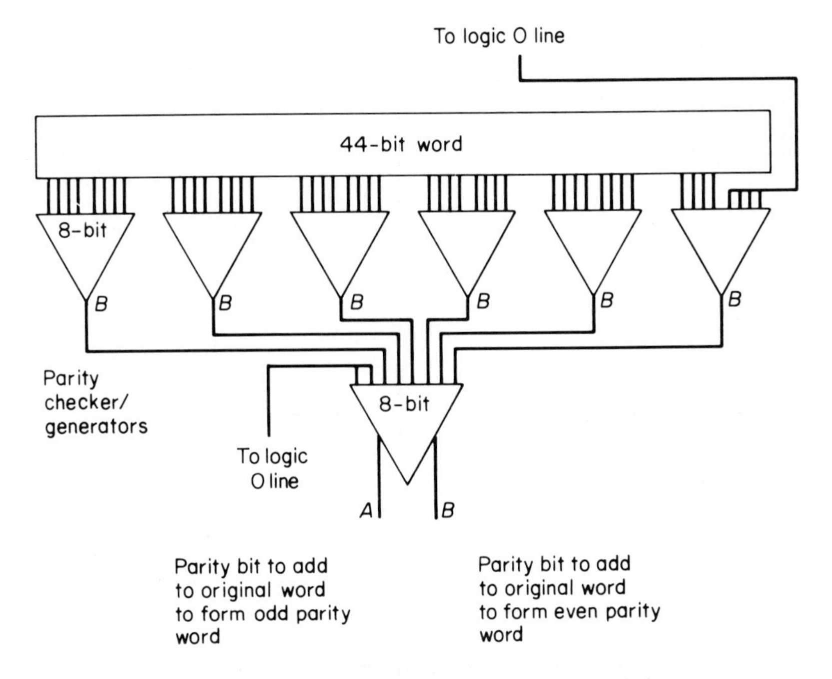

Fig. 6-29. Forty-four-bit-word parity generator. (Courtesy of Motorola.)

Fig. 6-30. Forty-four-bit-word parity checker. (Courtesy of Motorola.)

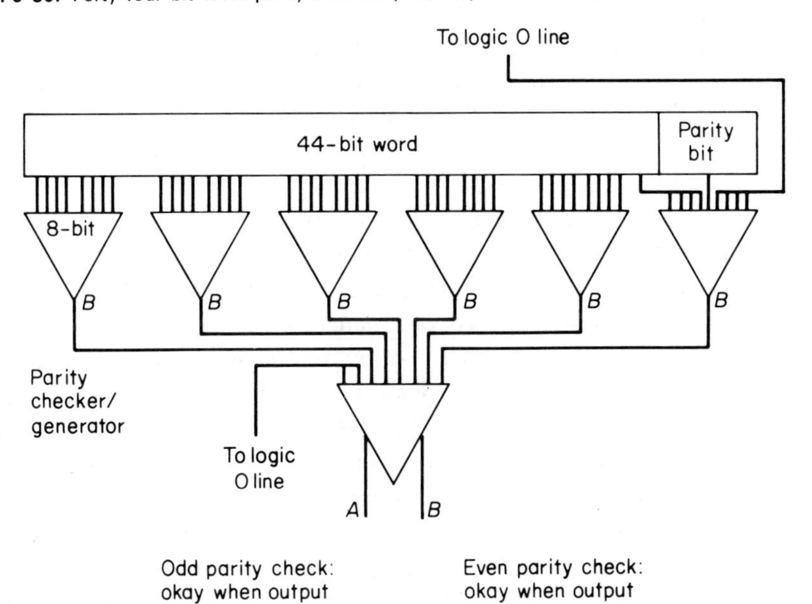

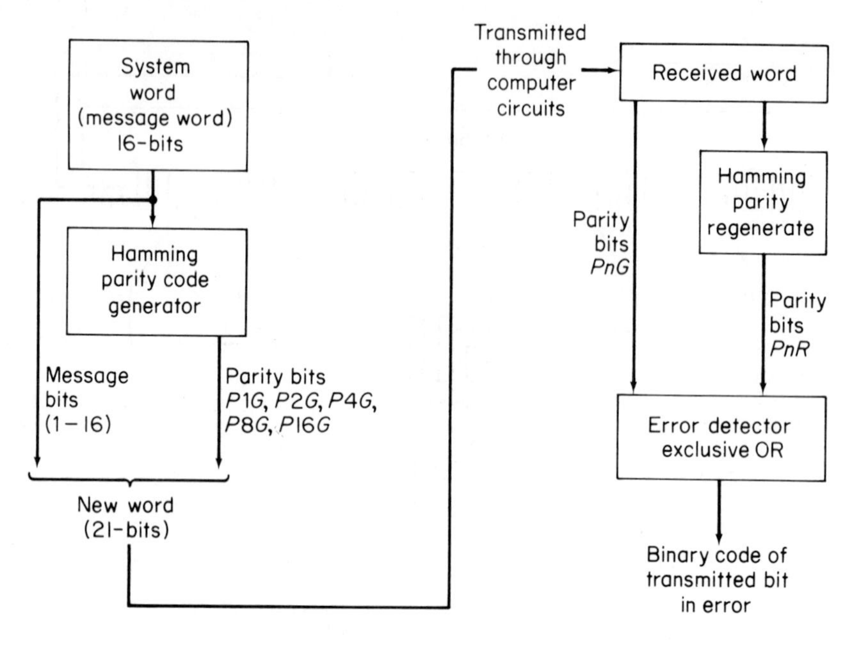

Fig. 6-31. Block diagram of Hamming code system. (Courtesy of Motorola.)

ming parity bits. The Hamming code generator calculates the five Hamming parity bits P1G, P2G, P4G, P8G, and P16G (the letter G indicates the parity bits calculated by the parity generator) from the 16 message bits, M1–M16. The parity bits are then inserted into the message word in a definite order, after which the parity word can be processed in the computer circuit where errors are likely to be introduced.

The table of Figure 6-32 indicates which message bits must be examined to calculate the five parity bits. The message bits are the headings for the 16 rows, with the Hamming parity bits as the column headings. An X is placed in the table to indicate which of the message bits must be examined in order to generate the corresponding parity bit. For example, P1 is generated by requiring the combination of P1, M1, M2, M4, M5, etc., to possess an even parity. Similarly, P2 is generated by requiring P2, M1, M3, M4, etc., to possess even parity. Note that the P1 calculation requires ten message bits to be examined. This can be performed with a ten-input parity tree.

The Hamming parity detector reexamines the input message exactly as the generator does. However, the parity bits generated at the receiving end of the system, P1R, P2R, P4R, P8R, and P16R, are compared

Message bits	Parity bits P1	P2	P4	P8	P16
M1	X	X			
M2	X		X		
M3		X	X		
M4	X	X	X		
M5				X	
M6		X		X	
M7	X	X		X	
M8			X	X	
M9	X		X	X	
M10		X	X	X	
M11	X	X	X	X	
M12	X				X
M13		X			X
M14	X	X			X
M15			X		X
M16	X		X		X
Total inputs to each parity tree in generator	10	9	9	7	5

Fig. 6-32. Hamming parity generation for 16 message bits. (Courtesy of Motorola.)

with the transmitted bits, P*n*G (where *n* represents 1, 2, 4, 8, and 16 for the example given). Each combination of parity bits (P1G transmitted and P1R received) is compared via an EXCLUSIVE OR circuit. The results of this comparison, P1E–P16E, form a binary word that indicates the *bit position* of any single bit in error.

For example, an output code of P16E = 1, P8E = 0, P4E = 1, P2E = 0, and P1E = 0, or 10100 (binary 20), indicates that the twentieth bit in the transmitted word is in error. In the circuits of Figures 6-33 and 6-34 (Hamming parity generator and detector, respectively), the parity bits are inserted into the message bits in the follow-

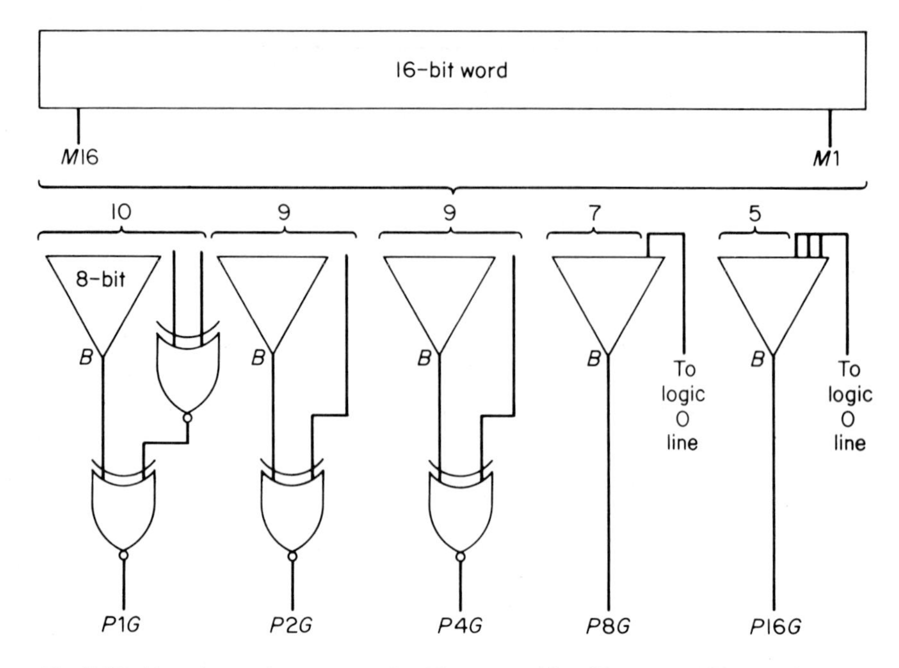

Fig. 6-33. Hamming parity generator for 16 message bits. (Courtesy of Motorola.)

ing sequence: P1G, P2G, M1, P4G, M2, M3, M4, P8G, M5, M6, M7, M8, M9, M10, M11, P16G, M12, M13, M14, M15, M16. Thus the twentieth bit in the transmitted word is M15 (message bit 15), which is in error.

The eight-bit parity trees of Figures 6-33 and 6-34 are equivalent to the circuit of Figure 6-28, with the OR output (output *B*) used. Note that any unused inputs are connected to a logic 0 line.

The output of the detector circuit (Figure 6-34) is the five-bit binary word that indicates which bit (if any) in the message is in error. If there are no errors after the bits have been transmitted through the computer system, the output is 00000. Also note that the generation circuit called for in Figure 6-34 is equivalent to the circuit of Figure 6-33.

6. Equality Comparator Networks

Many computer logic systems require techniques for comparing two binary or BCD numbers. The fastest method is to compare all bits of each word simultaneously, in parallel. Although these comparison

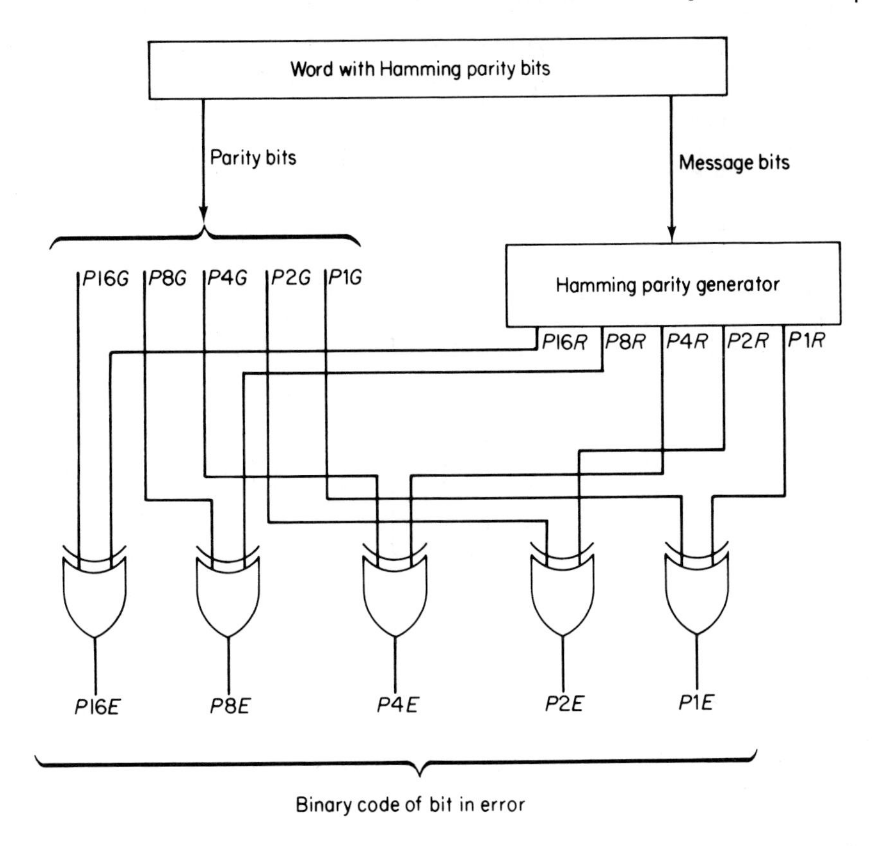

Fig. 6-34. Hamming parity detector for 16 message bits. (Courtesy of Motorola.)

Fig. 6-35. Four-bit by two-word equality detector. (Courtesy of Motorola.)

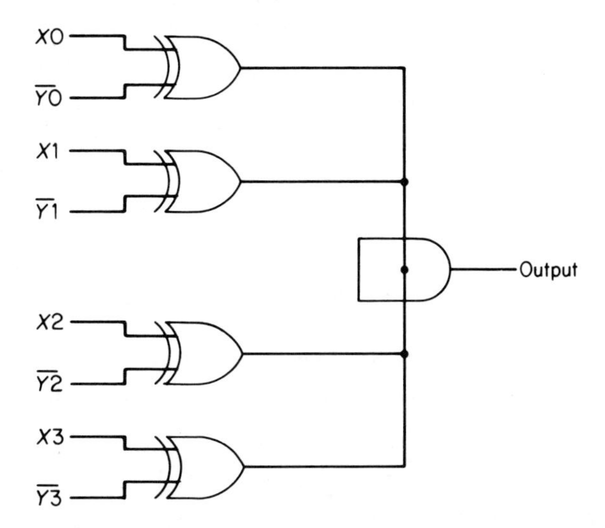

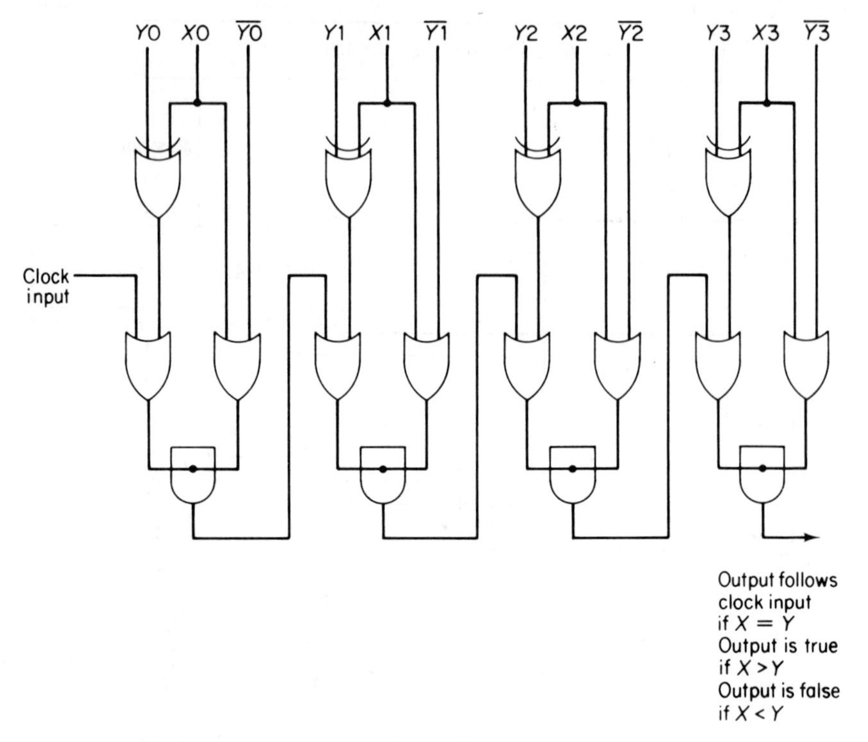

Fig. 6-36. Four-bit by two-word comparator. *Y*0, *Y*1, *Y*2, and *Y*3 represent word *Y* (*Y*0 is the least significant bit); *X*0, *X*1, *X*2, and *X*3 represent word *X* (*X*0 is the least significant bit). (Courtesy of Motorola.)

circuits are not true parity networks, they are often confused with parity systems.

The circuit of Figure 6-35 compares the *equality* of two words. That is, the circuit compares the direct correspondence of bits in like word positions. The circuit requires only EXCLUSIVE OR gates, provided that the complement for each bit of one word is available and that the word has no more than eight bits.

The circuit of Figure 6-36 can be used in similar applications where it is necessary to detect not only inequality but also to determine which word is larger.

J. DECODER AND ENCODER NETWORK

There are many types of decoders and encoders used in computers. Some computer decoders produce an output that indicates the state of input variables. For example, assuming that each variable can have only two states (0 or 1), there are four possible combinations for two variables (00, 01, 10, and 11). Thus a decoder of this type will have two inputs (one for each variable) and four outputs (one for each possible combination).

With other decoders, the function is to indicate the number of variables that are true (or false) on an *even or odd* basis. For example, assume that an odd decoder is used with three variables; the single decoder output is true only when an odd number (1 or 3) of the input variables is true.

Another type of decoder is used to indicate the majority (or minority) state of variables. For example, assuming that a majority decoder is used with three variables, the single output is true only when two or three of the inputs are true. A minority decoder with three variables produces a true output when one and only one input is true.

Still another type of decoder in common use is the code converter. Such decoders convert one type of logic code to another. For example, a binary-to-decimal decoder converts a four-bit binary number into a decimal equivalent. Such a decoder has four inputs and ten outputs. Only one of the outputs is true at a given time, depending on the state of the inputs (or binary number at the inputs). This last group of decoders are often referred to as *multiple-line decoders*.

Note that in many computer systems very complex or special-purpose decoders are essentially repetitions of the basic circuits. For example, in a computer with a six-digit counter readout, each digit has a separate decoder (usually binary to decimal). However, all parts of the decoder network are identical. Likewise, a six-variable decoder is essentially an interconnection of two three-variable decoders, and so forth.

Also note that such circuits as adders, subtractors, and parity comparators can be considered as decoders. However, owing to the special nature of these circuits, they are discussed individually in separate sections of this chapter.

1. Two-Variable Decoders

The circuit of Figure 6-37 is a two-variable decoder. In this circuit, one and only one output is true for each of the four possible input states. Both true and complemented outputs are available.

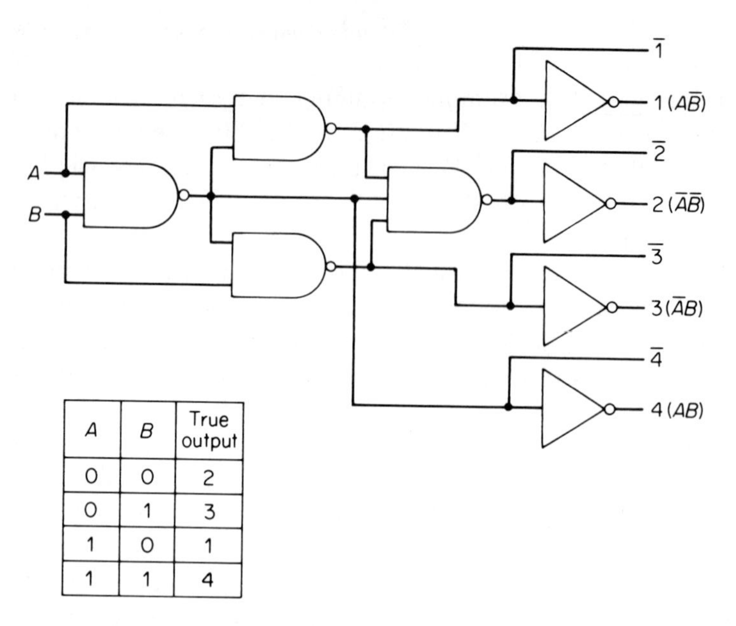

A	B	True output
0	0	2
0	1	3
1	0	1
1	1	4

Fig. 6-37. NAND gate two-variable decoder. (Courtesy of Texas Instruments.)

Fig. 6-38. Gated two-variable decoder. (Courtesy of Motorola.)

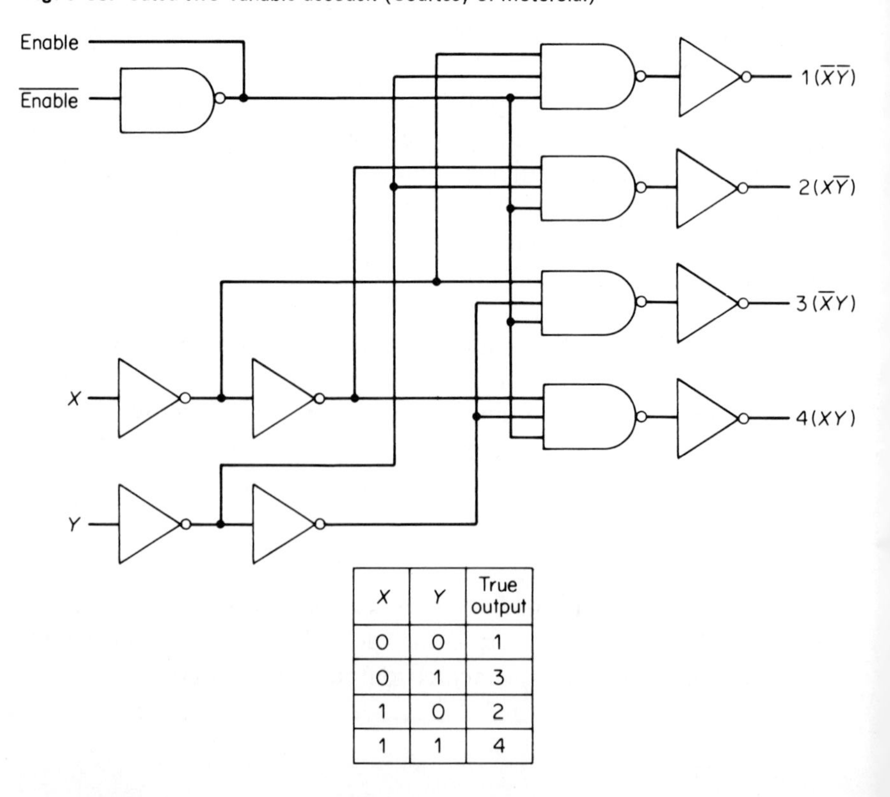

X	Y	True output
0	0	1
0	1	3
1	0	2
1	1	4

The circuit of Figure 6-38 is a gated two-variable decoder. That is, the outputs are available only when an enable, strobe, gate, or clock signal is present. Such *turn-on* signals can be in pulse form or can be a fixed d-c voltage controlled by a switch on the computer control panel. The enable signal can be either true or complemented. If the complemented enable is not required, the enable inverter is omitted. Likewise, if the complements of the X and Y inputs are available, the X and Y input inverters are omitted.

No matter what circuit configuration is used (true or complemented),

Fig. 6-39. Three-variable odd decoder. (Courtesy of Texas Instruments.)

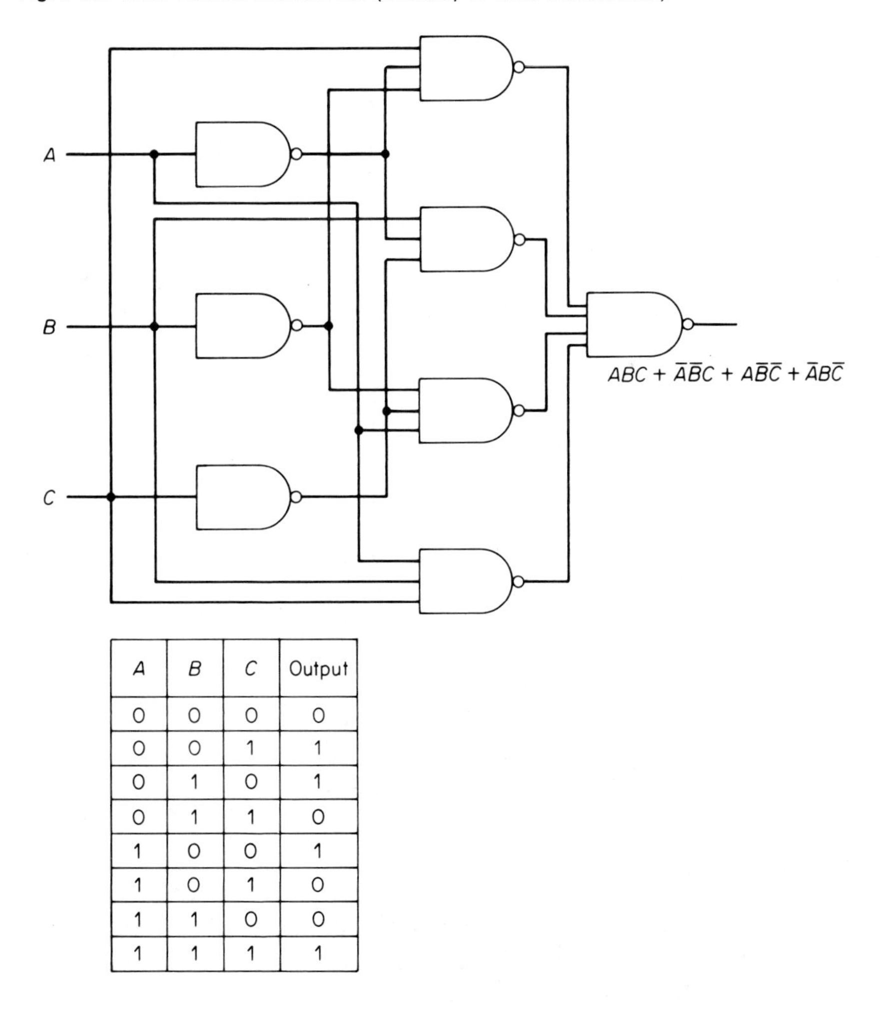

A	B	C	Output
0	0	0	0
0	0	1	1
0	1	0	1
0	1	1	0
1	0	0	1
1	0	1	0
1	1	0	0
1	1	1	1

when the enable signal is present, one and only one output is true for each of the four possible input states.

2. Odd and Even Decoders

The circuit of Figure 6-39 is a three-variable odd decoder. In this circuit, the output is true when an odd number of inputs (1 or 3) is true. Note that the circuit does not require a complemented input.

The circuit of Figure 6-40 is a three-variable even decoder. In this circuit, the output is true when two (an even number) and only two of the inputs are true. Again, complemented inputs are not required.

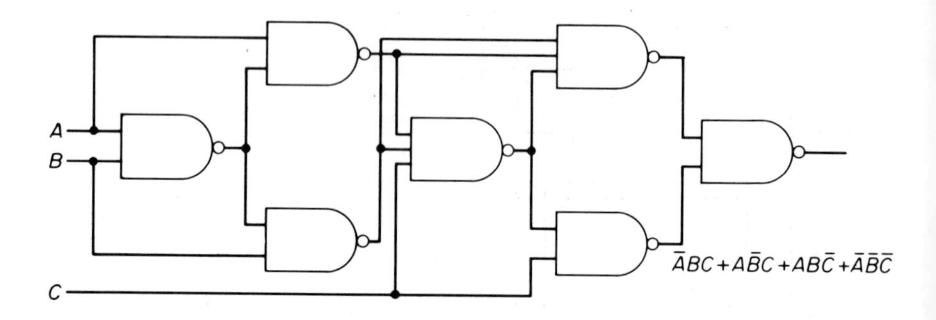

A	B	C	Output
0	0	0	1
0	0	1	0
0	1	0	0
0	1	1	1
1	0	0	0
1	0	1	1
1	1	0	1
1	1	1	0

Fig. 6-40. Three-variable even decoder. (Courtesy of Cambridge Thermionic Corporation.)

3. Majority Decoders

The circuit of Figure 6-41 is a majority decoder. That is, the output is true if two or three of the three inputs are true. If two or more input variables are false, the output is false.

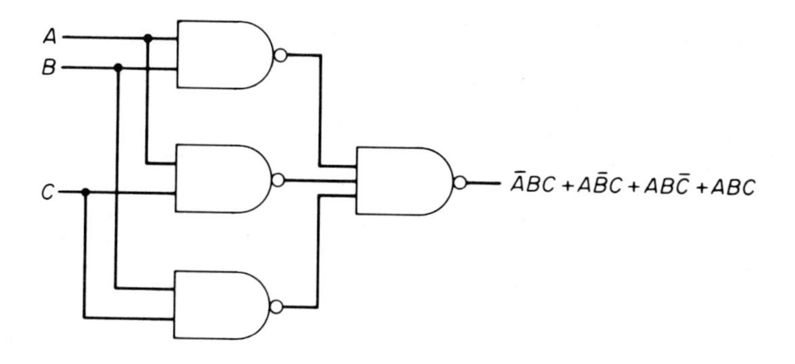

A	B	C	Output
0	0	0	0
0	0	1	0
0	1	0	0
0	1	1	1
1	0	0	0
1	0	1	1
1	1	0	1
1	1	1	1

Fig. 6-41. Majority decoder. (Courtesy of Motorola.)

4. Minority Decoder

The circuit of Figure 6-42 is a minority decoder. In this circuit, the output is true if any one of the inputs does not agree with the other two inputs. If all three inputs agree, either true or false, the output is false.

5. Encoder Networks

The term *encoder* is used here to indicate any logic circuit that performs the opposite function of a decoder. For example, the decoder of Figure 6-4 converts a four-bit BCD number to a ten-bit decimal equivalent (to operate a decade readout). An encoder, in this context,

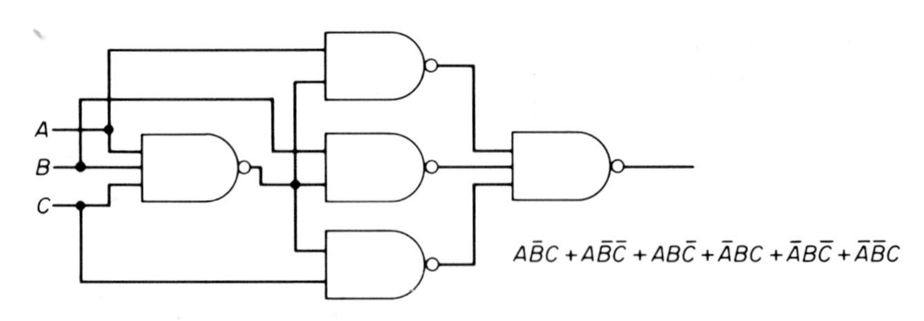

A	B	C	Output
0	0	0	0
0	0	1	1
0	1	0	1
0	1	1	1
1	0	0	1
1	0	1	1
1	1	0	1
1	1	1	0

Fig. 6-42. Minority decoder. (Courtesy of Cambridge Thermionic Corporation.)

will convert a ten-bit decimal number to its BCD equivalent. However, both encoders and decoders are forms of logic networks that produce an output (or outputs) only when certain inputs are present.

The circuit of Figure 6-43 is a decimal-to-BCD encoder. The circuit provides conversion from a 10-line (decimal) input to a four-bit binary equivalent. For example, assume that three of the decimal inputs are true and that all other inputs are false. (With this type of decoder, only one of the inputs can be true at the same time.) Under these conditions, the output of inverter gate 3 is false, while the output of all other inverter gates is true. Inverter gate 3 is connected to logic gates 1 and 2. Any false input to a NAND gate produces a true output. Thus logic gates 1 and 2 are true. The inputs to logic gates 4 and 8 are all true. All true inputs to a NAND gate produce a false output. Thus logic gates 4 and 8 are false. The binary output of the logic gates is then 0011 or decimal 3.

Note that the 0 decimal input line is not connected. When the

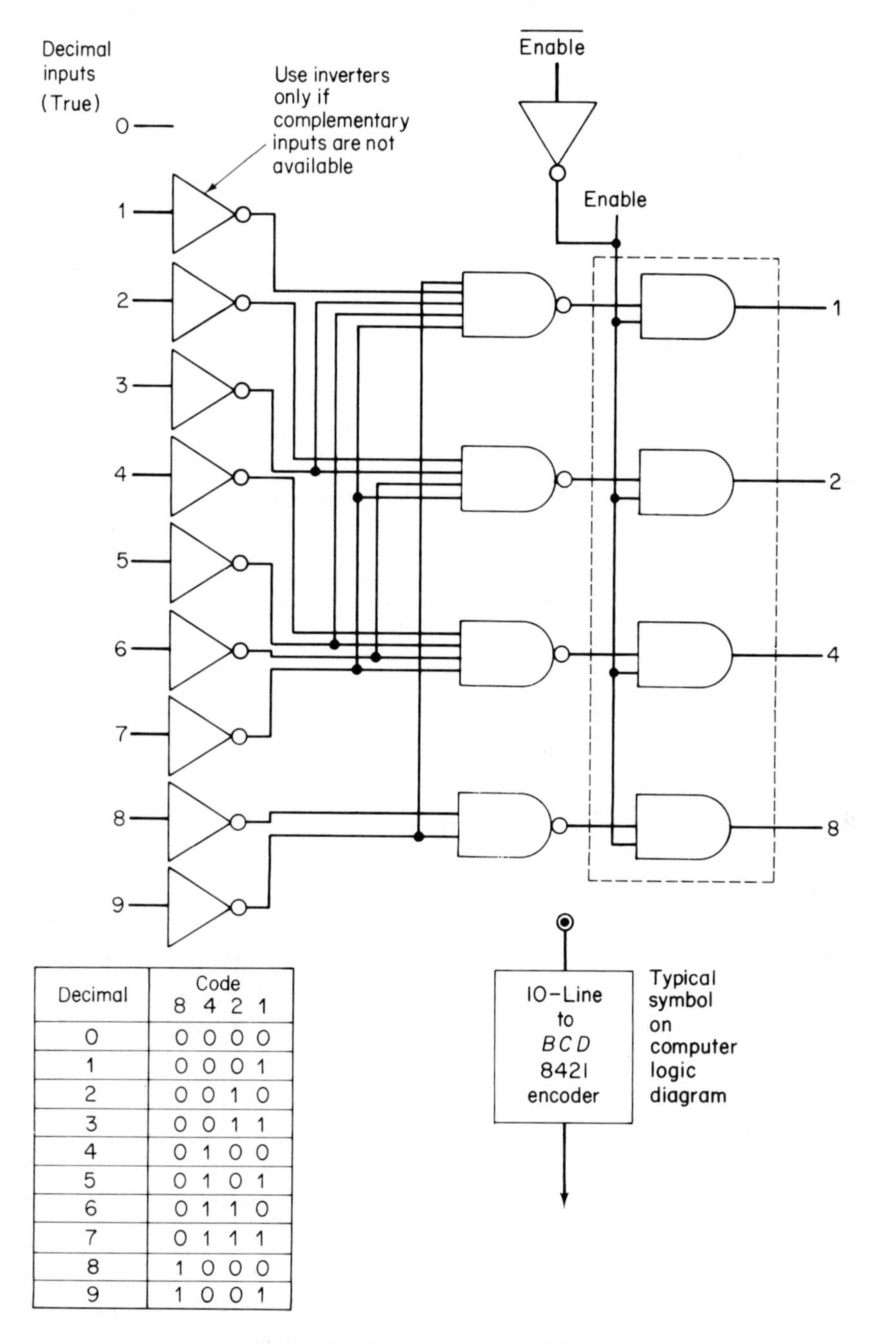

Decimal	Code 8 4 2 1
0	0 0 0 0
1	0 0 0 1
2	0 0 1 0
3	0 0 1 1
4	0 1 0 0
5	0 1 0 1
6	0 1 1 0
7	0 1 1 1
8	1 0 0 0
9	1 0 0 1

Fig. 6-43. Decimal-to-BCD encoder. (Courtesy of Motorola.)

decimal input is 0, the 1–9 lines are all false, the outputs of the inverter gates are all true, and the outputs of the logic gates are all false, producing a binary 0000 or decimal 0.

The AND gates (shown in a dotted enclosure) following the logic gates provide for gating the encoder. With such connections, the outputs are available only when an enable signal (either pulse or fixed d-c voltage) is present.

6. Multiple-Line Decoders and Encoders

Both decoders and encoders may have any number of inputs and outputs (various combinations of which are true at any given time). To simplify computer logic diagrams, both decoders and encoders are often shown in symbol form as rectangular boxes rather than showing the full circuitry. The type or function of the decoder/encoder is indicated within the symbol (such as 10-line to XS-3, 8421 to 10-line, etc.). An example of such a symbol is shown in Figure 6-43.

K. DATA DISTRIBUTORS AND SELECTORS

Basic data distributor and selector circuits are similar to decoders. The two basic circuits described here are universal in that they may be rearranged throughout the computer to meet any system need where data distribution or selection is involved.

The data distributor distributes a single channel of input data to any number of output lines, in accordance with a binary code applied to the control lines. Both two-channel and four-channel data distributor circuits are shown in Figure 6-44. Note that both inverters and AND gates are used. (If the distributor is used where the data are applied to several loads on the output line, the AND gates are usually of the power type.) Data applied to input X are distributed to outputs Z0–Z3, in accordance with the binary number applied to control inputs A and B (or the states, 0 or 1, of inputs A and B), as shown by the equations and truth table. Data applied to input Y are distributed to outputs Z4 and Z5, in accodance with the state of control input Y.

The data selector selects data on one or more input lines and applies the data to a single output channel in accordance with a binary code

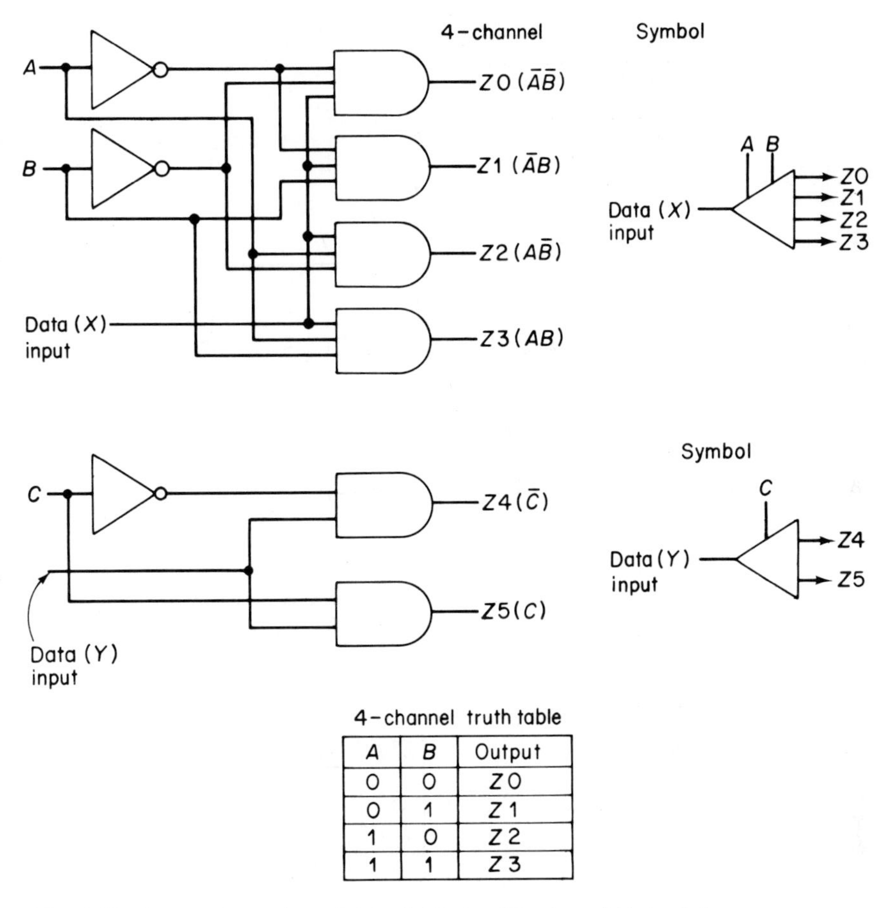

4-channel truth table

A	B	Output
0	0	Z0
0	1	Z1
1	0	Z2
1	1	Z3

Fig. 6-44. Four- and two-channel data distributor. (Courtesy of Motorola.)

applied to control lines. A four-input data selector circuit is shown in Figure 6-45. Note that inverters, AND gates, and OR gates are used. (If the selector must drive several loads at its output, the OR gate is usually of the power type.) Data present on input lines *X*0–*X*3 are transferred to output *Q*0, in accordance with the state of control inputs *A* and *B*, as shown by the equations and truth table.

For example, assume that input data line *X*3 is to be selected. With control lines *A* and *B* both at 1, the outputs of inverters 7 and 8 are at 1. These two logic 1 levels apply to 1 levels to AND gate 4, thus enabling its operation with data available on data line *X*3. All other AND gates (1, 2, and 3) are inhibited, thus disabling lines *X*0, *X*1, and *X*2.

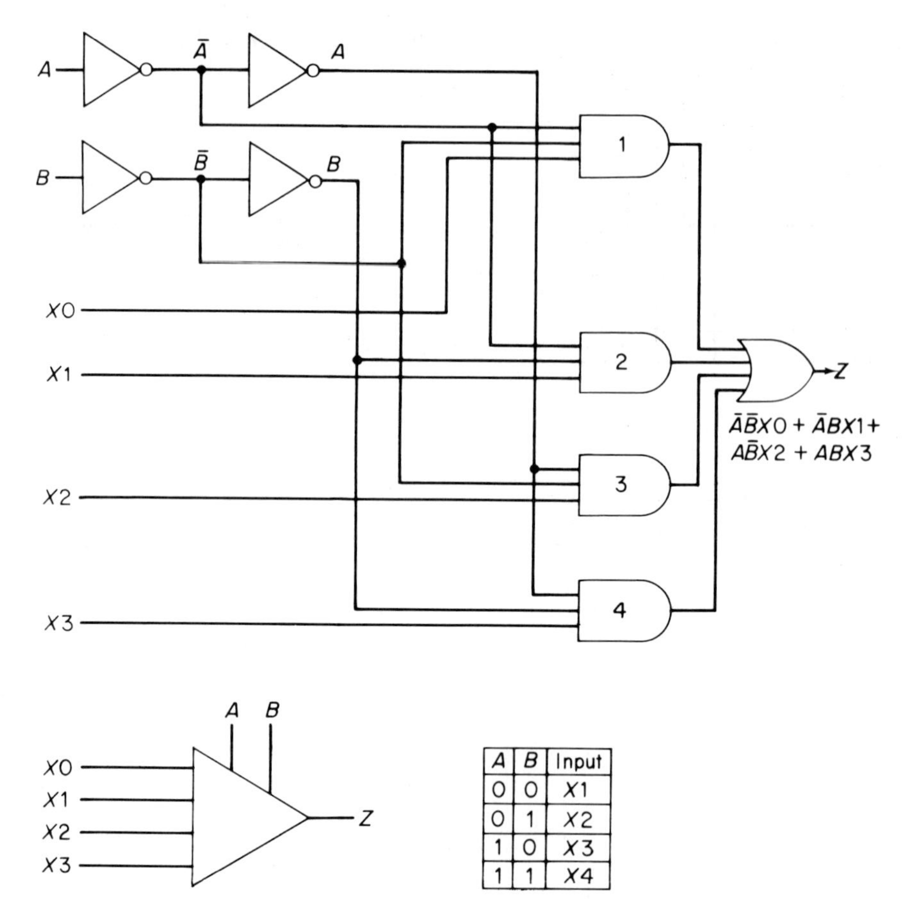

A	B	Input
0	0	X1
0	1	X2
1	0	X3
1	1	X4

Fig. 6-45. Four-channel data selector. (Courtesy of Motorola.)

1. Data Distributor Applications

The size of the distributor function may be increased by increasing the number of basic distributor circuits. For example, a system for distribution of one bit of information to one of eight locations is shown in Figure 6-46.

In this system, the data on the *Y* line are distributed according to the binary code applied to *A*, *B*, and *C* control lines. Note that the distribution system is implemented with two four-channel distributors and one two-channel distributor. Data are entered into the two-channel distributor and routed to one of the four-channel distributors.

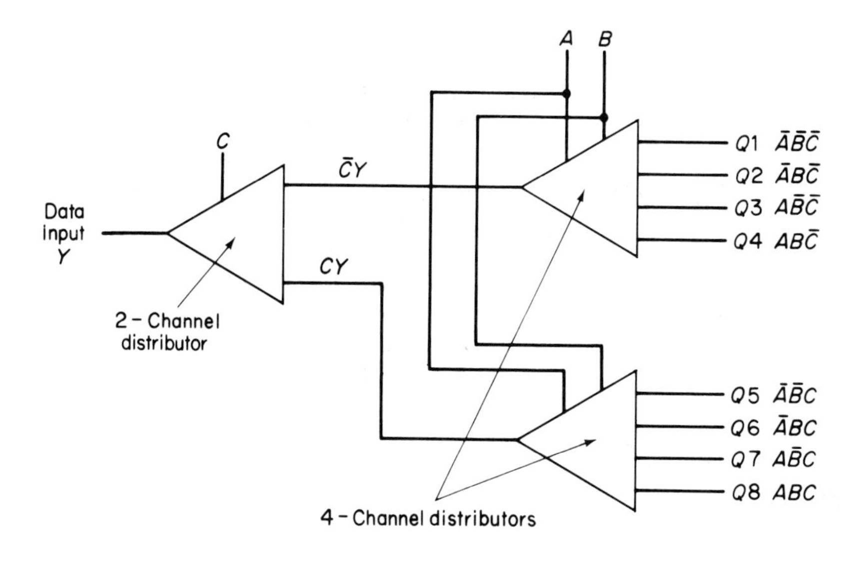

B	A	C	Output
0	0	0	1
1	0	0	2
0	1	0	3
1	1	0	4
0	0	1	5
1	0	1	6
0	1	1	7
1	1	1	8

Fig. 6-46. Data distribution for one bit of information to one of eight locations. (Courtesy of Motorola.)

For example, with information at 1 on the *Y* line, the *Y* line is ANDed with the *C* control line. This provides a 1 at either CY or $\overline{C}Y$. With $\overline{C}Y$ at 1, the control logic from the *A* and *B* control lines provides data outputs from one of the four locations *Q*1–*Q*4. With CY at 1, the control logic from the *A* and *B* inputs provides data outputs from one of the four locations *Q*5–*Q*8. This is shown in the truth table of Figure 6-46.

Distribution of more than one bit of information is also possible with the basic distributor circuits. For example, a system for distributing *N* bits of information, with each bit going to one of four locations, is shown in Figure 6-47. Data on inputs *X* and *Y*–*M* are distributed by control variables *A* and *B*, as previously described.

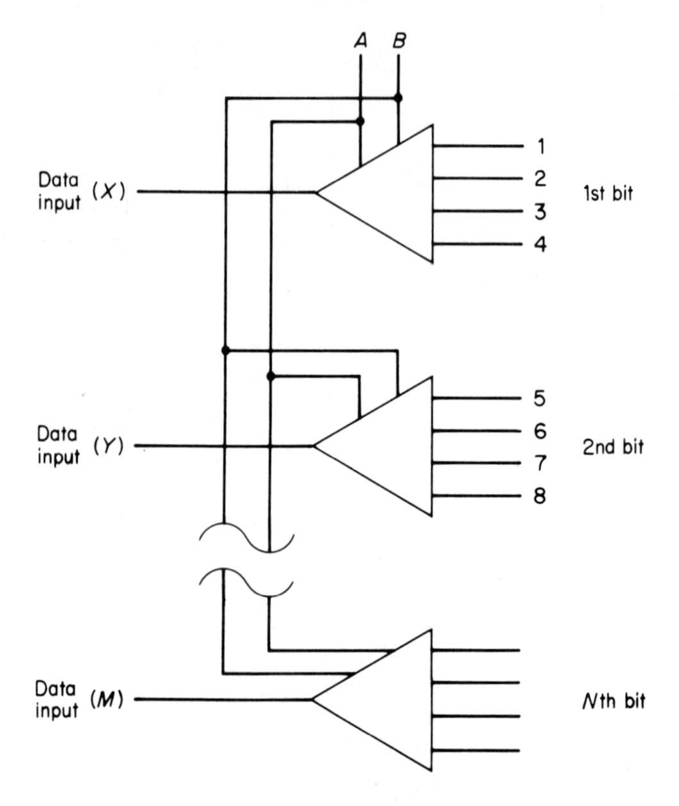

Fig. 6-47. Data distribution for *N* bits of information, each bit to one of four locations. (Courtesy of Motorola.)

A scheme to distribute *N* bits of information, each going to one of eight locations, is shown in Figure 6-48. Distribution of each bit is the same as previously described.

2. Data Selector Applications

Data selection from more than four locations (or inputs) can be implemented using multiple basic data selector circuits. An example of expanded selection is given in the one-bit selector network of Figure 6-49. This circuit selects data from one of the eight inputs, $X0$–$X7$, and transfers the data to output $Q0$, as indicated by the truth table.

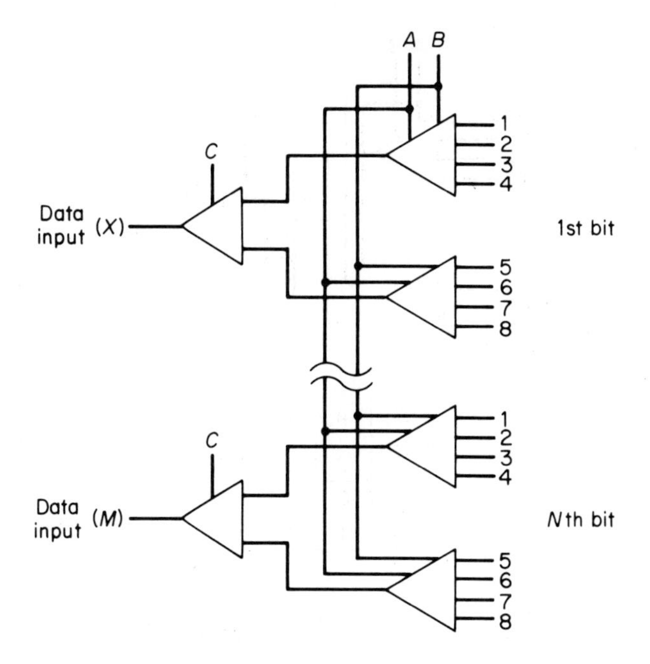

Fig. 6-48. Data distribution for *N* bits of information, each bit to one of eight locations. (Courtesy of Motorola.)

The basic data selector circuit can be used to implement a network that will provide multiple outputs from multiple inputs. Such an *N*-bit network is shown in Figure 6-50. Each output bit is selected from one of its own group of four different inputs. For example, with control lines *A* and *B* both at 1, data lines *X*3, *X*7, and *XM* are enabled, and all other data lines are inhibited. The truth table for each selector in the network is the same as for the basic selector (Figure 6-45).

L. LOGIC FORMS

The following paragraphs describe the various logic forms used in computers. Some of these forms first appeared as discrete component circuits, particularly in early computers. However, most of the forms are the result of packaging computer logic elements as integrated circuits.

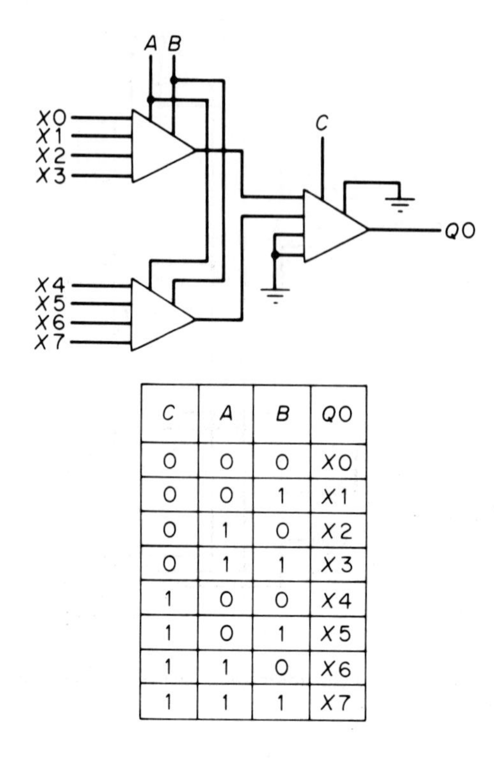

C	A	B	Q0
0	0	0	X0
0	0	1	X1
0	1	0	X2
0	1	1	X3
1	0	0	X4
1	0	1	X5
1	1	0	X6
1	1	1	X7

Fig. 6-49. Data selector: one bit from one of eight locations. (Courtesy of Motorola.)

Fig. 6-50. Data selector: *N* bits from one of four locations. (Courtesy of Motorola.)

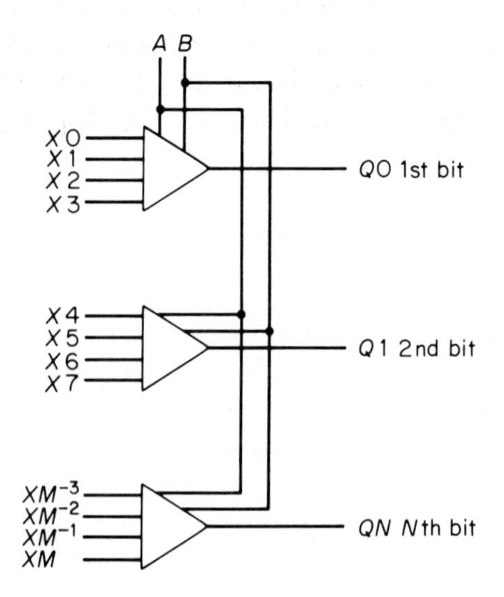

1. Direct-Coupled Transistor Logic

The direct-coupled transistor logic (DCTL) gate was one of the first to be integrated. A simple DCTL parallel gate is shown in Figure 6-51A. A more practical DCTL parallel gate is shown in Figure 6-51B. Note that these circuits are often confused with the resistor-transistor logic network (RTL), since only resistors and transistors are involved. However, DCTL is a better term.

In the DCTL type of gate circuit, there is no separate transistor to provide amplification (and inversion), usually found in present-day logic ICs. Instead, the amplification function is distributed among the

Fig. 6-51. Direct-coupled transistor logic (DCTL).

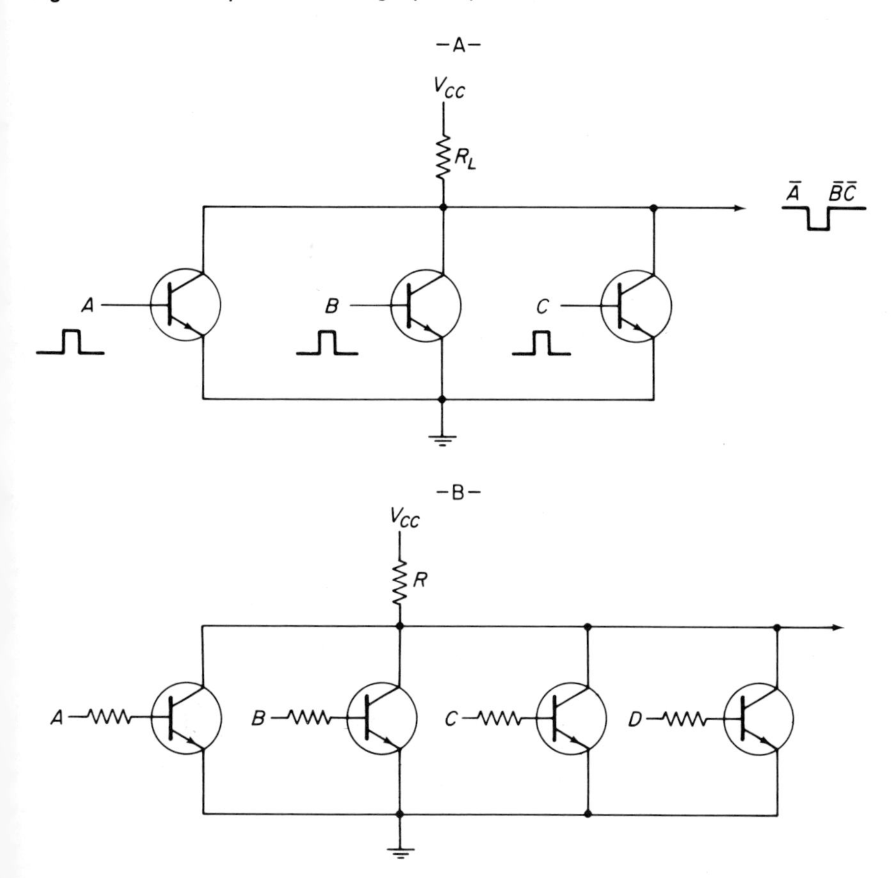

four input transistors (one transistor and one resistor for each input). The circuit of Figure 6-51B is a NOR gate in that if any input is high, the output is low. This circuit was popular in early computers but is generally replaced in late-model computers.

2. Resistor-Transistor Logic

Figure 6-52 shows two bonafide RTL circuits. Note that, unlike the DCTL circuits, the base-emitter junctions of all transistors are biased. This keeps current drain at a minimum. (One major drawback with DCTL is excessive current drain.)

The circuit of Figure 6-52A is a four-input NOR gate. The switching function is provided by the four input resistors, while amplification is accomplished by the transistor. This circuit usually exists only in discrete form, since it is difficult to integrate precision resistors.

Fig. 6-52. Resistor-transistor logic (RTL).

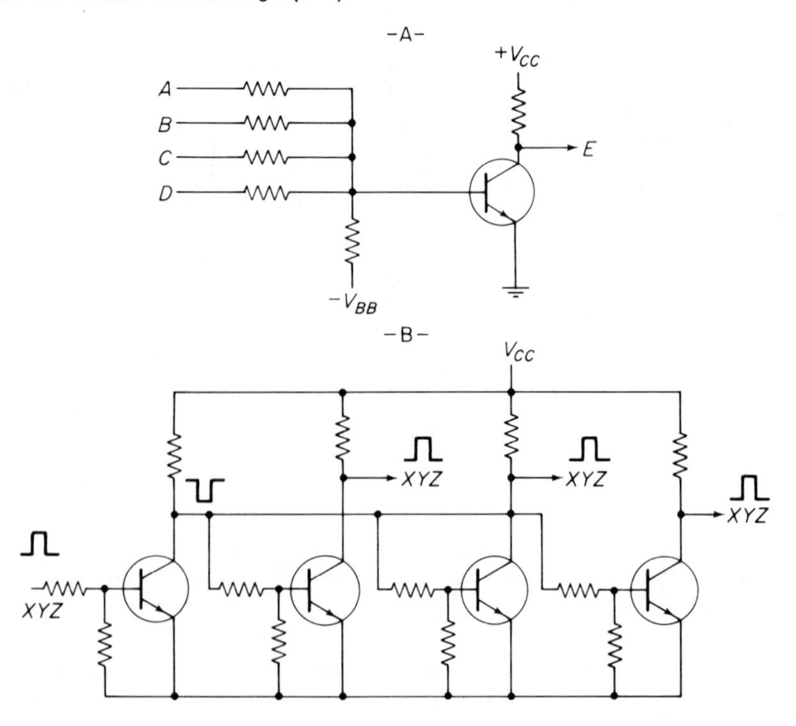

The circuit of Figure 6-52B is a buffer. Each of the three outputs is an amplified version of the input, without inversion. The input transistor inverts the input and applies this to all three output transistors, which, in turn, invert the pulse back to its original form.

3. Resistor-Capacitor Transistor Logic

As shown in Figure 6-53, the addition of a speedup capacitor across the base resistor of an RTL circuit improves the high-frequency characteristics of a gate by providing a low impedance for the leading and trailing edges of input pulses. The disadvantage of the resistor-capacitor transistor logic (RCTL) circuit from an IC standpoint is that it requires a large IC chip area. Also, the RCTL does not track the temperature-sensitive saturation characteristics of the transistor and is noise-sensitive. Low-amplitude noise signals will easily pass through the capacitor.

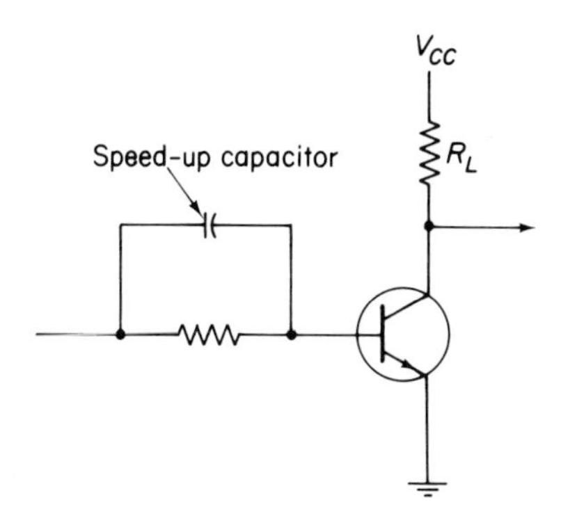

Fig. 6-53. Resistor-capacitor transistor logic (RCTL).

4. Diode-Transistor Logic

The diode-transistor logic (DTL) circuit (Figure 6-54) provides an AND function with an output transistor as an inverter-amplifier. The total circuit is then a NAND gate for positive logic and a NOR gate for negative logic. The DTL circuits have moderately high speeds with good noise immunity. Low-amplitude noise signals will not overcome

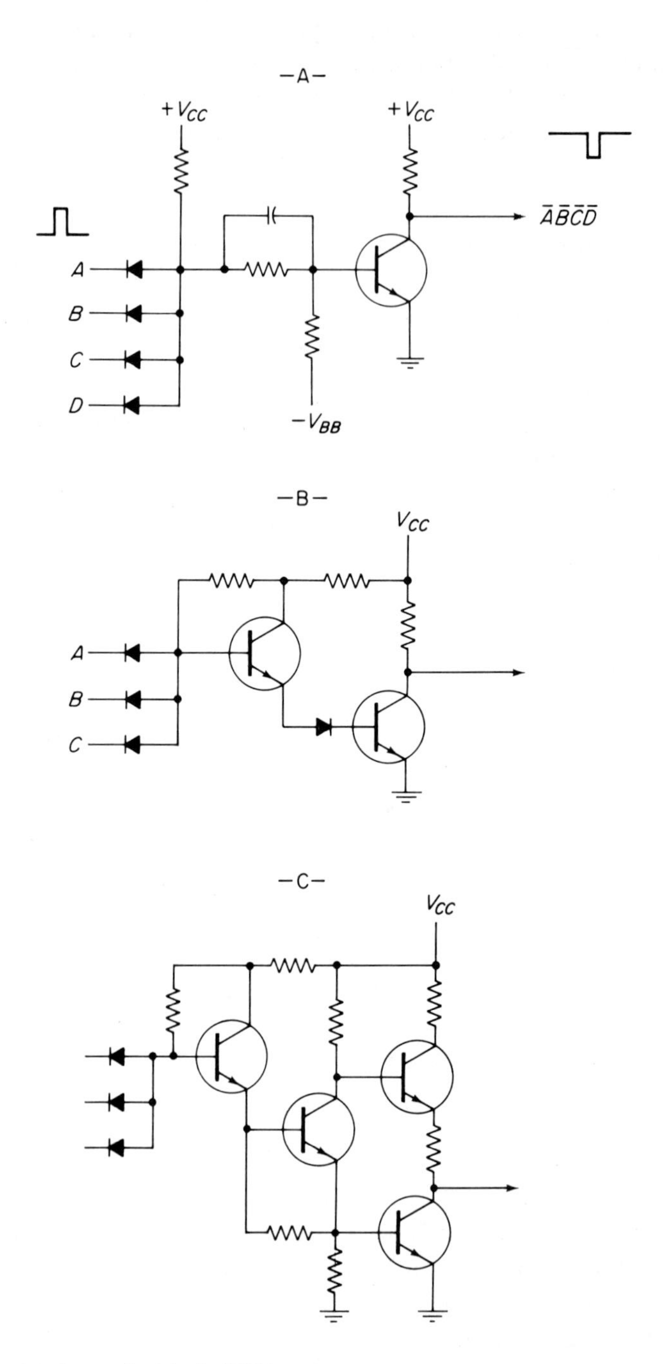

Fig. 6-54. Diode-transistor logic (DTL).

the input diode resistance (forward voltage drop) and thus do not appear at the output. Note that in the circuit of Figure 6-54 the speedup capacitor is used. This increases the speed of the gate, while the diodes act to block the noise signals.

5. Current Mode Logic

Current mode logic (CML), also referred to in some computer service literature as current steering logic (CSL), is shown in Figure 6-55. This type of circuit uses one transistor for every input and an additional transistor for biasing.

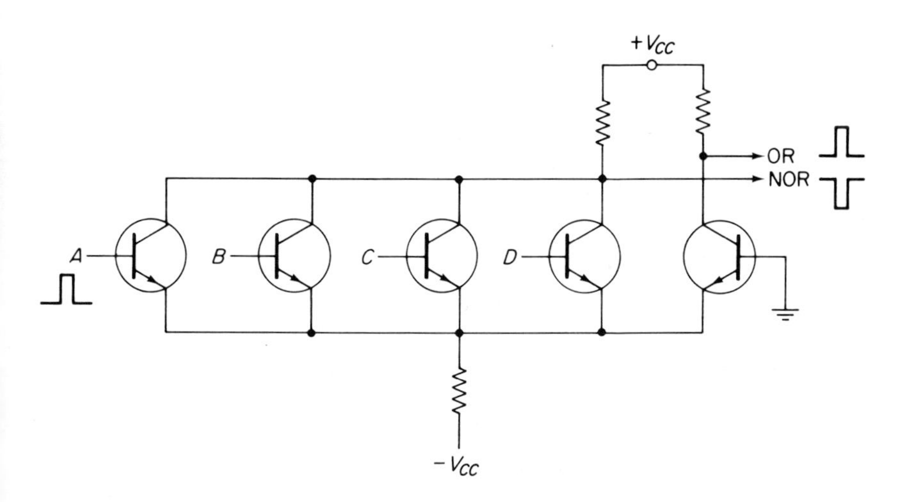

Fig. 6-55. Current mode logic (CML).

Because the circuit operates in the current mode, current flows either through the bank of input transistors or through the biasing transistor. Thus both the inverted and noninverted outputs are always present. The presence of both outputs from a single circuit is advantageous in many computer applications. Also, because the circuit does not operate in the saturated voltage mode (full on or off switching), the circuit is much faster than most other logic forms. The circuit of Figure 6-55 is both OR and NOR. If any input goes positive, the OR output also goes positive, and the NOR output goes negative.

6. Transistor-Transistor Logic

The transistor-transistor logic (TTL or T^2L) circuits shown in Figure 6-56 use transistors at the inputs for the AND function. Otherwise, the TTL is similar to the DTL circuit.

In the circuit of Figure 6-56A, a bank of four transistors provides for the inverting and amplifying function. This is the basic discrete component form of the TTL.

In the IC version, Figure 6-56B, the TTL changes slightly in that the bank of input transistors is replaced with a multiemitter transistor. The amplifying transistor is also replaced with a more elaborate scheme using transistors in a push-pull configuration. In this form, the output can supply a large amount of current **both when it is high and low**.

The TTL circuit is faster than the DTL and switches at approximately the same logic levels. The TTL has a wide frequency range and is therefore more sensitive to noise than the DTL. The TTL and DTL are logically and electronically compatible. Thus many computers use DTL in all cases, except where very high-speed TTL is required.

7. High-Threshold Logic

High-threshold logic (HTL) is intended for application in noisy environments where slow speeds can be tolerated. A typical noise margin is about 5 V. The basic HTL gate circuit is similar to the DTL circuits except that a zener diode replaces the coupling diode.

The basic HTL gate is shown in Figure 6-57A. Note that this is similar to the modified DTL shown in Figure 6-57B. The basic difference is in diode D_1, the resistor values, and the collector supply voltage (V_{CC}).

In the modified DTL, D_1 is a base-emitter diode operated in its forward direction and having a drop of approximately 0.75 V. The input threshold level of DTL is a net of two forward diode drops (the input diode offsets a diode drop in the other direction), or about 1.5 V.

In HTL, D_1 is a base-emitter junction operated in its reverse direction (commonly called zener operation). Conduction occurs when the junction has approximately 6.7 V across it. Thus the threshold voltage for HTL is equal to one forward diode drop plus one reverse diode

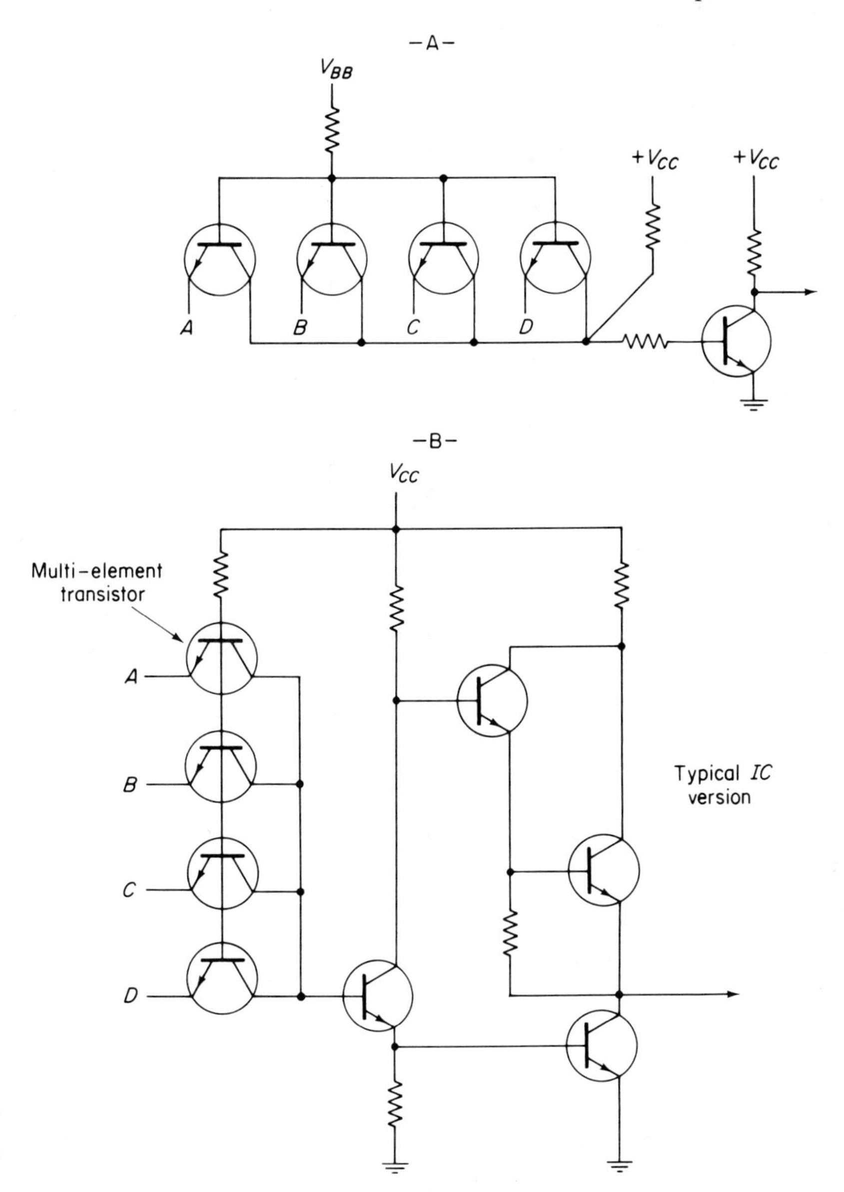

Fig. 6-56. Transistor-transistor logic (TTL or T²L).

drop, or about 7.5 V. This is at least 6 V higher than a DTL. Since 90 percent of the electrical noise found in a typical computer system is less than 5 V, the HTL threshold prevents most noise from entering the circuits.

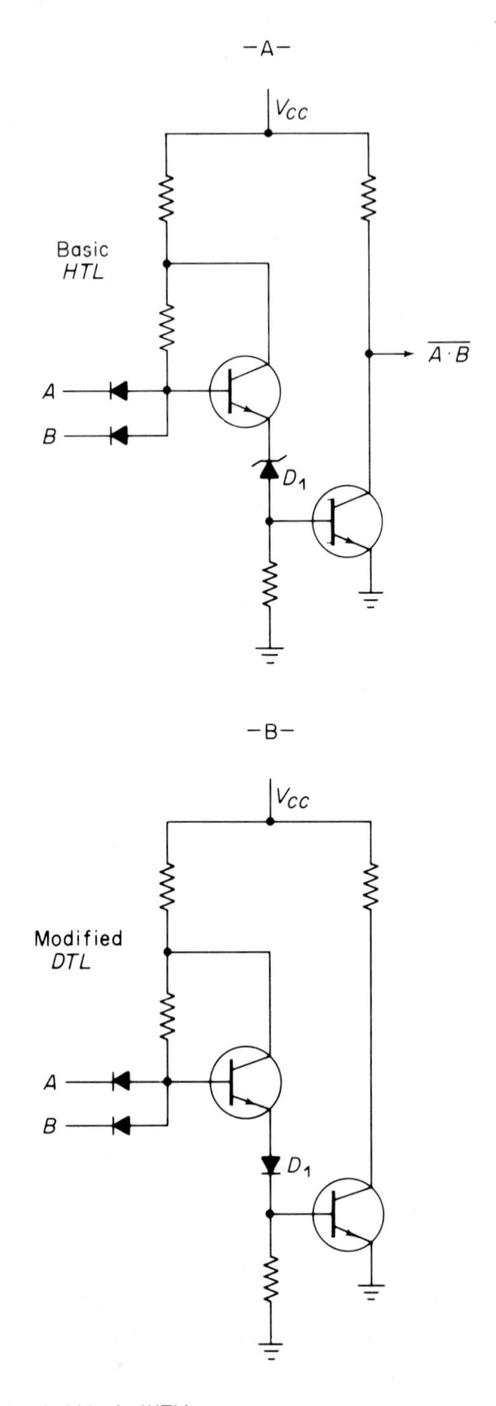

Fig. 6-57. High-threshold logic (HTL).

8. Emitter-Coupled Logic

Emitter-coupled logic (ECL), shown in Figure 6-58, operates at very high speeds. Computers can be operated at frequencies up to about

Fig. 6-58. Emitter-coupled logic (ECL).

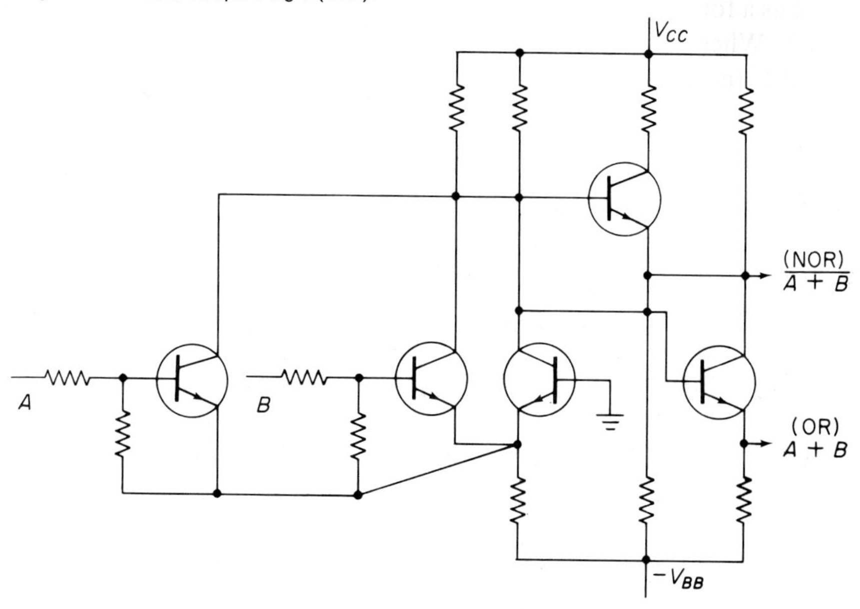

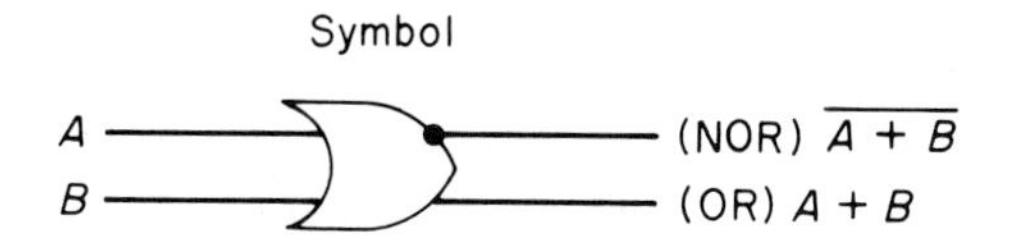

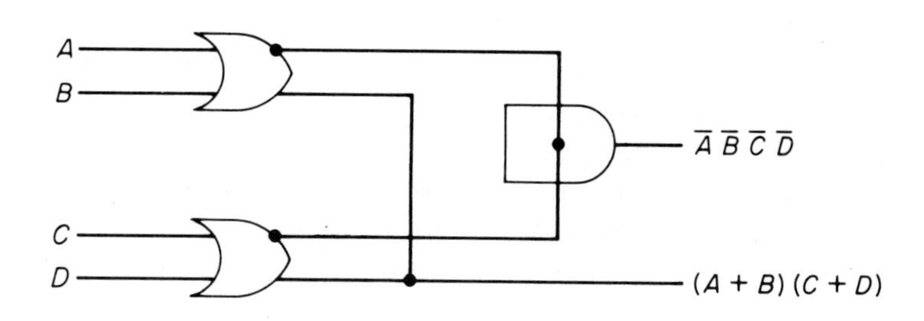

300 MHz using ECL. Another advantage of ECL is that both a true and complementary output is produced. Thus both OR and NOR functions are available at the output. Note that when the NOR functions of two ECL gates are connected in parallel, the outputs are ANDed, thus extending the number of inputs. For example, as shown in Figure 6-58, when two two-input NOR gates are ANDed, the results are the same as a four-input NOR gate (or a four-input NAND gate in negative logic). When the OR functions of two ECL gates are connected in parallel, the outputs are ANDed, resulting in an OR/AND function.

9. Field Effect Transistors in Computer Logic

Field effect transistors (FETs) are being used to simplify logic circuits in computers. Particularly useful are the MOSFET (metal-oxide-semiconductor FET) elements found in IC form. It is assumed that the reader is already familiar with the basic theory, physical construction, and characteristics of FETs. Such information is covered in John D. Lenk's *Practical Semiconductor Databook for Electronic Engineers and Technicians* (Englewood Cliffs, N.J.: Prentice-Hall, Inc., 1970).

The basic use of FETs in computer logic is the complementary inverter of Figure 6-59. Type C (enhancement mode only) MOSFETs are used in this circuit. The logic levels for the inverter are $+V$ for a 1 and ground (or 0 V) for a 0.

With a true input ($+V$), the P-channel stage has zero gate voltage and is essentially cut off. The P channel conducts very little drain current (identified as I_{DSS} and typically a few microamperes for a C-type FET). The N channel element is forward-biased and its drain voltage (with only a few picoamperes of I_{DDS} allowed to flow) is near ground or false (0). The load capacitance, C_L, represents the output load plus any stray circuit capacitance.

With a false input (ground), the N-channel element is cut off and permits only I_{DSS} to flow. The P-channel element is forward-biased, and its V_{DS} (drain-source voltage) is low. Thus the drain terminal of the P channel is near $+V$, and C_L is charged to $+V$. The power dissipation is extremely low since both stable states, true and false (or 1 and 0), conduct only leakage current. Power is dissipated only during switching, an ideal situation for logic circuits. In addition to the lower

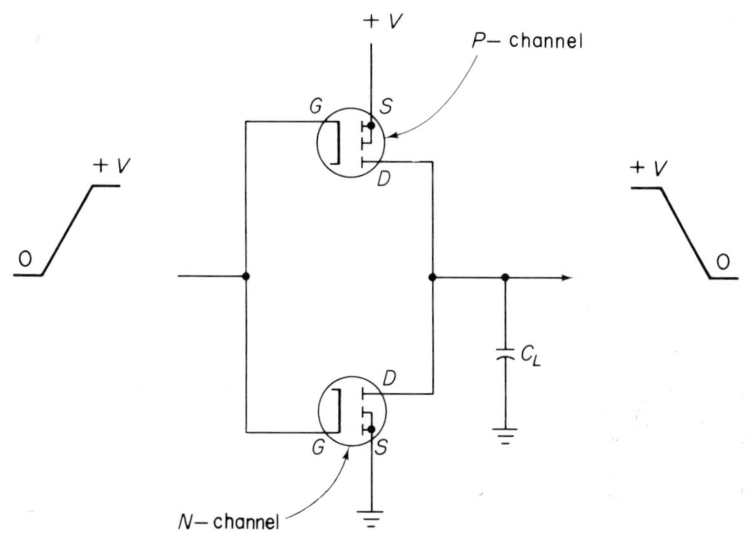

Fig. 6-59. Basic FET complementary inverter logic circuit.

power dissipation, another advantage of FETs for logic circuits is that no coupling elements are required. The input to a MOSFET is an insulated gate, which resembles a capacitor in effect.

Without the need for a coupling capacitor function, it is relatively simple to fabricate MOSFET logic elements in IC form. OR, NOR, AND, and NAND gates with either positive or negative logic can be implemented with MOSFETs. Thus almost any logic circuit combination can be produced. FET logic can also be used over a wide range of power supply voltages.

An R-S FF, a two-input NOR gate, and a two-input NAND gate are shown in Figures 6-60, 6-61, and 6-62, respectively.

In the NOR gate circuit of Figure 6-61, the gates of Q_1 and Q_3 are tied together to form input 1. Elements Q_1 and Q_3 act together as an inverter circuit in that they form a push-pull combination. Element Q_2 acts as a series resistance, which is either extremely high or low, in the inverter formed by Q_1 and Q_3. Likewise, Q_1 acts as a series resistance in the inverter formed by Q_3 and Q_4.

Input 2 is the control input for the second inverter. The output of the gate is at +10 V only when elements Q_1 and Q_2 are switched on. This occurs only if both inputs 1 and 2 are at ground. Thus the output is a logic 1 only when both inputs are at a logic 0.

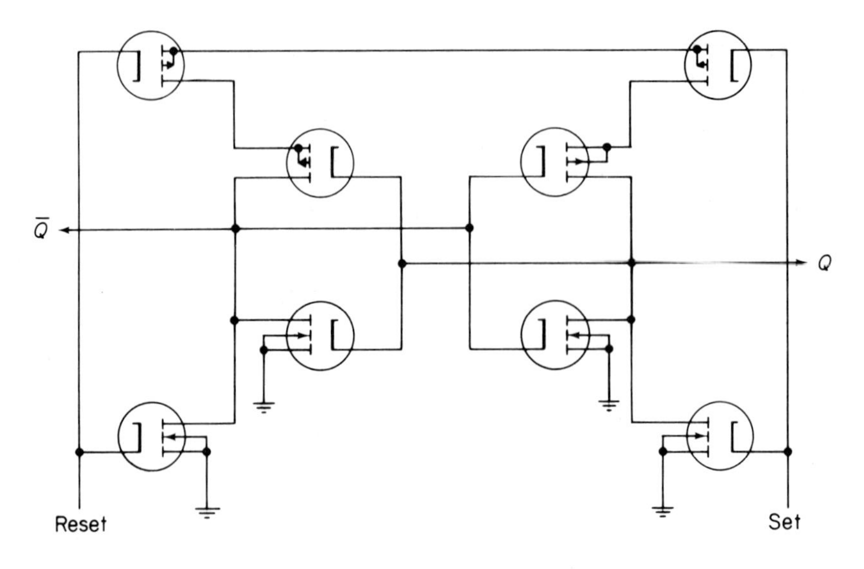

Fig. 6-60. Complementary FET R-S FF. (Courtesy of Motorola.)

Fig. 6-61. Two-input NOR gate using MOSFETs. (Courtesy of Motorola.)

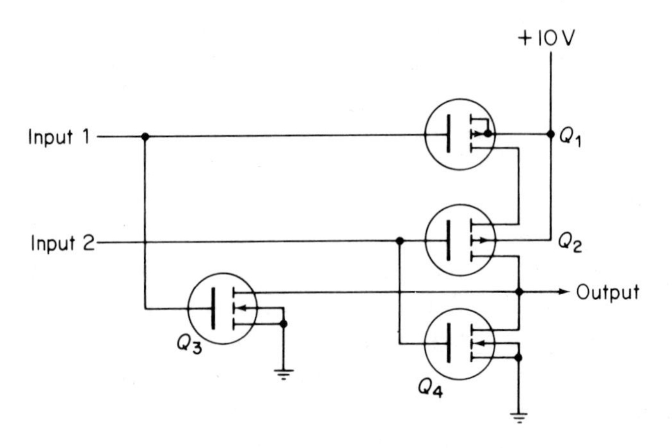

0 = 0 V	1 = +10 V	
Input 1	Input 2	Output
0	0	1
0	1	0
1	0	0
1	1	0

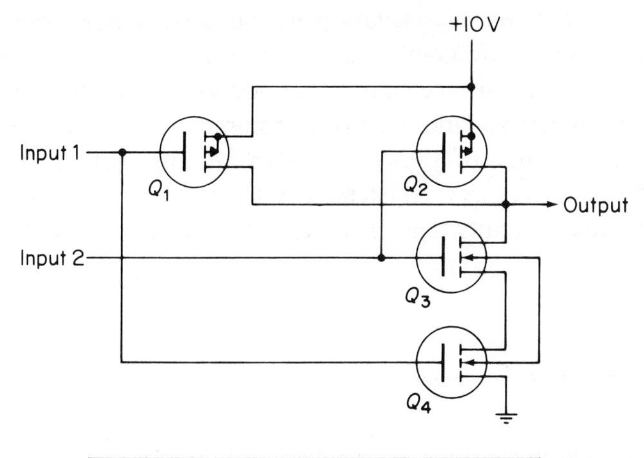

0 = 0V	1 = +10 V	
Input 1	Input 2	Output
0	0	1
0	1	1
1	0	1
1	1	0

Fig. 6-62. Two-input NAND gate using MOSFETs. (Courtesy of Motorola.)

Since a NOR gate using positive logic becomes a NAND gate when using negative logic, the NOR gate can be converted to a NAND gate by interchanging P- and N-channel elements and flipping the circuit upside down. This is done with the two-input NAND gate of Figure 6-62.

M. ARITHMETIC CIRCUITS

Digital computers can be designed to perform all known arithmetic operations, depending on the intended use of the computer. A computer that can perform addition, subtraction, multiplication, and division can solve almost any problem since most arithmetic operations are based upon these four functions.

Basic binary addition and subtraction can be accomplished using the circuits described in previous paragraphs of this chapter. In some computers, special circuits are developed to perform multiplication and division. In most computers, however, the basic adder, shift register, and storage register are combined to perform the four basic functions. One reason for this arrangement is that adders and registers are readily available in integrated circuit form. A computer arithemtic section can be made up entirely of these integrated circuits, with proper interconnection of adders and registers. The following paragraphs describe the combination circuits that make up the majority of computer arithmetic units.

1. Subtraction by Complementing

As discussed in Chapter 3 (subdivision B, 2), it is possible to accomplish binary subtraction by complementing. In a practical circuit, this is done by complementing (or inverting) the subtrahend before it enters either of the inputs (augend or addend) of a full adder. An example of this method is shown in Figure 6-63, which is a combined parallel adder and subtractor circuit.

When the circuit is to be used for subtraction, the subtract line is made true by a control panel switch or by a programmed pulse. With the subtract line true, the subtract AND gates pass the inverted subtrahend through the OR gate to the corresponding input of the full adders. At this same time, the end-around-carry gate is opened (by the subtract line being true), inserting C_4 (carry four) back into C_1 (carry 1). The process of complementing and "adding back" the end-around carry produces the correct difference on D_1, D_2, and D_3.

For example, assume that 011 is to be subtracted from 111. Using normal binary subtraction,

```
 111    (minuend)
−011    (subtrahend)
────
 100    (difference).
```

Now, using the complement method circuit of Figure 6-63, the 111 minuend is entered into the minuend input of FA_1 (full adder 1), FA_2, and FA_3. The 011 subtrahend is entered at the inverters so that 0 is applied to I_3 (inverter 3), 1 is applied to I_2, and the least significant 1 is applied to I_1. The inverters produce the complement 100, which appears at the subtract AND gates (1 at gate 3, 0 at gate 2, and least

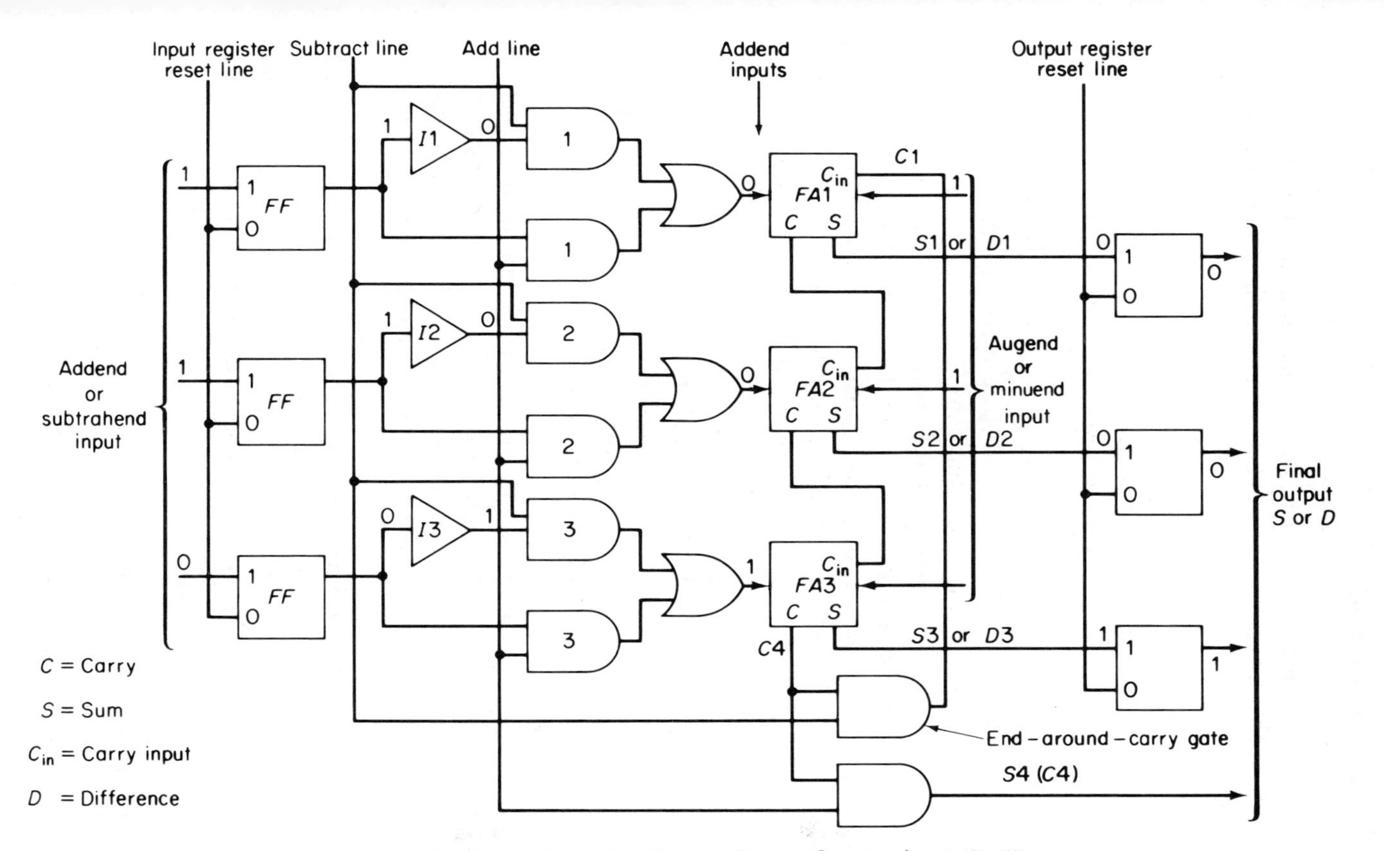

Fig. 6-63. Subtraction by complementing. C, carry; S, sum; C_{in}, carry input; D, difference.

signficant 0 at gate 1). In turn, the normal addend input of all three adders receive this complement. This results in the addition of 111 and 100, or

$$\begin{array}{rrl} & 111 & \text{(minuend)} \\ & +100 & \text{(complement)} \\ \hline 1 & 011 & \text{(sum before end-around carry).} \end{array}$$

However, the end-around carry (C_4) of 1 is applied to the carry input (C_1) of FA_1. Since the sum-before carry of FA_1 is 1, the end-around carry of 1 changes the sum (now difference) output of FA_1 to 0. Likewise, the carry output of FA_1 is applied to the carry input of FA_2, changing the sum-before carry of 1 to a difference output of 0. In turn, the carry output of FA_2 is applied to the carry input of FA_3, changing the sum before carry of 0 to a difference output of 1, with no additional carry output from FA_3. This can be shown as follows:

$$\begin{array}{rrl} & 111 & \text{(minuend)} \\ & +100 & \text{(complement)} \\ \hline 1 & 011 & \text{(sum-before carry)} \\ & +\ \ 1 & \text{(end-around carry)} \\ \hline & 100 & \text{(difference).} \end{array}$$

Note that the registers shown in Figure 6-63 are used to hold the numbers or count at the input and output of the adder/subtractor circuit. Typically, such registers are made up of FF that can be reset to zero (by the operator or a timing pulse) before and after arithmetic operations.

When the circuit of Figure 6-63 is to be used for addition, the addition line is made true, permitting the add AND gates to pass the non-inverted addend through the OR gate to the corresponding addend input of the full adders. The circuit then acts as a conventional adder.

2. Multiplication by Shifting

As discussed in Chapter 3 (subdivision B, 3), it is possible to accomplish binary multiplication by adding and shifting, because multiplication is the process of adding the multiplicand to itself as many times as the multiplier dictates. For example,

```
    1111      (multiplicand)
   ×1101      (multiplier)
    1111      A )
   0000       B |
  1111        C } (partial products)
 1111         D )
11000011      (product).
```

In binary multiplication (where only 1s or 0s are used), the partial products are always equal to zero, or to the multiplicand. The final product is obtained by the addition of as many partial products that are equal to the multipliand as there are 1s in the multiplier. In our example, there are three 1s in the muliplier. Thus three partial products (*A*, *C*, and *D*) are equal to the multiplicand and must be added. Of course, the addition must take place in the proper order, since each partial product is shifted by one digit for each digit in the multiplier (whether a 1 or 0). In our example, there are four digits in the multiplier. Thus there must be four shifts.

Figure 6-64 shows a typical shift multiplication circuit. Note that the circuit consists of three registers (multiplicand, multiplier, and accumulator) all made up of FF, gates, and inverters, three parallel full adders, and a *shift* FF. The shift FF provides two bit times for each step of operation. This is necesscary because a shift must occur whether an add takes place or not. Thus one bit time is required for adding or not adding, and a second bit time is necessary for the shift. The shift FF alternately sets and resets, thus providing a true signal (S) to the various gates every other bit time. The output of the shift FF controls the action of the "add" or "not add" during one bit time (S*) and the shift during the next bit time (S).

Assume that the circuit of Figure 6-64 is to multiply binary 101 by 111 ($5 \times 7 = 35$). All the multiplier and multiplicand register FFs are reset to zero; then the appropriate digits (1 or 0) are set into each FF as applicable. (The reset and preset lines are omitted from Figure 6-64 for clarity.)

The multiplication process is started by a clock pulse from the computer timer. This clock pulse resets the shift FF, making the S output false and the S* output true. Thus the first action that can occur (in conjunction with the first clock pulse) is an add or not add, depending on the state of multiplier FF FMR_3.

With the shift FF reset, the S* output is true. The output of FMR_3

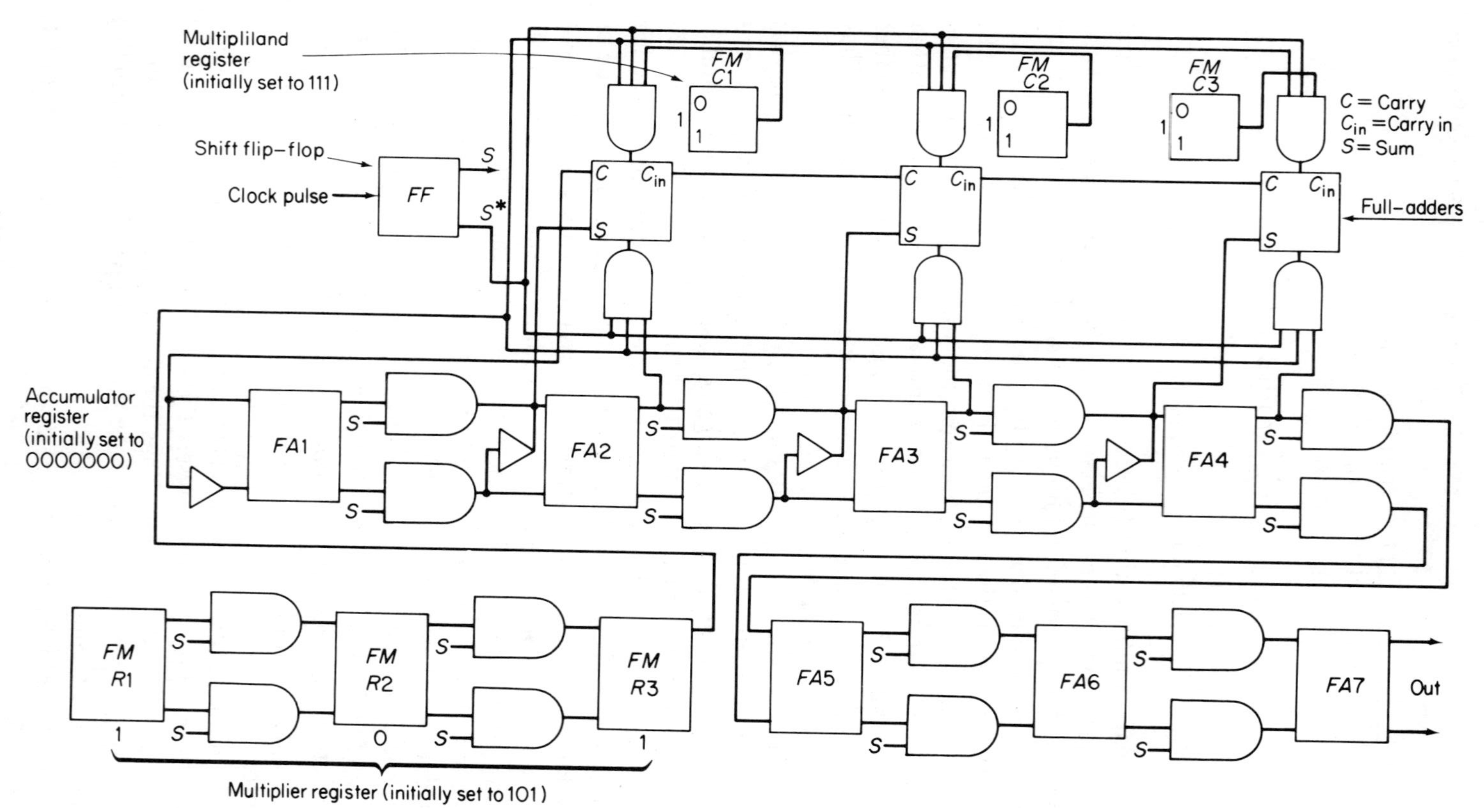

Fig. 6-64. Multiplication by shifting. See Figure 6-63 for explanation of symbols.

is also true, since the multiplier register is initially set to 101. Under these conditions, all the parallel adder AND gates are enabled. The contents of the multiplicand register (FMC_1–FMC_3) and the accumulator register (FA_2–FA_4) are added. Then the sum and carry outputs of the full adders are put back into the accumulator register FFs (FA_1–FA_4). Since the accumulator register is initially reset to all zeros, the sum is equal to the multiplicand (111), and this value is the sum answer in accumulator FFs FA_2–FA_4.

At the next clock pulse, the S output is true, and the S* output is false. Thus no more adding can take place, but a shift occurs in both the multiplier and accumulator registers (since the AND gates for these registers are enabled by the S output).

At the next clock pulse, S* is again true, and S is false. The full adders again try to add the contents of the multiplicand register (FMC_1–FMC_3) to the accumulator register (FA_2–FA_4). However, the output of multiplier FF FMR_3 is now false, keeping the full-adder gates closed. FF FMR_3 is false because it has been shifted one digit by the clock pulse. Originally, FMR_1 was at 1, FMR_2 at 0, and FMR_3 at 1. After the shift, however, both FMR_1 and FMR_3 are at 0 (false), with FMR_2 at 1.

At the next clock pulse (S*, false; S, true), another shift occurs. The accumulator register FFs are now at $FA_1 = 0$, $FA_2 = 0$, $FA_3 = 0$, $FA_4 = 1$, $FA_5 = 1$, $FA_6 = 1$, and $FA_7 = 0$.

At the next clock pulse (S*, true; S, false), an add does take place since the MSD of the multiplier (101) has shifted into FMR_3. The addition that takes place is

111	(multiplicand register)
0001110	(accumulator register)
100011	(final true product).

Although the correct product now exists in the accumulator register, the next shift will take place automatically, placing the product's LSD into FA_7.

In a typical computer, a *stop multiplication* pulse from the control section will halt action of the multiplication circuit at this time. In some computers, the contents of the accumulator register can be read out by front-panel lights connected to show the state of individual accumulator FFs (the light is on if the FF is in the 1 state). Typically, the next operation in the computer program is to transfer the contents of the accumulator register (now 0100011) to another register, or perhaps into the computer memory, for further processing.

3. Simultaneous Multiplication

In some computers, particularly the special-purpose computers, the arithmetic operations must be performed at high speeds. Instead of adding (or subtracting), complementing, and shifting two sets of binary digits, each digit is processed simultaneously with all other digits. A separate logic network (adder, subtractor, control gates, etc.) is required for each digit, similar to the circuit of Figure 6-63. Of course, the circuits that provide simultaneous arithmetic operations add many components to the computer (thus increasing the size and cost), since the computer's regular adder and shift register circuits cannot be used.

Figure 6-65 shows a circuit for simultaneous multiplication of two four-digit binary numbers, producing an eight-digit output. The circuit is made up of AND gates, full adders, and half-adders. The best way to understand the operation of this circuit is to trace through the multiplication of two numbers. The binary numbers used in the explanation for Figure 6-64 (111 × 101) are shown in Figure 6-65. The input and output states of all gates and adders are shown. Note that the final product is 00100011.

4. Repeated-Addition Multiplication

Since multiplication is the process of adding the multiplicand to itself as many times as the multiplier dictates, it is possible to perform multiplication by repeated addition. For example, to multiply 111 by 101 (7 × 5) the multiplicand 111 is added to itself 101 (or 5) times. Thus

$$
\begin{array}{rl}
111 & (1) \\
+111 & (2) \\
+111 & (3) \\
+111 & (4) \\
+111 & (5) \\
\hline
100011 &
\end{array}
$$

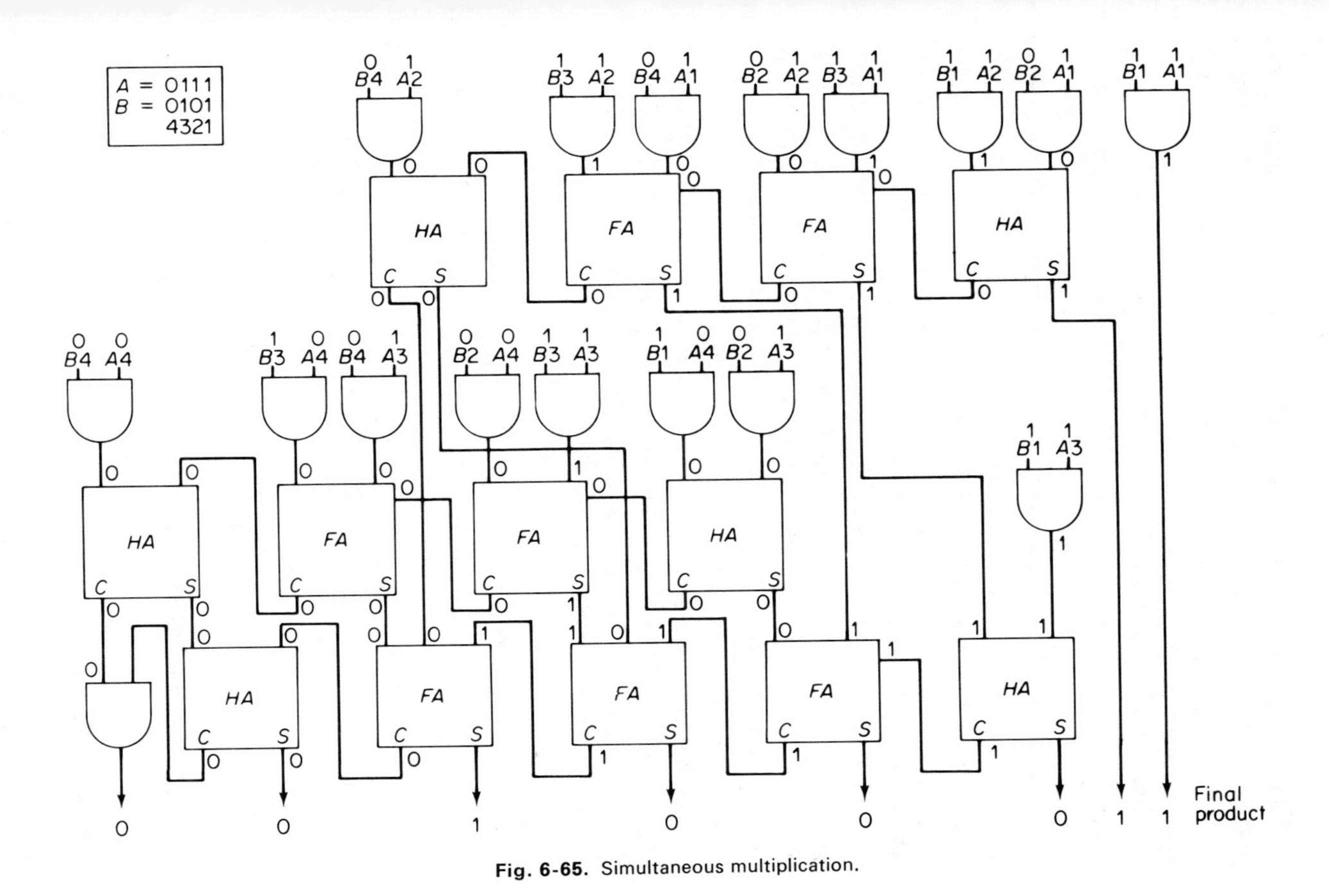

Fig. 6-65. Simultaneous multiplication.

Some computers use the repeated-addition system of multiplication. However, the trend today is toward the shifting method (for simple, general-purpose computers) or simultaneous multiplication (for high-speed, special-purpose computers).

Figure 6-66 is a block diagram of a repeated-addition multiplier circuit. In such a circuit, the value of the multiplicand is put into the multiplicand register, and the value of the multiplier is put into the multiplier counter. The counter counts down (from the multiplier value) to 0. For example, if the multiplier is 101, the counter registers 101 before the first count, 100 after the first count, 011 after the second count, and so forth, down to 000. At count zero, the multiply control gate is closed, halting the repeated-addition process.

As long as the gate is open, the value of the multiplicand register is added to the existing value in the accumulator register. Note that the accumulator must have as many FFs as the sum of the multiplier and multiplicand. In our example (101 $\times$ 111) there is a total of six digits. Thus the accumulator must have at least six FFs.

The multiplicand and accumulator outputs comprise the augend and addend inputs to the adder circuit. The accumulator starts at 0 and holds the answer from the last addition. Thus the accumulator value increases as the repeated addition continues.

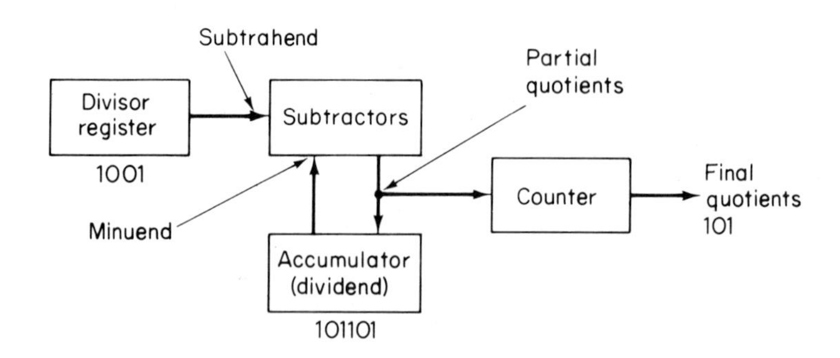

Fig. 6-66. Repeated-addition multiplication.

5. Division Circuits

As with multiplication, a separate circuit is sometimes used in computers to perform division only. Such circuits are used where arithmetic operations must be performed at high speeds, without regard to increased size and cost. High-speed circuits for simultaneous division are similar to those for multiplication (Figure 6-65), except that subtractors and gates are used (instead of adders and gates) since division is essentially a process of repeated subtraction, or subtraction and shifting.

The basic repeated-subtraction divider circuit is shown in the block diagram of Figure 6-67. In such a circuit, the value of the divisor is put into the divisor register, and the value of the dividend is put into the accumulator. The divisor and accumulator outputs comprise the subtrahend and minuend inputs to the subtractor circuit. The counter starts at zero and holds the partial quotients until the last subtraction takes place.

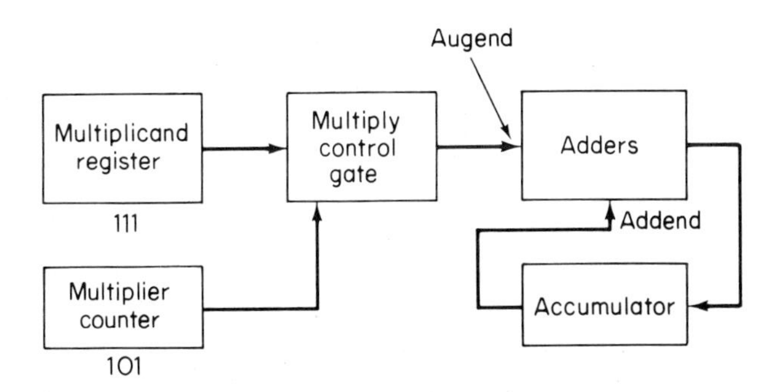

Fig. 6-67. Repeated-subtraction divider.

As each subtraction occurs, the value in the accumulator becomes smaller, while the count in the counter becomes larger, finally producing the correct quotient. One problem with such a divider is that it does not stop when the accumulator reaches 0 (or some remainder). Instead, the subtractor trys to continue subtracting beyond the point of 0 remainder. When this occurs, the value in the accumulator register becomes a negative quantity. In a practical circuit, this problem is overcome with a sign comparator (discussed in previous sections of this chapter). When the sign comparator notes a negative quantity in the accumulator, the divide process is stopped and the overage is added back to the accumulator total.

The basic subtraction-shifting divider circuit is shown in the block diagram of Figure 6-68. In such a circuit, the dividend is put into the accumulator, and the divisor is put into the divisor register. The

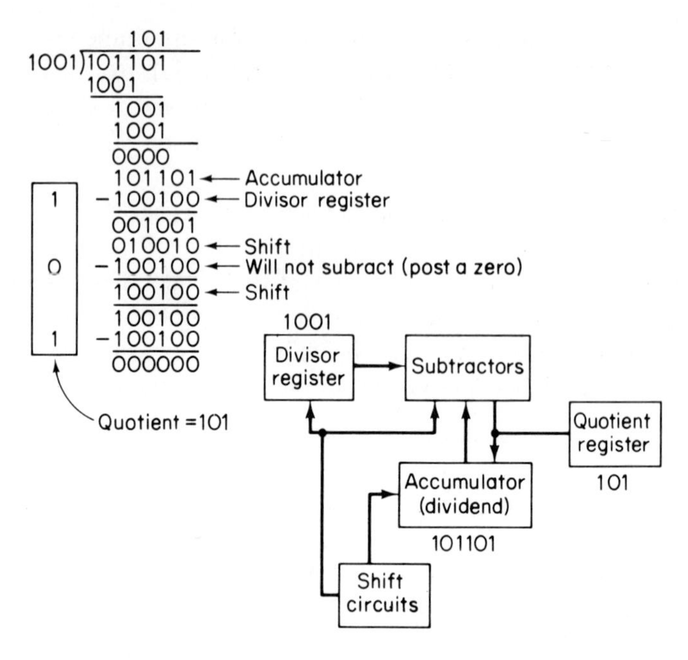

Fig. 6-68. Subtraction-shifting divider.

quotient register holds the quotients produced by repeated subtraction.

For each step (or timing pulse) a shift occurs in the accumulator and quotient register. Thus a 0 or a 1 is posted in the quotient register for each step. A 0 is posted when a subtraction cannot be performed, and a 1 is posted when a subtraction can be performed. Note that the divisor is fed into the subtractor in a manner corresponding to the digits of highest order of the dividend. The 1s and 0s posted in the quotient register become the final quotient, as shown by the sample division problem of Figure 6-68.

N. TIMING AND CONTROL CIRCUITS

The main units of any computer (input/output, memory, arithmetic, control) must be logically gated together. Likewise, the internal circuits of each unit are gated together. Obviously, the computer cannot be allowed to perform any of its functions in a random fashion. For example, two units cannot be simultaneously trying to fill the output register.

Operations must proceed in order. Thus a timing signal is applied at the gates that interconnect units (and circuits within units). The timing signals open and close gates in a predetermined order, causing the computer to perform its function in a logical manner.

The timing signals (called clock pulses in some computer service literature) must originate from the same source, even though they may occur at different intervals and are distributed to many different circuits. The most common source for timing signals is a crystal-controlled oscillator that produces a sine wave at some fixed frequency (typically in the 1–10-MHz range). The sine-wave output is shaped into pulses and/or square waves, using conventional shaping circuits. The pulses are then applied to frequency dividers, counters, and triggers, which set the duration of the timing signals.

Figure 6-69 shows the block diagram of a typical computer timing system. (The computer using this timing system is discussed further in Chapters 9 and 10.) The circuits involved in the timing system are not discussed in detail, since all the circuits (crystal oscillators, FFs, counters, etc.) are conventional and not unique to computers. However, the timing diagram that shows the relationship of all timing signals used in the computer is shown in Figure 6-70. Note that Figure 6-70 shows the theoretical timing of pulses and pulse shapes, as they appear in the service literature for the computer. Figure 6-71 shows the actual pulse shapes and time relationships of two pulses, as they appear on an oscilloscope.

Fig. 6-69. Typical computer timing system.

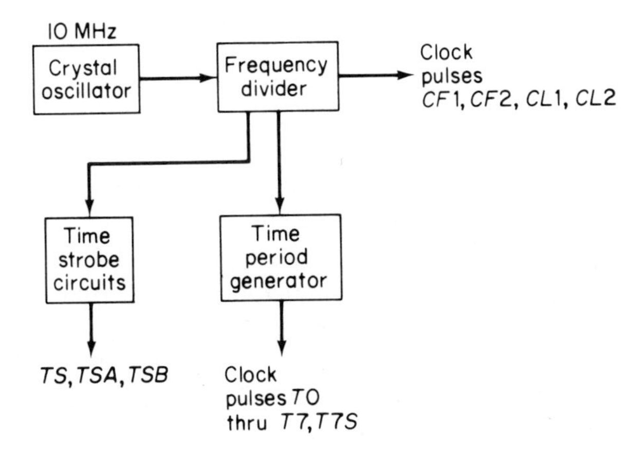

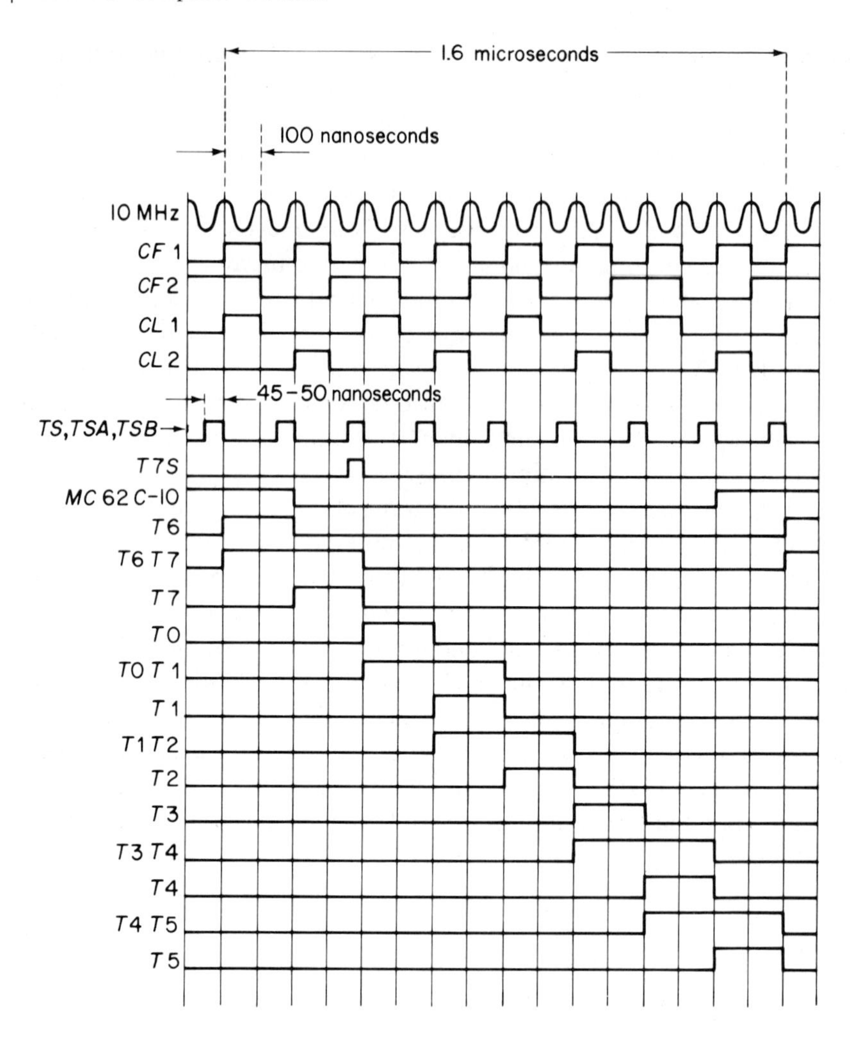

Fig. 6-70. Typical computer timing diagram.

The following is a brief description of how the timing signals are produced by the various blocks in the timing system.

The oscillator produces a frequency-stable (crystal-controlled) 10-MHz sine wave that is amplified and applied to the frequency divider. The major components in the frequency divider are two FFs and various gates. One FF (shown as CF1 in Figure 6-70) divides the 10-MHz output from the oscillator by 2, producing a square wave with a period of 200 nanoseconds (nS). The other FF (CF2) divides the

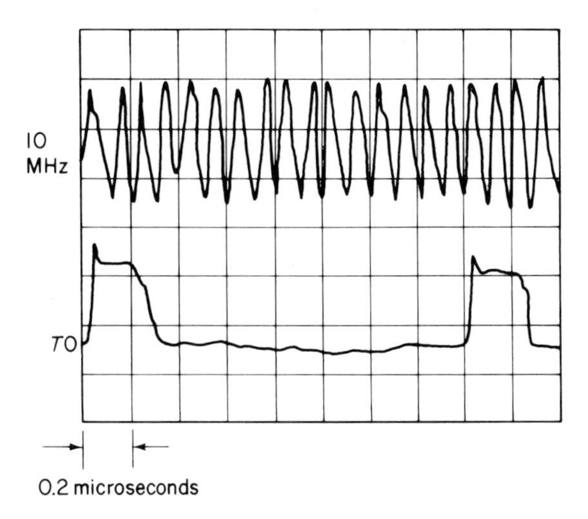

Fig. 6-71. Actual wave forms of computer timing signals.

CF1 output by 2, producing another square wave with a period of 400 nS. Gates within the frequency divider combine the CF1 and CF2 outputs to produce the CL1 and CL2 pulses shown in Figure 6-70.

The time strobe circuits produce three timing signals (TS, TSA, and TSB) with durations of 45 to 50 nS. These timing signals are locked to the CF1 output from the frequency divider.

The time period generator consists of a counter and associated AND gates. The unit produces eight clock pulses, *T*0–*T*7, each lasting 200 nS. The time period generator also produces double-length pulses, each true for the duration of two clock pulses (such as *T*6*T*7). One more pulse produced is the *T*7S pulse, which is true during the last quarter of *T*7. (The use of these clock pulses by other computer circuits is discussed in Chapter 9.)

INPUT/OUTPUT CIRCUITS

7

The input/output circuits of a computer are located within the external accessory (or peripheral) units and within the computer itself. The function of these circuits is to translate the instructions and data into the computer language and from computer language into a form suitable for readout. In effect, the input/output circuits reconcile the "outer world" with the remaining computer circuits.

There are two major reasons for this reconciliation or translation. First, the outer world rarely expresses anything in digital terms, while the computer always uses some form of digital number (binary, BCD, octal, etc.). Second, the computer operates at extremely high speeds when compared to the outer world. For example, in the fraction of a second that it takes to strike a key on an input typewriter, a computer can perform hundreds or even thousands of operations.

To best use the available computer time, the information to be processed is prepared in advance and stored. Common storage forms include paper tape, punch cards, and magnetic tape. The basic relationship between the computer and the accessory devices is shown in Figure 7-1. Note that the terms **on-line** and **off-line** are used to indicate **direct** and **indirect** connection to the computer. For example, a paper-tape punch that is operated by an electric typewriter is an off-line device for indirect input to the computer. The paper-tape reader that converts holes in the paper tape into pulses applied to the computer is an on-line device for direct input. Information is put into the off-line devices by human operators. The on-line devices then automatically convert the data into pulses (or control signals) for application to the computer. On-line devices require only that the operator load the tapes or cards and turn on the unit.

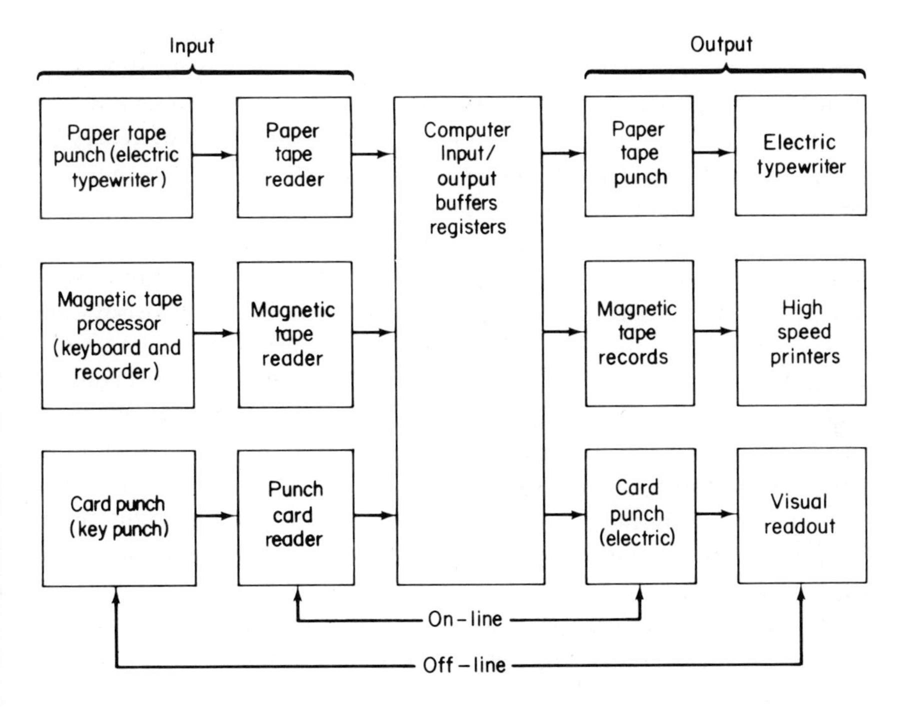

Fig. 7-1. Basic relationship between the computer and input/output accessories.

With a system such as the one shown in Figure 7-1, the computer does not have to wait for the operator to type out messages, since the computer can read directly from the punched tape, card, or magnetic tape. Large quantities of tapes or cards can be made in advance by many operators, handling different problems on separate typewriters.

The computer can look at all the tapes or cards from the appropriate reader. After processing, the computer controls the on-line tape or card punch (or magnetic-tape recorder) to store the processed data. The tapes or cards containing the processed data are then read out on output printers or typewriters (or other visual display devices).

These output readout devices are not so fast as the computer's internal circuitry. However, the devices are very fast in comparison to human operators and have a chance of keeping pace with the computer, since many internal computer calculations require repeated steps.

It should be noted that not all computer input/output sections operate as shown in Figure 7-1. Some computers operate on a **real-time** basis, where the computer stands ready to solve problems presented by the human operator. Where human operators must command a computer, a straight manual keyboard (similar to a typewriter keyboard) is the simplest form of input/output device. The commands are typed and applied directly to the computer (in the form of pulses or command signals). The processed output signals then "type out" the answers on the same keyboard.

It should also be noted that some special-purpose computers receive continuously changing inputs and produce corresponding readouts. Computers used to monitor (and control) industrial processes are an example. There are generally no off-line devices with such systems. Instead, these computers receive inputs from transducers, which convert such factors as process temperature, flow rate, and volume into electrical voltages. The voltages, which are analogs of the temperature, flow, and volume, are converted into digital form by an a/d circuit (Chapter 6, subdivision B). The automatic readout from the computer, in addition to supplying a permanent record on the keyboard, is also used to control the industrial process. At the computer output, the digital data are converted to a corresponding electrical voltage (or analog) by a d/a circuit. The output electrical voltages are then applied to control valves, switches, etc., as needed to control the industrial process.

A. THE BASIC INPUT CIRCUIT

No matter what system or input/output device is used, any computer input must (1) convert the data into a digital form that is compatible with the computer's internal circuits and (2) store the digital data until they can be entered into the computer's circuits without disrupting normal computer operation. This procedure is sometimes referred to as a **service routine**.

The conversion is done by a decoder circuit, while the storage and timing is done by a register (operated from the computer's timing or clock signals). Refer to Chapter 6, subdivisions C, D, J, and N.

A circuit illustrating the basic input to a computer is shown in Figure 7-2. It is assumed that the computer logic is in BCD form, whereas the input device (a standard on-line keyboard) produces a decimal output. (Only the number keys, 0–9, of the keyboard are shown.) When any key is pressed, the corresponding switch is closed, applying a fixed voltage (typically about 5 V) to the decoder. Note that the decoder (10-line to BCD) is shown as being within the computer. In some systems, the decoder is part of the input device or is an auxiliary unit separate from both the computer and the input device.

The BCD output of the decoder is applied to a register. This register is generally located in the computer and is often known as a *buffer register* or simply *buffer*. As in the case of other registers, the buffer consists of FFs (one for each digit handled) and gates. The state of the FFs is indicated by lights on the computer control panel. One light is provided for each FF. Generally, the FF is in the 1 when the light is on. By means of such lights (known as **interpolation lights** or **register lights**) the operator can tell the existing state of each bit in the register. The register FFs and gates are controlled by timing pulses from the computer's internal timing circuits. At time $T1$, the FFs are set to 0000. At time $T2$, the register input gates are opened. (When this occurs, the input gates are said to be *strobed* or *enabled*.) At time $T3$, the output gates are opened.

Since the register gates are opened and closed by the computer pulses, the slow speed of the input device is reconciled with the high speed of the computer. For instance, assume that timing pulses $T1$, $T2$, and $T3$ occur 10,000 times/sec and that it takes 1 second for the typewriter key to be pressed and released. No matter what time the signal (momentary voltage) from the keyboard starts and stops, the register has thousands of times to read in, store, and read out the data to the computer.

Note that the timing pulses are applied through gates and that these gates are controlled by signals from the input device and computer.

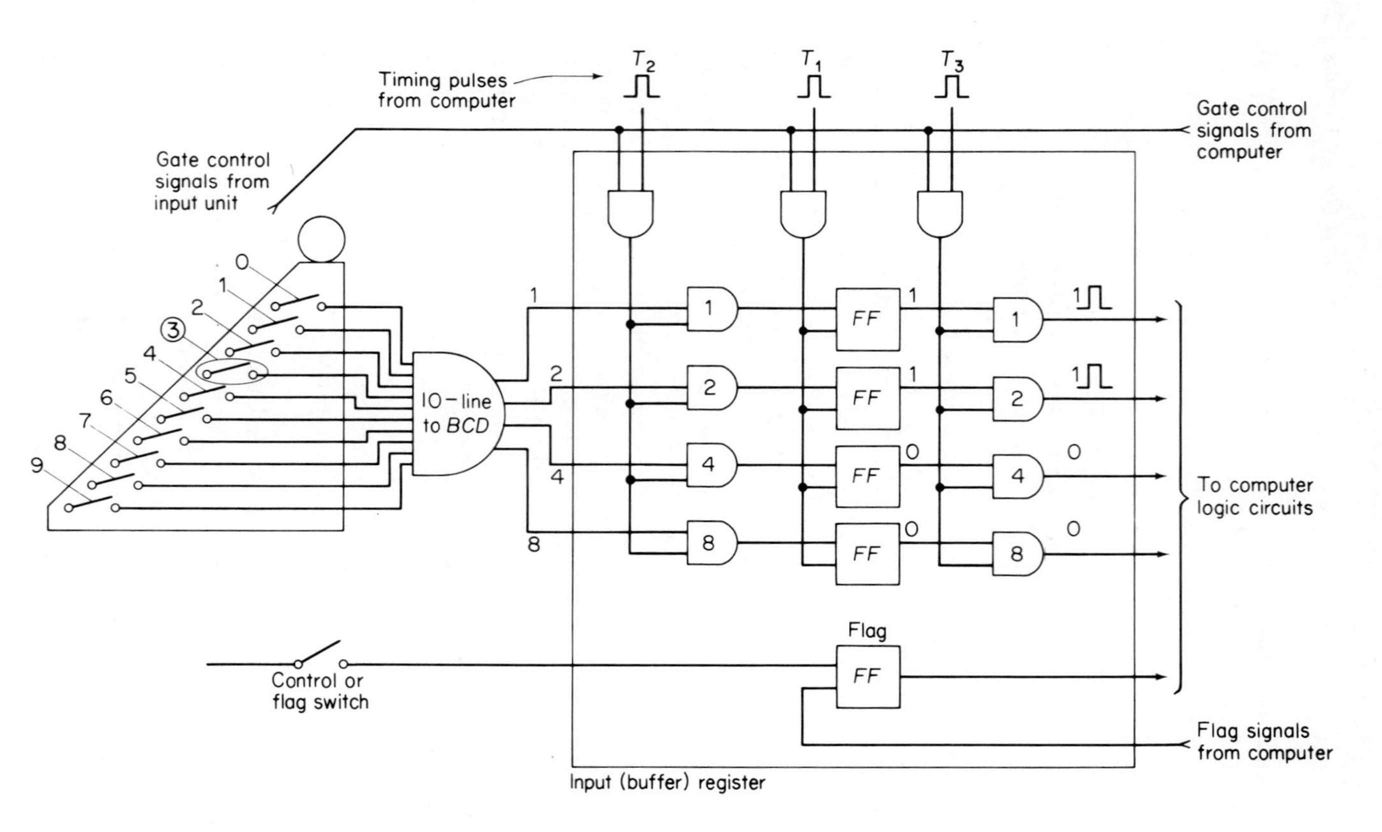

Fig. 7-2. Basic computer input circuit.

The gate signals are generally referred to as *control* or *flag* signals (or in some cases as *interrupt* commands).

The control, flag, and interrupt gates are necessary to prevent undesired conflict between the input device and the computer's internal circuits. Assume, for example, that the computer is performing a series of mathematical calculations on data previously entered by the keyboard and that the operator starts to enter more data. In the normal sequence, a control or flag signal is sent to the flag FF in the register, setting it to a 1. This indicates to the computer logic circuits that there is new information to be entered in the buffer. If the old information in the buffer has been read out into the computer, then pulse *T*1 sets the FFs to 0000; pulse *T*2 opens the input gates, allowing the FFs to be set to the new value; and pulse *T*3 opens the output gates, allowing the new value to be read out into the computer circuits. Generally, there is an indicator on the input device and/or computer console to show that the flag FF is set and that the computer is accepting new data.

Now assume that the computer is not ready to accept new information (previous data are still being processed). Then the timing pulse control gates remain closed, preventing data from entering or leaving the register, as well as preventing the existing data (FF settings) from being set to 0 (by *T*1).

Keep in mind that since the computer operates at such a high speed, the operator does not usually have to "wait" until the computer is finished before he can strike the next key (although this can happen).

Note in Figure 7-2 that key number 3 (decimal 3) is closed. This applies a voltage to the 3 input of the decoder, making the 1 and 2 output lines of the decoder true (with the 4 and 8 output lines false). Input gates 1 and 2 are opened (at time *T*2), and FFs 1 and 2 are set to 1 (with FFs 4 and 8 remaining at 0). Output gates 1 and 2 are opened (at time *T*3), producing pulses (or 1s) on lines 1 and 2 to the computer, with no pulses (or 0s) at lines 4 and 8. Thus the decimal 3 is entered into the computer as two pulses representing a binary 3 (0011).

Also note that the input voltages to the decoder could come from a paper tape or punch-card reader or from tracks on a magnetic-tape reader. The source of the input voltages is of no consequence to the computer input. Of course, the voltages must be of the correct level and duration. Likewise, the input voltages must be applied in a decimal format if the decimal-to-BCD decoder of Figure 7-2 is used.

B. THE BASIC OUTPUT CIRCUIT

Computer output circuits are essentially the reverse of input circuits. The output circuits must (1) convert the processed data into a form (usually decimal or alphanumeric) that is compatible with the readout device and (2) synchronize the high-speed computer output with that of the lower-speed readout device.

As in the case of input, the conversion is done by a decoder (or encoder) circuit, while the synchronization is done by registers and the computer timing circuits.

A circuit illustrating the basic output from a computer is shown in Figure 7-3. Again, the computer logic is in BCD form, whereas the output device (keyboard) operates in decimal form. Only the number key (3) of the keyboard is shown. In the readout mode, the keys are operated by solenoids, which receive voltage from the decoder (BCD to decimal). When the buffer register output gates are opened, a voltage is produced on one of the ten lines from the decoder. This voltage is applied to the corresponding solenoid and causes the appropriate key to strike.

In the normal sequence, a control or flag signal is sent to the flag FF, setting it to a 1. This indicates to the computer that the readout device (keyboard) is ready to receive data from the output buffer. If there is information (from the computer processing circuits) at the input of the buffer, pulse $T1$ sets the buffer FFs to 0000; pulse $T2$ opens the input gates, allowing the FFs to be set to the new value; and pulse $T3$ opens the output gates, allowing the value to be applied to the keyboard (through the decoder).

It is obvious that the computer can solve problems faster than the keyboard can type them out. This means that two conditions must occur. First, the output register must be held in the existing state long enough for the key to be struck. Second, the normal routine of the computer must be interrupted so that the answers to several problems are not computed while the output buffer is held open. In actual practice, the interruption occurs at some convenient point in the computer operation (usually at the end of a timing cycle). The subject of control, flag, and interrupt commands for input/output systems is discussed throughout Chapter 9.

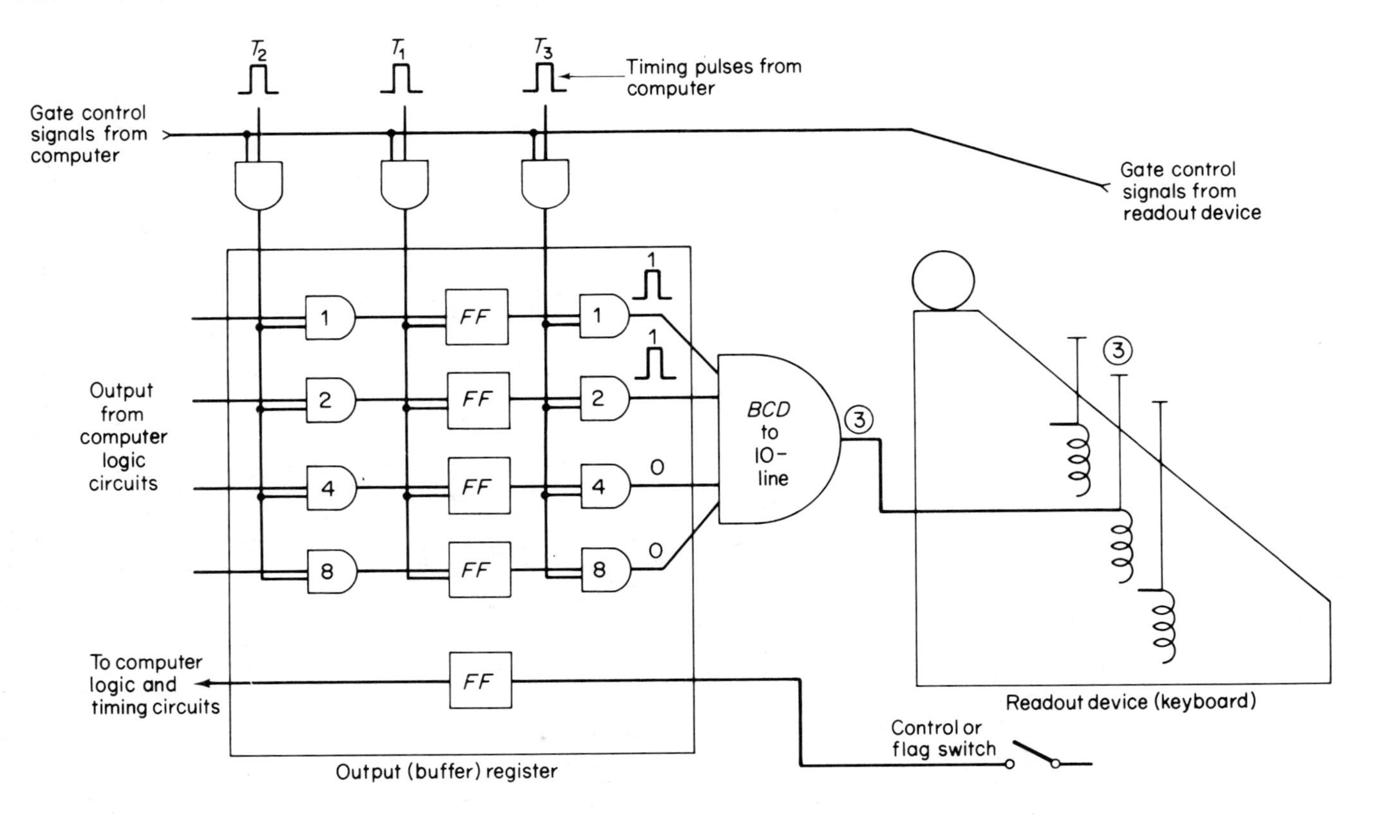

Fig. 7-3. Basic computer output circuit.

C. MAGNETIC-TAPE, DRUM, AND DISC INPUT/OUTPUT CIRCUITS

Magnetic-tape recorders, as well as magnetic-drum and -disc units, are often used as computer input/output devices. However, these units are also storage devices, and their operation is closely associated with that of the computer's internal storage or memory units. For this reason, the operation of magnetic tape, drums, and discs is covered in Chapter 8, along with other storage or memory devices.

D. PAPER-TAPE INPUT/OUTPUT CIRCUITS

A paper-tape reader provides direct input to a computer by reading prepunched data in paper (or thin metallic) tape. The reader also provides output from a computer by punching output information in the paper. Generally, paper tape is used in systems where information is received over wire communication circuits and in scientific applications involving limited input and output.

Recording on paper tape is done by machines that punch data by a direct connection to a typewriter or a keypunch. Other machines are used to transmit data punched into paper tape over telephone or telegraph lines in order to produce a duplicate tape at the other end of the line, where the newly punched paper tape can be used for further processing. Information stored on paper tape is recorded in patterns of round punched holes, located in parallel tracks (or channels) along the length of the tape. A character is represented by a combination of punches across the width of the tape. Paper tapes vary according to the number of channels they contain. Most paper tapes have either five or eight channels, as illustrated in Figure 7-4.

Paper-tape systems are ideally suited to the binary (or two-state) digital logic used in computers, since the basic indication of paper tape is either "hole" or "no hole." Two methods of sensing the digits are shown in Figure 7-4.

In the system of Figure 7-4A, wire brushes complete a circuit through the tape holes to a metal plate underneath the tape. As the tape is drawn across the plate, the brushes either complete the circuit through a hole (producing an output pulse across the load resistor)

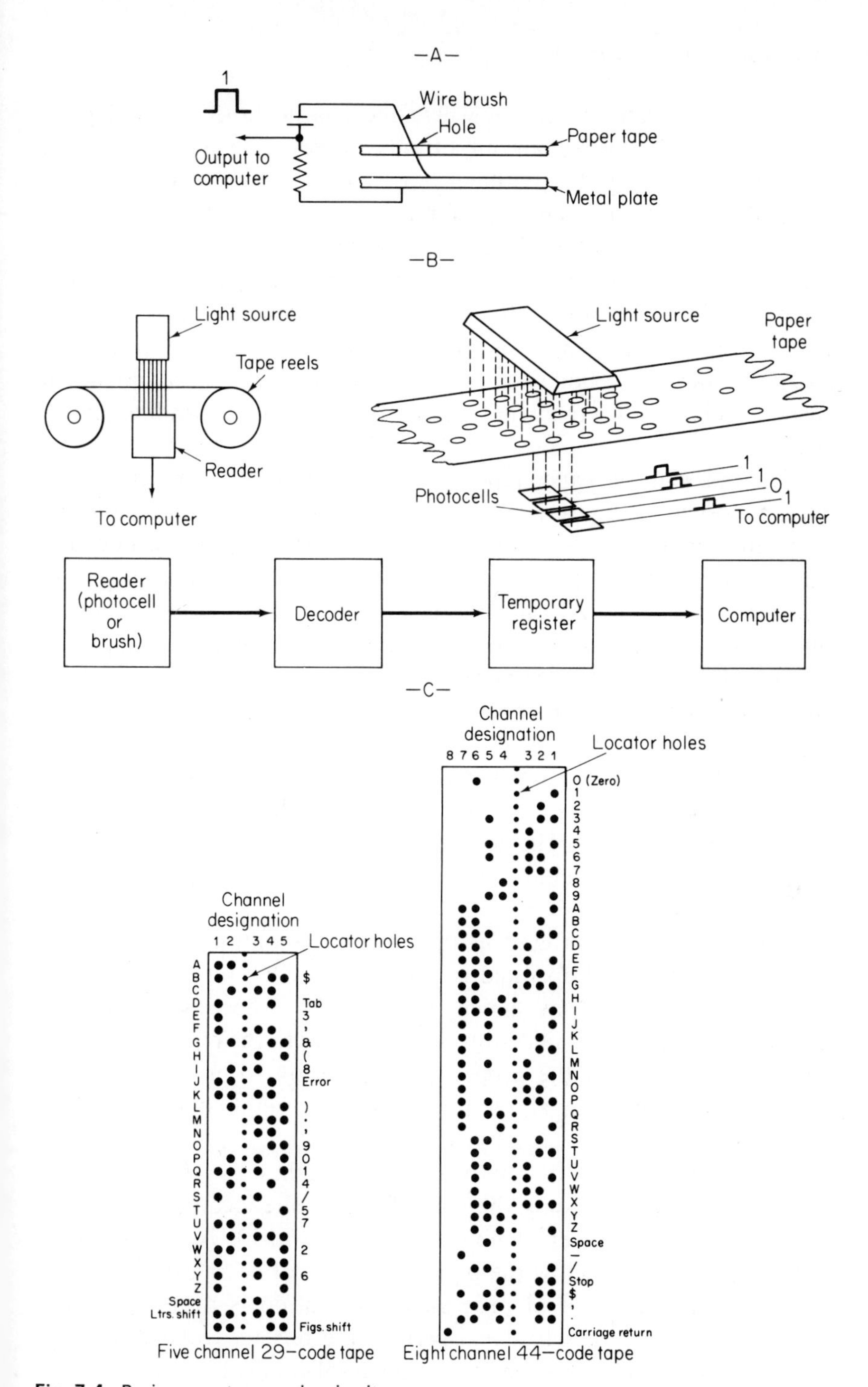

Fig. 7-4. Basic paper-tape reader circuits.

or fail to complete the circuit where there is no hole (producing no output pulse). Generally, an output pulse (hole) represents a binary 1, whereas no output pulse (no hole) represents a 0. Note that one brush is used for each track or channel of holes.

In the system of Figure 7-4B, a light source is placed on one side of the paper tape, while photocells are located on the opposite side of the tape. One photocell is used for each track or channel of holes. As the tape moves, the light strikes a photocell wherever there is a hole, producing an output or binary 1. No output (binary 0) is produced when there is no hole, since the light cannot pass to the corresponding photocell.

The holes in the paper tape can be located only at predetermined sites, as shown in Figure 7-4C. Each set of holes across the tape represents one character. A series of characters makes up a word. Location holes guide the tape through the reader and hold the tape in proper position for reading. At each character, the tape is stopped momentarily for reading, after which the character is stored in a temporary register. The use of this temporary register between the reader and the computer's input buffer compensates for the difference in speeds of the reader and computer.

No matter what paper-tape coding (five- or eight-channel) is used, a decoder network is required between the reader and the computer, as shown in Figure 7-4. The decoder converts the five- or eight-channel output into a format suitable for the computer's logic system (binary, BCD, octal, etc.).

When paper tape is used at the computer's output, the holes are produced by solenoid-operated metal punches. One punch is used for each track or channel, as shown in Figure 7-5. The output from the computer's register is applied through a decoder to the punch solenoids. The decoder converts the processed information from computer language (binary, BCD, octal, etc.) into a five- or eight-channel code, as applicable.

The paper tape is driven below the punches by the same gear mechanism used in reading the tape. There is one locator hole on the tape for each frame (set of holes across the width). As the frame is pulled into position below the punches, a control or flag signal is sent to the register. If a set of processed information is available in the computer register, the flag signal permits the register to be strobed so that the information is passed to the punch solenoids. If no information

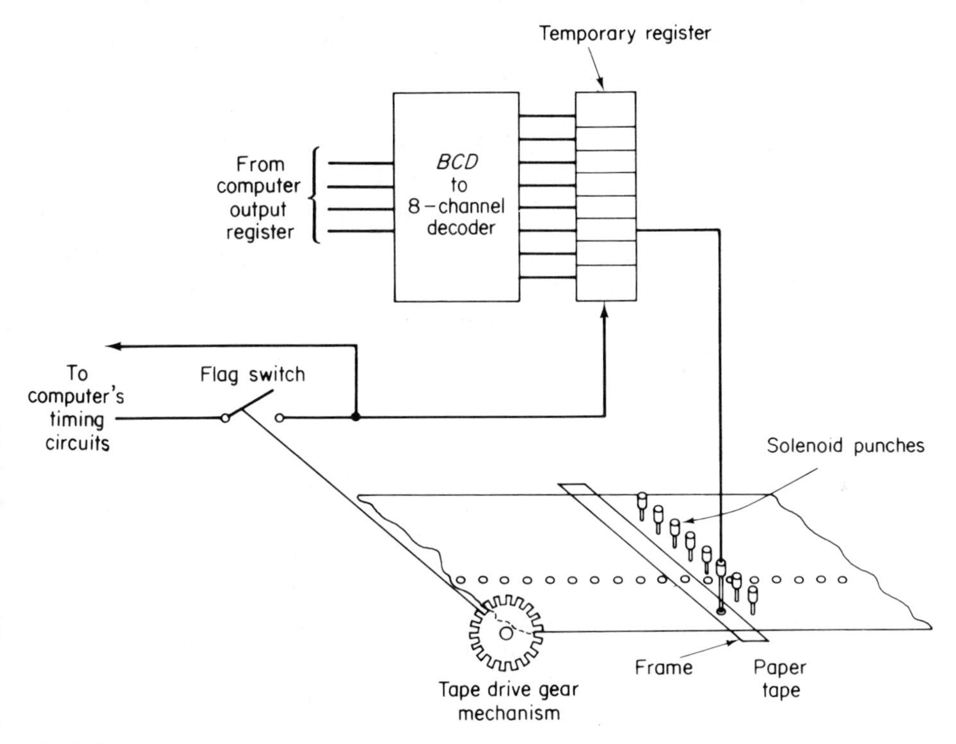

Fig. 7-5. Basic paper-tape punch circuits.

is available at the register, the tape drive is stopped until new information is available. Thus the output of the computer is synchronized with the timing of the tape punch. Of course, under normal circumstances, the computer will produce outputs faster than can be punched by the tape unit. For this reason, a temporary storage register is often used between the computer register and the tape unit.

E. PUNCH-CARD INPUT/OUTPUT CIRCUITS

Punch-card data systems were in use many years before the digital computer was invented. These early punch-card systems were essentially electromechanical, using relays instead of solid-state gates. The systems were capable of punching data into the cards, sorting or rearranging the cards in any desired sequence, and reading the data out (usually on a typewriter or some form of printer).

The punch-card readers used with computers are essentially the same as the original units, except that the output is translated into computer language, and the input register of the computer is synchronized with the timing of the card reader.

Information stored on punch cards is recorded in patterns of rectangular punched holes, located in rows and columns on the card. Figure 7-6 shows the standard arrangement for a typical IBM punch card. (There are other formats for punch cards. However, the patterns shown in Figure 7-6 are in common use.)

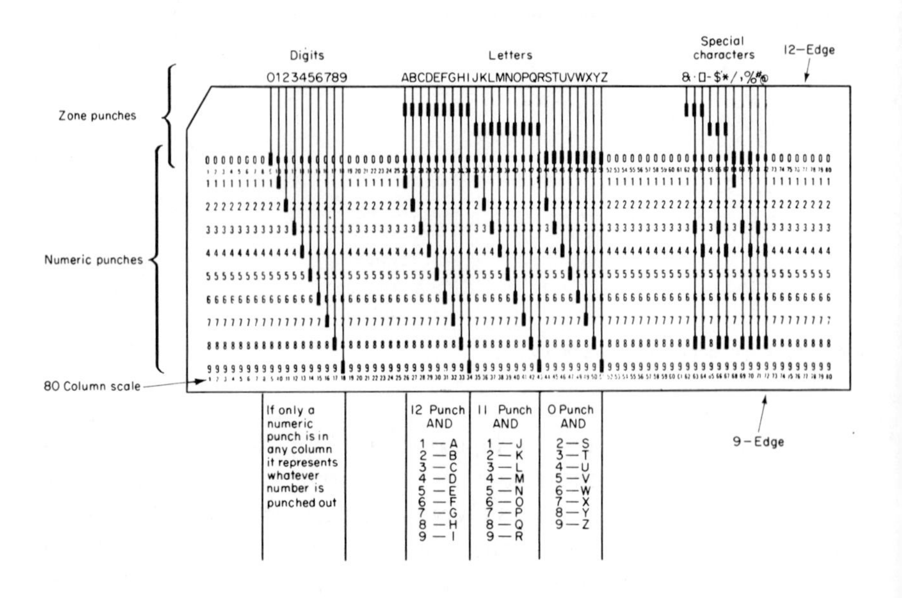

Fig. 7-6. Typical IBM punch card. (Courtesy of International Business Machines.)

As shown, there are 80 columns and 12 rows. (The two rows above the 0 row are considered as the 11 and 12 rows, respectively.) A character is represented by a combination of punches in any one column. For example, the letter L is represented by punches in the 11 and 3 rows of any one column.

As in the case of paper-tape systems, the reading process is done in one of two ways: (1) via the brush-type reader or (2) with the photoelectric reader. These methods are illustrated in Figure 7-7. With the brush method, a reading brush on the top of a card makes contact

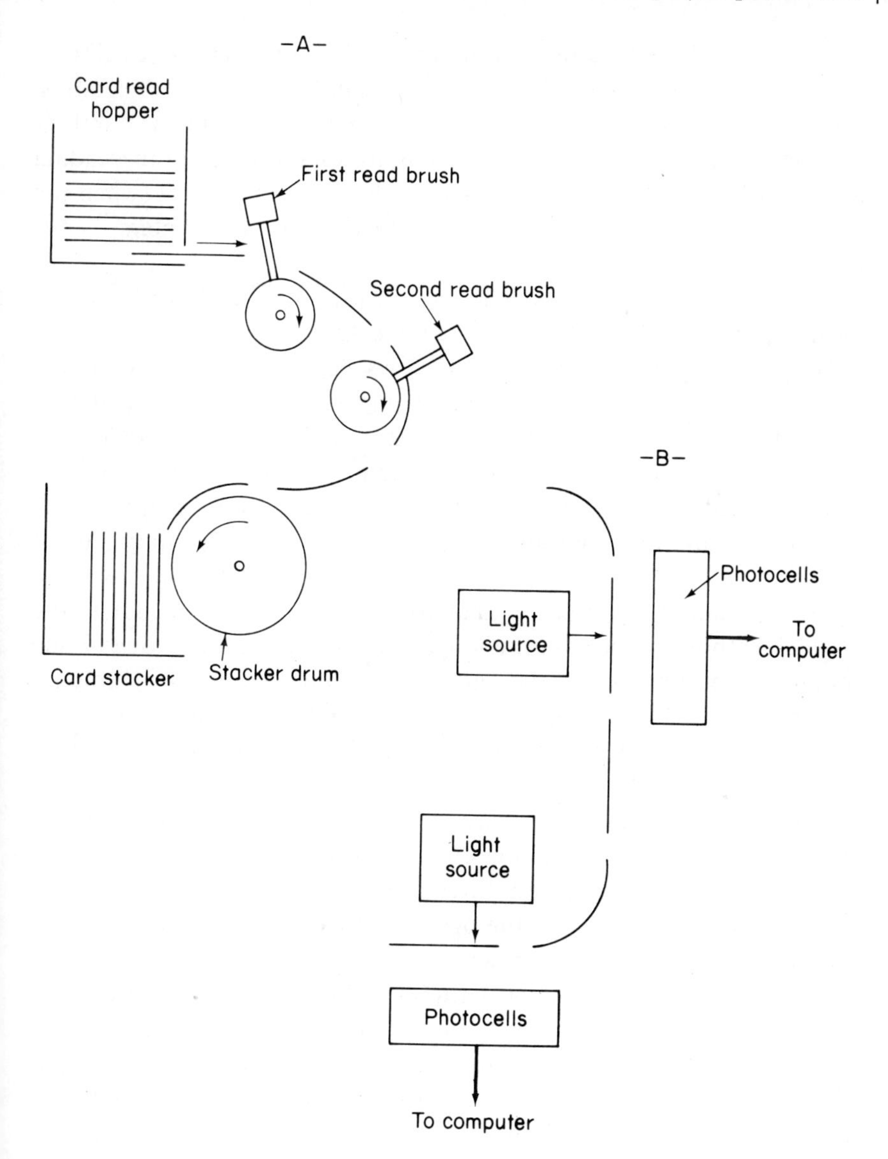

Fig. 7-7. Basic punch-card reading methods.

with a roller beneath the card every time a hole is detected (producing an output pulse). In the brushless method, a light source is placed on one side of the card, while photocells are located on the opposite side. Holes in the card allow the light to shine through them, thus producing an output.

Punch cards can be read in either serial or parallel modes. Either way, one column is required for each character. Any number of columns (up to 80 per card) can be used to make up words, groups of numbers or symbols, etc. The serial method is a column-by-column reading (columns 1–80); the parallel method reads either rows 12–9 (when the card enters 12-edge first), or rows 9–12 (when the card enters 9-edge first).

With the parallel method, the entire card must be read before any meaning can be realized from any of the columns. That is, there are no distinguishing punches until all the rows have been read. A hole is judged to be part of a particular character, based upon the hole's distance from the leading edge of the card and the amount of time it takes the reading brushes to reach that hole. Assuming a constant card-reading speed, the holes in the 0 row, for instance, are read at 0 time (0 being a prescribed amount of time away from the leading edge of the card).

Serial reading has been popular for several years, even though the parallel method has been in use longer. It is more practical to read one column at a time, since the information punched in each column is a complete character. Serial reading more nearly resembles the read-out methods for paper tape (and magnetic tape, described in Chapter 8).

No matter what system is used, a card reader usually has a built-in device (or set of error-detecting circuits) to discontinue reading when an invalid character is sensed. Should an invalid character occur, say owing to an unwanted hole, the operator must check the tape of error and correct it before any further reading can be done. For example, there is no valid character that requires a simultaneous punch in rows 7 and 8. An AND gate can be used to detect this error. The output of the 7 and 8 rows are connected to the AND gate input, with the output of the AND gate connected to an alarm indicator. If there are holes at rows 7 and 8 in any one column, the AND gate receives two true inputs and produces an output to the alarm system.

Output card punching is done by a set of punches that make holes in corresponding locations on the card, depending on information received by the punches. Generally, the punches are solenoid-operated. However, some off-line units use mechanical punches.

A typical output card punch arrangement is shown in Figure 7-8. The output from the computer's register is applied through a decoder

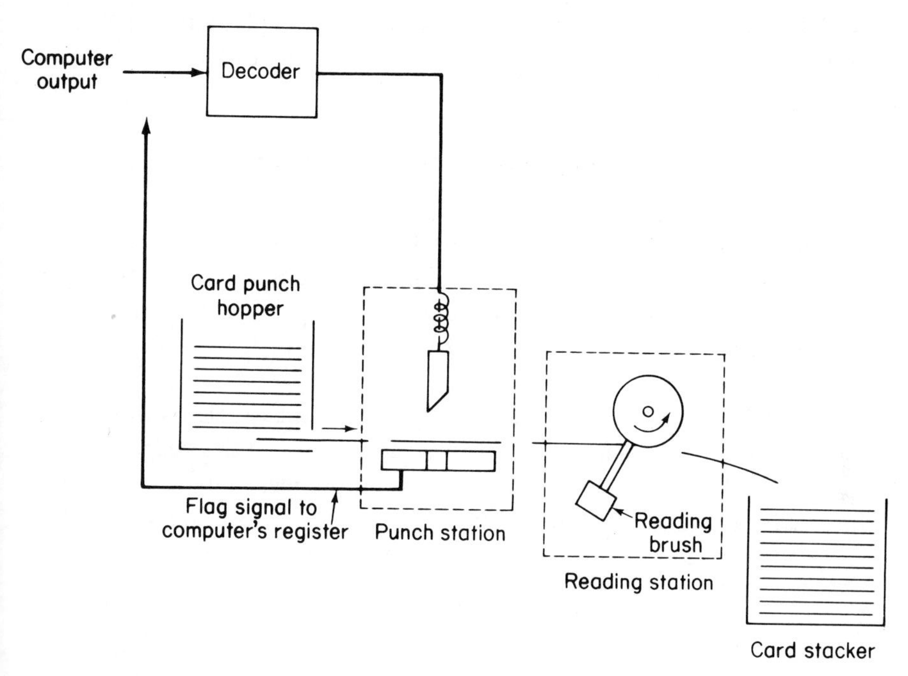

Fig. 7-8. Basic card punch circuits.

to the punch solenoids. The decoder converts the processed information from computer language into a corresponding card code. Punching, like reading, can be either serial or parallel. The card punch moves blank cards (one card at a time) from the hopper to the punches, which punch according to the pulses received from the computer memory. If a set of processed information is available in the computer register, the flag signal permits the register to be strobed so that the information is passed to the punch solenoids. If no information is available at the register, the card unit stops until new information is available. Thus the output of the computer is synchronized with the timing of the card unit. Even high-speed card punches operate at a limited speed, a feature that restricts the effectiveness of punching a card as output compared to the use of other devices.

Once the holes are punched, the columns are read at a reading station (brush type, in this case) to check on the accuracy of the punched data (invalid characters, parity check, etc.). If no errors are detected, the punched card is ejected into its designated pocket in the card stacker. Depending on the make and type of equipment used, some card punch devices are integrated as a part of the card reader.

F. VISUAL DISPLAY (CRT) INPUT/OUTPUT DEVICES

The cathode-ray-tube (CRT) visual display unit is often used as an input/output device, particularly in inquiry/response situations where information is required for immediate use. Unless the CRT unit is attached to a printing device, no permanent record of displayed data is kept.

As shown in Figure 7-9, the visual display unit is essentially a cathode-ray tube (complete with vertical and horizontal sweep circuits, similar to those used in TV sets and oscilloscopes) plus a keyboard. Information is displayed on the face of the CRT immediately after it is received from the computer or entered from the keyboard.

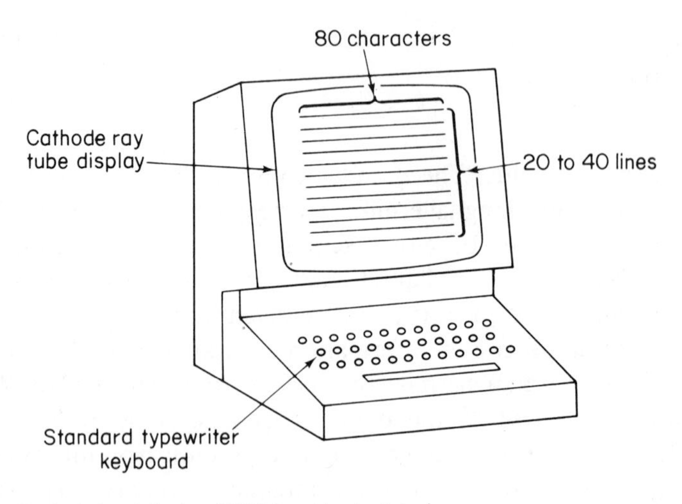

Fig. 7-9. Typical visual display (CRT) input/output device.

The input function is accomplished by the keyboard in a manner similar to that described for the basic input circuit (subdivision A of this chapter). The output function is performed by the CRT. The horizontal and vertical sweep deflection circuits of the CRT are standard. The electron beam is swept across the CRT face several hundred (or thousand) times per second. Typically, the deflecting circuits sweep out 20 to 40 rows or horizontal lines of alphanumeric characters, with each line devided into 80 spaces (for 80 characters).

There are many systems used to produce the characters. Figure 7-10 shows one method. Here, the characters are produced by modulating the CRT electron beam intensity with timing pulses that occur at precise intervals as the beam passes a given point on the CRT face. With this system, the timing of the pulses is controlled by outputs from the decoders.

The relationship of timing pulses to the horizontal and vertical deflection voltages is synchronized by master timing pulses. In the example shown, two vertical sweeps are required for each character. Thus, to produce 80 characters across one line, the master pulses must trigger 160 vertical sweeps for each horizontal sweep.

The master pulses are applied to a gate that is controlled (to modulate the electron beam) by operation of the decoders. In turn, the decoders receive input from the computer's output register. In the absence of output from the decoders, no pulses pass to the CRT, the screen is blanked, and no characters appear, even though the vertical and horizontal deflection voltages are available. When there is information at the computer's output registers, this output is applied to the decoders, unblanking the screen at appropriate points on the vertical and horizontal sweeps.

The relationships of the vertical and horizontal deflection voltages, together with the blanking and unblanking (modulation), are shown in Figure 7-10C. The heavy lines on the vertical and horizontal sweeps indicate when the CRT is unblanked and producing a character (the numeral 8 in this case). For example, to form the upper-right-hand side of the numeral 8 (arbitrarily labeled as time interval 1) the upper vertical deflection plate goes negative, causing the beam to move down. During the same time interval 1, the right-hand horizontal plate also goes slightly negative, causing the beam to move slightly to the left. The beam is unblanked during time interval 1, so the upper-right-hand portion of the 8 is traced out.

The remaining segments of the numeral 8 can be traced out by comparing the status of the horizontal and vertical sweep voltages and the blanking condition for all time intervals during a complete character cycle (two vertical sweeps). Note that neither the vertical nor the horizontal sweeps are perfectly linear.

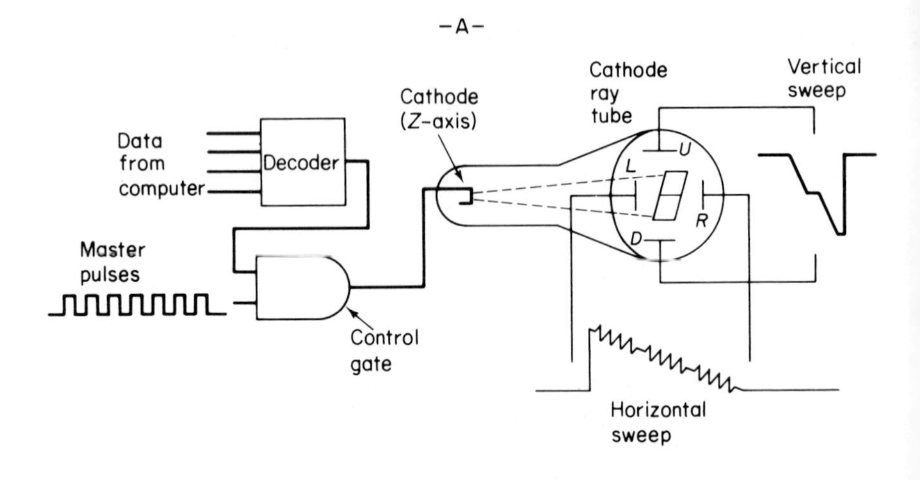

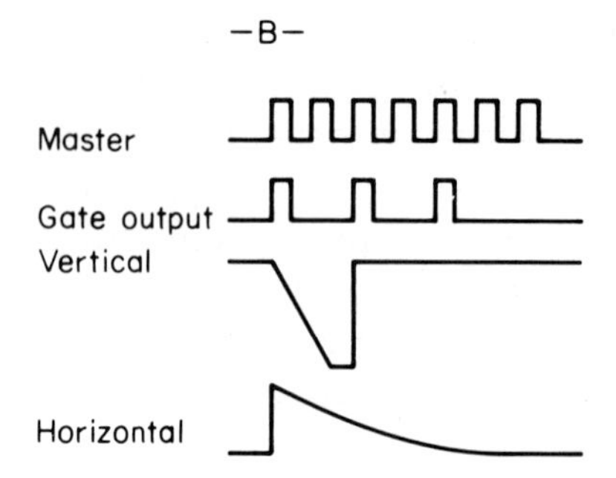

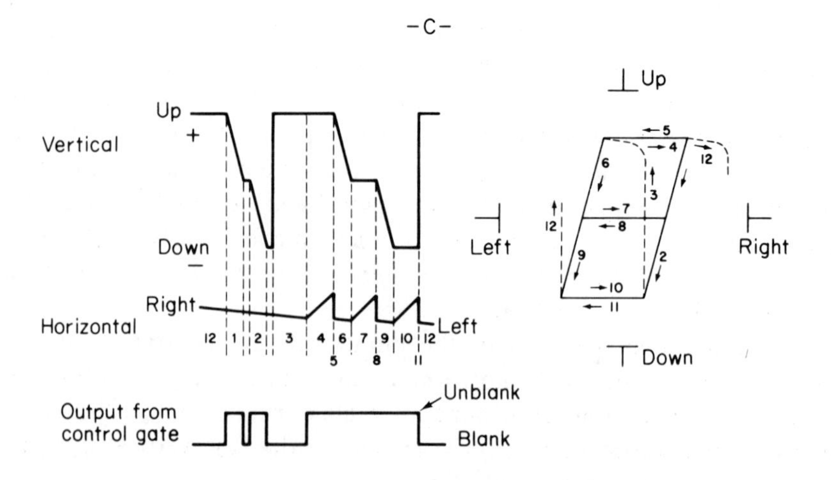

Fig. 7-10. How visual display is formed.

In all systems, the persistence of the CRT screen is fairly short. This is necessary so that the readout is removed in a reasonable period of time (to permit new information to be read in). Some visual display units contain storage registers that permit the displayed data to be retained on the screen until the operator clears the readout.

G. MAGNETIC INK CHARACTER RECOGNITION INPUT DEVICES

Magnetic ink character recognition (MICR) devices have been used in the banking industry for many years. These devices read the characters at the bottom of checks (account numbers and the like). In most cases, when MICR devices are used with computers, the output of the MICR unit is recorded on punch cards, paper tape, or magnetic tape. The recorded information is then read into the computer for processing in the normal manner. However, there are MICR readers that can be connected directly to the computer's input register.

No matter what recording system is used, the reading process is fairly standard. The reader consists of a transport unit, a scanning unit, and a recognition unit, as shown in Figure 7-11. The scanning unit is essentially a set of magnetic heads. As the check passes the scanner, the fixed head magnetizes the ink used to print the characters at the bottom of the check. (The ink contains a magnetic material similar to that used in magnetic tape.) The check then passes the read head. Some units use a single read head, while other readers have multiple heads.

A multihead system is shown in Figure 7-11. Each element of the read head is connected to a FF. The output of the FFs is fed to a decoder for conversion to the computer logic code. The FFs are placed in a condition to be set as each character passes the center of the read head. Movement of the check past the read head induces a voltage in the head elements. Only those head elements across from the magnetized ink characters produce voltages sufficient to set the FFs. Thus some FFs are set to 1, while others remain at 0, depending on the character. The combinations of 1 and 0 are converted to a corresponding code by the decoder matrix.

Not all magnetic readers use the system described here. In some systems, characters are recognized by density and polarity of the magnetic field. For example, the horizontal portion of a character

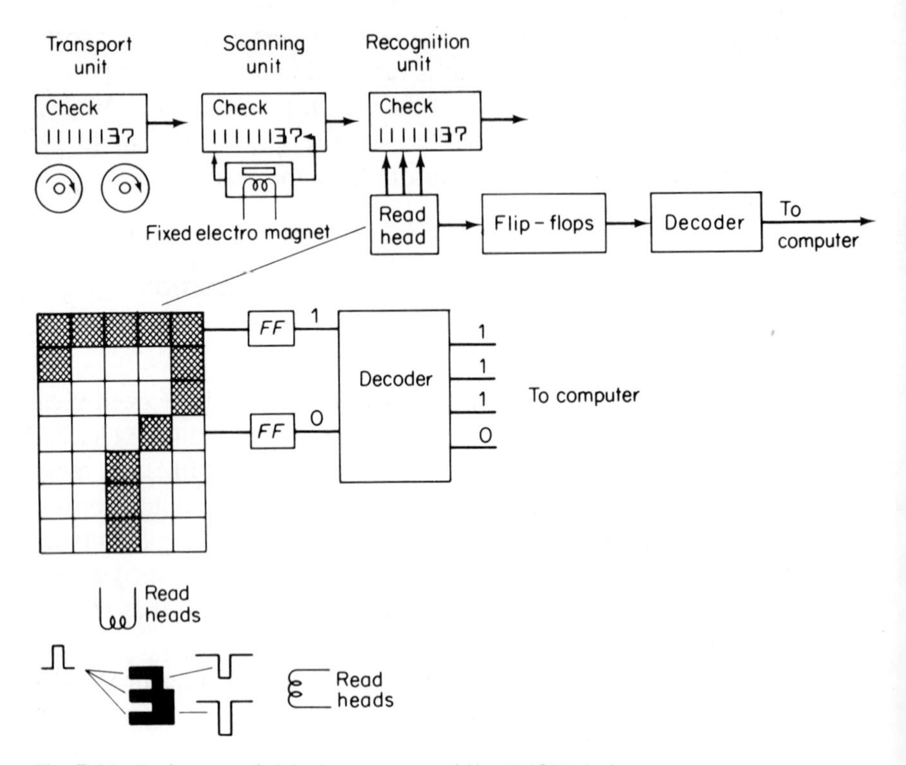

Fig. 7-11. Basic magnetic ink character recognition (MICR) devices.

induces a voltage of different polarity than the vertical portion. Likewise, a wide portion of the character (such as the lower-right-hand portion of the numeral 3 shown) produces a greater voltage than the narrower portions. These differences in polarity and amplitude are compared with fixed values in the decoder, which produces an output code compatible with the computer's input register.

H. OPTICAL CHARACTER RECOGNITION INPUT DEVICES

Optical character recognition (OCR) devices have been in general use since the 1950s. OCR devices read standard characters (both letters and numbers) on printed documents. There are many types of OCR units. Three generalized classes include

1. *Journal tape readers*, designed to read paper tapes such as those used in cash registers or adding machines.
2. *Document readers*, capable of reading a maximum of three lines of information on a document, regardless of the size of the document.
3. *Page reader*, capable of reading multiple lines of typed or printed matter from a normal page layout (typically $8\frac{1}{2}$ by 11 in.).

OCR units are further divided into the classification of type faces (or type fonts, as they are known) that can be read. Four generalized classes include

1. *Bar code readers*, which read a given numeric character printed on paper by a special keyboard imprinter or by an embossing process.
2. *Mark sense readers*, which read pencil marks placed in predetermined positions on a paper document.
3. *Stylized font readers*, which read one or more type faces specifically designed for both machine and human legibility.
4. *Generalized font readers*, which read several standard typewriter or printed fonts (both upper- and lowercase), as well as some hand-printed letters and numbers. Unlike the stylized font reader, the generalized font reader eliminates the need for equipment to produce the specially designed stylized font on input forms.

As in the case of magnetic ink input units, OCR devices used with computers usually record information on punch cards, paper tape, or magnetic tape. The recorded information is then read into the computer by corresponding read-in units. The output of some OCR devices can be fed directly to the computer.

There are many OCR systems. All have some characteristics in common. The reader consists of a transport unit, a scanning unit, and a recognition unit, as shown in Figure 7-12. With the particular reader system shown, the scanning unit consists of a light source and multiple photocells arranged in a matrix. The photocell outputs are connected to FFs, which are placed in a condition to be set at each character. As the document passes the photocell matrix or vice versa, the corresponding photocells produce pulses that set FFs in the recognition unit. Only those photocells across from the character produce sufficient voltage

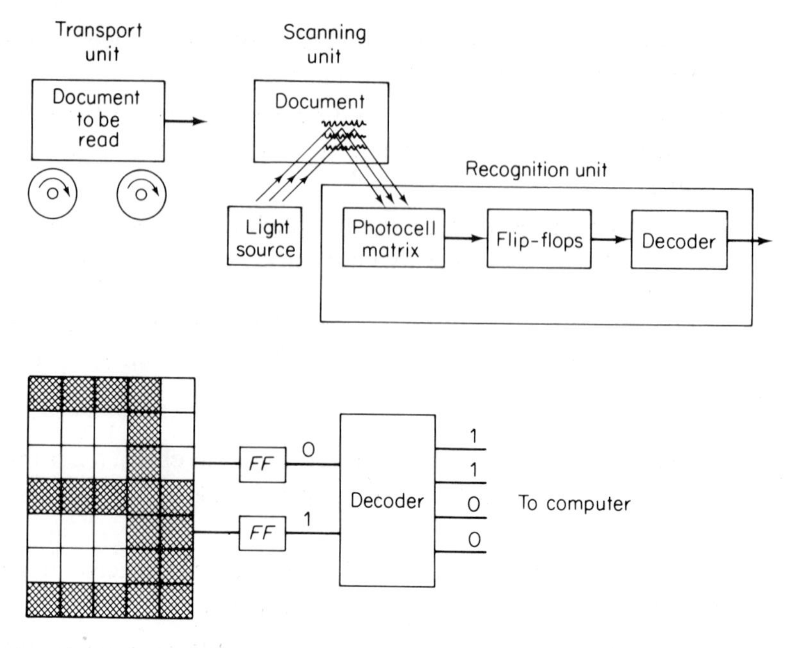

Fig. 7-12. Basic optical character recognition (OCR) devices.

to set the FFs. Thus some FFs are set to 1, while others remain at 0, depending on the character. The combinations of 1 and 0 are converted to a corresponding computer code by the decoder.

I. OUTPUT PRINTERS

When there is a limited amount of information to be read out of a computer, the standard electric typewriter is the most convenient and in most common use. Such printers are knowns as console, message, or supervisory printers. Long rolls of paper are put into the typewriter carriage to record both the entry of data (by the operator at the keyboard) and the readout of processed data (as described in subdivisions A and B of this chapter).

When high-speed readout is required or a large quantity of information is to be read out, various forms of printers are used. Note that many of these printers were used with electromechanical data-processing equipment long before digital computers were invented. With a standard typewriter, only one letter can be typed at a time. Likewise, the up and down movement of type bars in a typewriter is far too slow for computers. Output printers overcome these problems.

There are two basic types of printers:

1. *Line-at-a-time printers*, which print all characters on a given line simultaneously.
2. *Character-at-a-time printers*, which print each character serially, a position at a time, similar to the way a typewriter prints (but at much higher speeds).

No matter what printer is used, the printer receives signals from a decoder, which converts data from the computer into a form that is compatible with the printer. Output of the computer's register is synchronized with operation of the printer to overcome the difference in operating speeds (between the computer and the printer). These problems are discussed in subdivision B of this chapter.

1. Line-at-a-Time Printers

The *bar* or *gang printer* prints one line at a time by means of solenoid-operated hammers and type bars. As shown in Figure 7-13, the type bars are positioned side by side, with one type bar for each print position across the line. The number of print positions varies but is

Fig. 7-13. Basic bar printer.

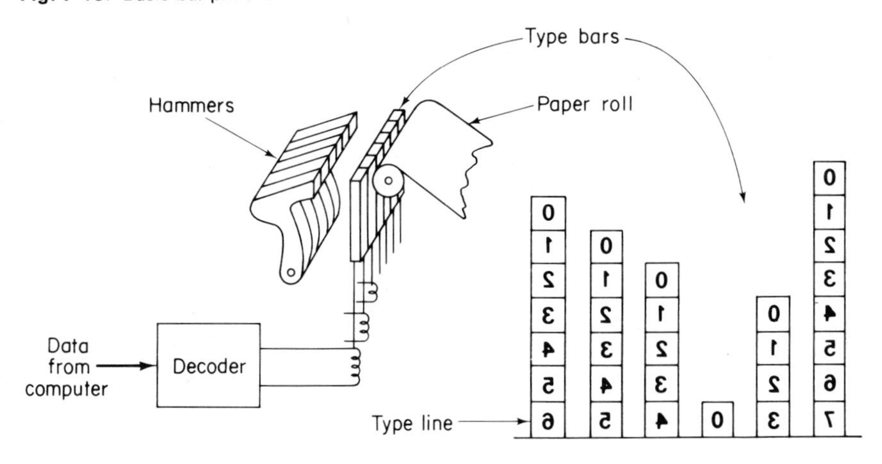

usually about 80, making one line of type comparable with a standard typewriter line (80 characters). In the example shown in Figure 7-13, there are six type bars, each with the numbers 0–9, raised to the proper position for the desired number (730456 in this example).
All bars are struck simultaneously by the hammers. Positioning of the bars is determined by output from the decoder. Note that the numbers on the type bars are backward so that they will print correctly.

A typical bar printer has a rated speed of about 150 lines/min for straight number printing and about 100 lines/min for alphanumeric readouts.

The *wheel printer* is an improvement over the bar printer. As shown in Figure 7-14, the numbers and letters are placed around the circumference of a wheel. This wheel can be spun much faster than a bar and need not reverse direction at the end of each stroke. A number of

Fig. 7-14. Basic wheel printer.

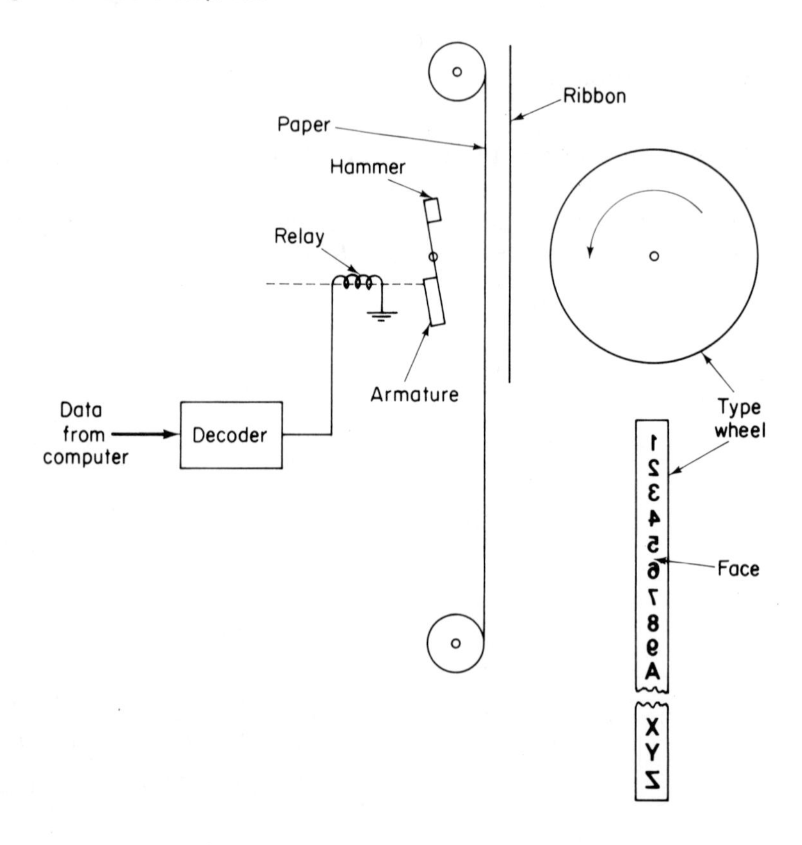

wheels are mounted side by side (for example, 80 wheels in a row), enabling a number of characters to be printed simultaneously. All wheels spin in one direction. When the proper characters are in place, as determined by outputs from the decoder, a signal input to the relay draws the armature, causing the corresponding hammers to strike and print. Even though the wheels spin very rapidly, the hammers strike and lift even faster, and the wheels need not be stopped when struck.

The wheel printer has a rated speed of about 150 lines/min for alphanumeric readouts.

A *drum printer* uses a solid cylindrical drum, around which characters are embossed, as shown in Figure 7-15. The drum rotates at a constant speed. As the A row passes the line to be printed, hammers behind the paper strike the paper against the drum, causing one or more As to be printed. As the B row moves into place, any print position requiring the letter B is printed in the same manner. One complete revolution of the drum is required to print each line. Drum-printer speeds range from 700 to 1600 lines/min.

A *chain printer* consists of a series of "links" arranged side by side, as shown in Figure 7-16. Each link contains a letter or number. Several sets of adjacent links contain the complete alphabet, numbers 0–9, and assorted symbols (such as the dollar sign and the like). The printer of Figure 7-16 contains seven sets of 50 characters each. The chain

Fig. 7-15. Basic drum printer.

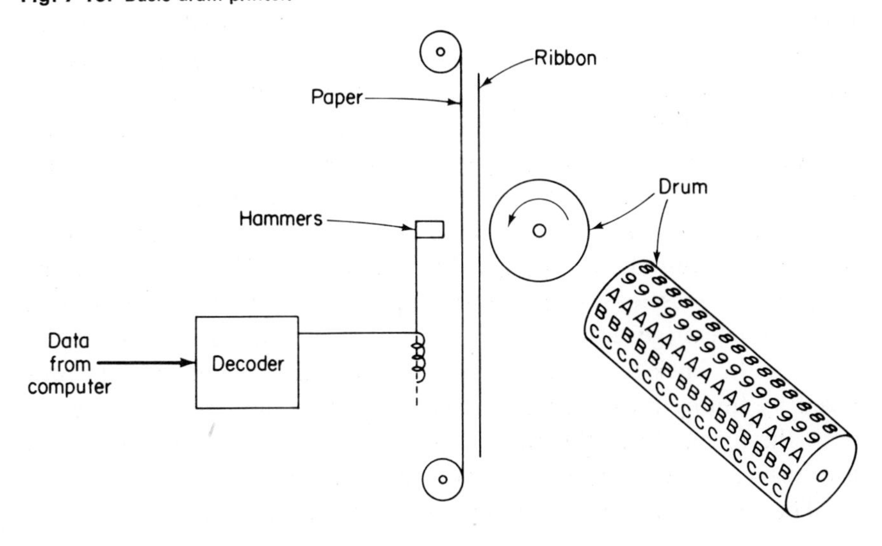

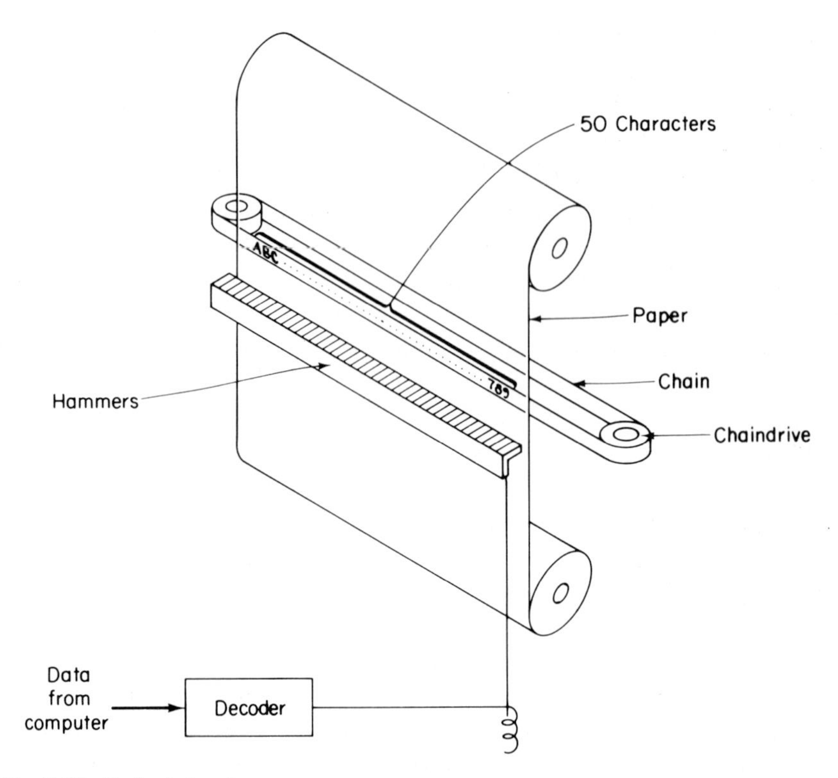

Fig. 7-16. Basic chain printer.

is mounted horizontally and revolves at a constant speed. While rotating, hammers behind the paper are timed (by the decoder matrix) to select the desired characters and strike the back of the paper to force it against the designated character. Inked ribbon between the character and the form leaves an imprint of the selected character. Chain-printer speed is generally about 1000 lines/min but can go higher.

A *comb printer* is used where a relatively simple, inexpensive printout is required but high speed is not essential. Comb-printer speed is rarely in excess of 150 lines/min. Only one set of characters is used. The characters (generally about 50 total) are mounted on a solid bar, which slides back and forth in front of the paper. Hammers, synchronized by timing pulses from the decoder, strike the desired characters onto the form. When the bar has passed over the width of the paper, it returns to a home position to print another line.

The *electrostatic printer* is the fastest method of printing, since it is limited only by the speed at which paper can be moved. The printing process involves placing electrostatic "spots" on a special paper that holds the charge. The spots are assembled to form characters. The paper then moves through a powdered ink bath, which clings to the paper wherever a character has been placed. The ink is then melted in a high-temperature area. Electrostatic-printer speed is on the order of 2000 to 5000 lines/min.

2. Character-at-a-Time Printers

The *teletype printer* prints one character at a time in a manner similar to that of an electric typewriter. However, all the type is placed on a

Fig. 7-17. Basic matrix printer (wire printer).

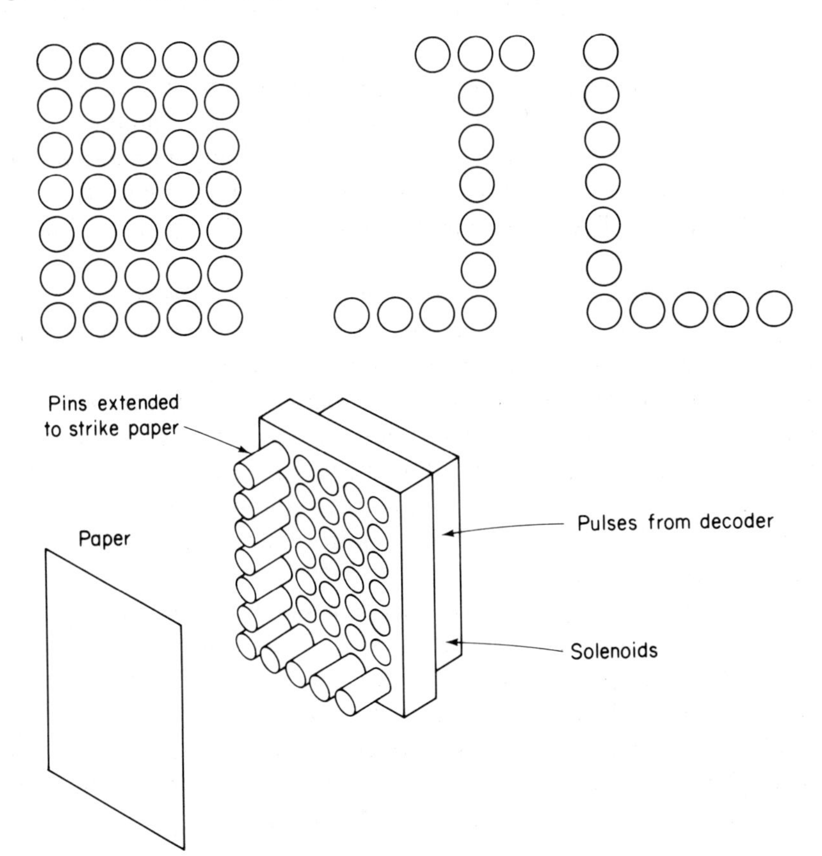

square block rather than on individual hammers. The type block moves from left to right, positioning the proper character at each print position. As the block stops at each position, a hammer strikes the proper character from behind. The character is depressed against an inked ribbon, which, in turn, imprints the character on the paper. Teletype-printer speed is about 8 lines/min.

The *matrix printer* consists of pins placed in a 5 by 7 matrix, as shown in Figure 7-17. The characters are formed when the appropriate pins strike against the paper. (In some matrix printers, the pins burn spots onto the paper. However, this burning technique is not in general use.) The pins are selected by pulses from the decoder. Some matrix printers are capable of printing about 700 to 800 lines/min, making the unit comparable in speed to most line-at-a-time printers.

J. DATA COMMUNICATIONS AND TERMINAL DEVICES

Data communications is the transmission of bits of data from one point to another. For example, the data from one computer can be transmitted to another computer in the same building, in the same city, or to a city across the country. Likewise, a central computer can serve several users on a **time-sharing** basis, with each of the users at a different remote location.

At present, most data transmission systems use the telephone and telegraph lines already available. This requires the translation of computer information (generally in the form of digital pulses) into a form suitable for transmission across the telephone lines. A **data set** is the device used to perform the translation. In most data sets, the digital pulses are used to modulate an audio tone (or tones) that can be transmitted over the lines. At the receiving end, the audio tones are demodulated and converted back to digital pulses. Both serial and parallel transmission methods are used.

Most data sets in present use include a standard telephone, in addition to the circuits for modulation and demodulation of the digital pulses. This permits the operators to communicate before and after the transmission of data. In a typical situation, the operator will dial a number, putting him in touch with operators at the opposite end of the line. After making the necessary arrangements, data can be transmitted back and forth between the locations via the data sets.

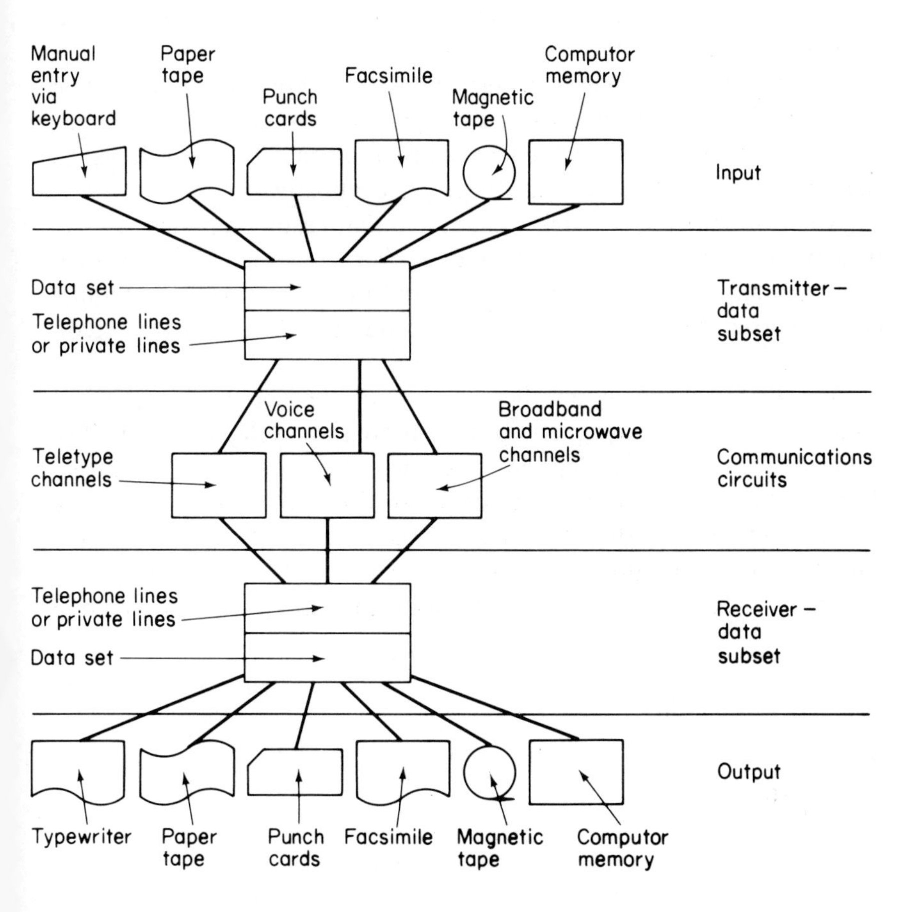

Fig. 7-18. Data transmission systems in common use. Teletype channels include typewriter and paper tape; voice channels include typewriter, paper tape, punch cards, and fascimile; broadband channels include typewriter, magnetic tape, and computer memory.

Any of the input/output units described thus far can be used as terminal devices, in association with the data set. The visual display (CRT) unit (described in subdivision F of this chapter) is probably the most popular terminal device. For example, a time-sharing user can have a visual display unit and a data set at an office location connected by telephone lines to a computer at some remote point. The input and output of the visual display unit is connected through the data set to the telephone lines. With this arrangement, the visual display unit is (in effect) connected directly to the computer.

In addition to the visual display unit, there are other devices that were specifically developed for the transmission of data over telephone lines. Two such units (called **touch tone** devices) have been developed by the American Telephone and Telegraph Company.

The *card dialer* is a touch tone device that reads prepunched holes in a plastic card at the rate of 8 to 9 characters/sec. This system is ideally suited to information retrieval and in applications that require entry of fixed data (such as the account numbers punched in a credit card).

The *Call-A-Matic* is another touch tone device; it stores several hundred entries on a magnetic belt by means of a telephone dial. The data are read into the telephone line when the user presses a button. The belt then moves at high speeds for readout. With this system, the data are entered into the belt on an off-line basis and then read into the computer as an on-line operation.

Figure 7-18 summarizes the data transmission systems in common use.

MEMORY AND STORAGE CIRCUITS

8

The terms *memory* and *storage* are often interchanged. Actually, any device that has a memory is capable of data storage. Before going into how memory and storage circuits operate, let us summarize some common terms used.

Storage can be internal or external. Punch cards, punched paper tape, and magnetic tape are some examples of **external storage**. These items are also examples of permanent storage and **nondestructive storage**, since the stored information will remain permanently and is not destroyed during readout. Moreover, the cards and paper tape are **nonerasable**, while the magnetic tape is **erasable**. The magnetic drum and magnetic disc are forms of permanent but erasable storage.

The most common forms of **internal storage** are registers and ferrite cores, although magnetic drums and discs are used internally in some computers. Generally, ferrite cores are used as **primary storage**, while registers are used for **secondary storage** or for **transfer**. Ferrite cores are erasable. Thus it is necesary to **rewrite** data into them after readout. Although erasable and destructive, ferrite cores will retain information when power is removed. Thus ferrite cores have greater **permanence** than registers.

The FFs that make up registers have a memory since they can be set to a given state and will remain in that state until a specific condition changes them. For example, if a FF receives a 1 input, it will set to the 1 state. If another 1 input is applied, the FF will "remember" that it is in the 1 state and will not change. Only a 0 input can change the state. Usually, one FF is used for each bit of data. Thus a register with 16 FFs has a **storage capacity** of 16.

Ferrite core memories have a short **access time** (typically 1 to 5 μS), which is the time required to retrieve data from storage. Storage units can have different **modes of access**. Some have **serial access** or **sequential access**, where each bit is read out one after another. Other units use **parallel access**, where all bits of a computer word are read out simultaneously. When data can be read out of storage at a particular address, without reference to other addresses, the storage is said of have **random access** or **direct address**. Ferrite core memories provide random access.

A. MAGNETIC STORAGE BASICS

Magnetic tape, drums, discs, and ferrite core memories all operate on the principle of electromagnetism. Therefore we shall review electromagnetism as it applies to computer storage.

Fig. 8-1. Basic principles of magnetic storage showing metal magnetized in opposite directions by opposite currents. N and S, original polarity of magnetism in metal.

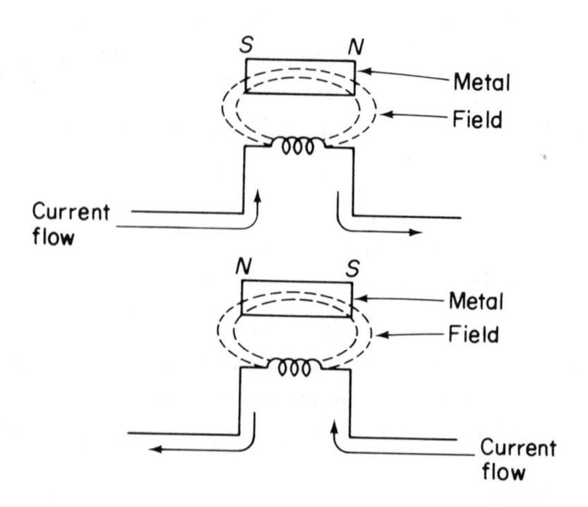

As shown in Figure 8-1, current through a coil creates a magnetic field. If a metal capable of being magnetized is placed in this field, the metal will become magnetized in one direction. If current flow is reversed, the metal will be magnetized in the opposite direction. As shown in Figure 8-2, if metal is magnetized in one direction and an opposite magnetizing current is applied to change the direction of magnetism, the changing magnetic field produces (or induces) a current in another conductor (in or near the field). However, if the magnetizing current is applied so as not to change the direction of magnetism, there is no change in the magnetic field and no induced voltage. Thus the magnetized metal has a "memory" and is ideally suited to the two-state binary logic (1 or 0) used in digital computers.

There are two ways in which this magnetic principle can be used in digital logic. In the case of magnetic tapes, drums, and discs, the presence or absence of magnetism is used to indicate the binary state. (Generally, the presence of magnetism indicates a binary 1, while a

Fig. 8-2. Basic principles of magnetic storage showing effect of currents on previously magnetized metal storage elements.

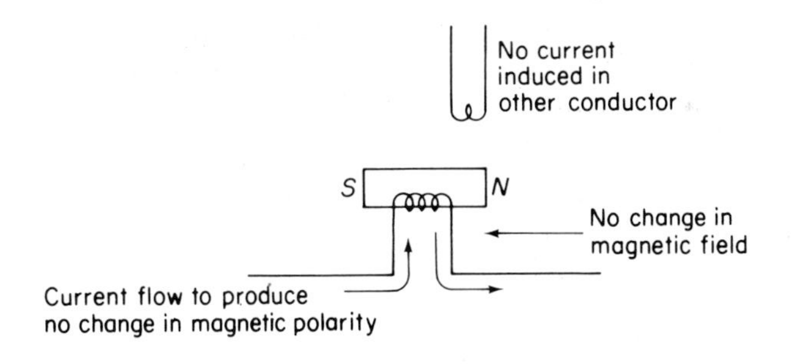

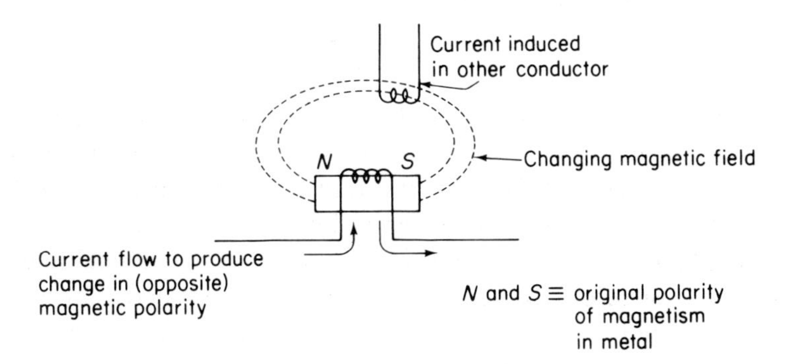

binary 0 is indicated by the absence of magnetism.) In the case of ferrite cores, the direction of magnetism is used to indicate the state. As is discussed in later paragraphs, ferrite cores are circular and can be magnetized in the clockwise or counterclockwise direction, depending on the direction of current flow. If new currents are applied, the cores will "remember" their existing state and will change states or remain in the existing state, as applicable.

Whenever metal is magnetized in one direction and an opposite magnetizing force is applied, there is some lag before the magnetic field changes. This lag is known as **hysteresis**, which can be shown by means of a graph or *loop*, as illustrated in Figure 8-3. Such a graph shows the relationship between magnetic force (current in the case of

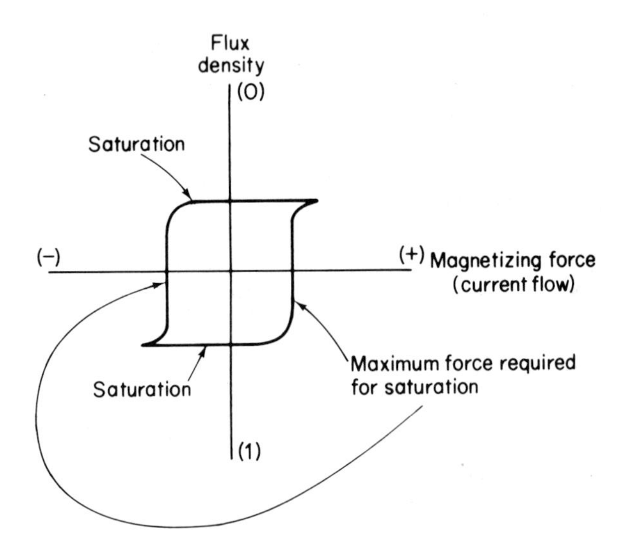

Fig. 8-3. Hysteresis graph or loop showing relationship of magnetizing force to flux density in magnetic storage elements.

an electromagnet) and magnetic flux density. Magnetic force is shown on the horizontal line, with any point to the right of the vertical center line indicating current flow in one direction (arbitrarily labeled +). Points to the left of the vertical center line indicate current flow in the opposite direction (−). Flux density is shown on the vertical line. Any point above or below the horizontal line can be considered (arbitrarily) as north or south, clockwise or counterclockwise, etc. In our example, we shall consider the 0 binary state as being above (with 1 as below) the horizontal line.

The vertical sides of the hysteresis loop represent the maximum magnetizing force required to produce saturation of the magnetic flux (represented by the horizontal sides of the loop). Note that the loop is rectangular, almost square. This is the ideal condition for magnetic devices used in computer memories.

A perfectly square hysteresis loop (rarely found in any magnetic device) means that the device is perfectly linear. That is, a given current in either direction produces the same flux density in the corresponding direction. Next, and particularly important for ferrite core memories, the flux density remains at about the same level when the magnetizing force is returned to 0 and even when an opposite magnetizing force is applied. In fact, it takes about twice the magnetizing force (or current) to change states (1 to 0 or 0 to 1) as is required to go from a demagnetized condition to either state. A square loop device has considerable hysteresis or lag and thus a good "memory."

A nonsquare loop magnetic device begins losing flux density when the magnetizing force is removed and loses density quickly in the presence of an opposite force, making it a poor "memory."

B. FERRITE CORE STORAGE BASICS

Ferrite core memories used in computers consist of metal rings arranged on a wire matrix, as shown in Figure 8-4. The core rings are made of metal alloys that possess rectangular or square hysteresis loop qualities. Note that each core has four wires passing through it, as shown in Figure 8-4B. The wires labeled *W* and *A* are the address wires. Currents passing through the address wires set the state (1 or 0). The core state is dependent on the direction of current flow.

Although shown at right angles, the address wires are placed on the core so that the effects of their currents are additive. That is, if current is applied to both the *A* wire and *W* wire simultaneously, the core receives double current. The currents normally applied to each of the address wires are about one-half that necessary to change states. Thus current must be applied to both wires to produce a change in states.

The sense wire is positioned so that it will produce an output current whenever there is a change of states (the core magnetism changes from clockwise to counterclockwise and vice versa).

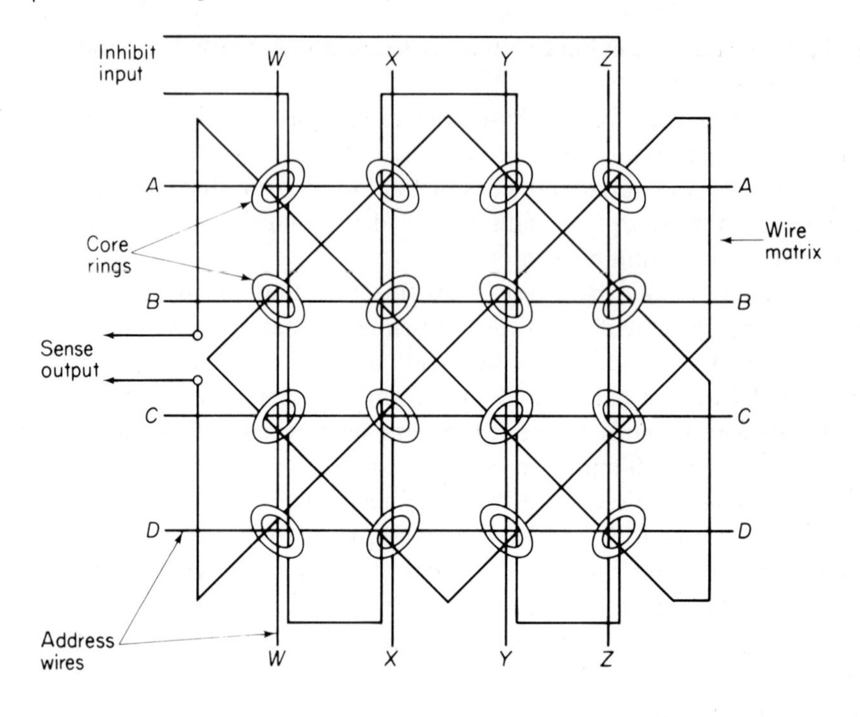

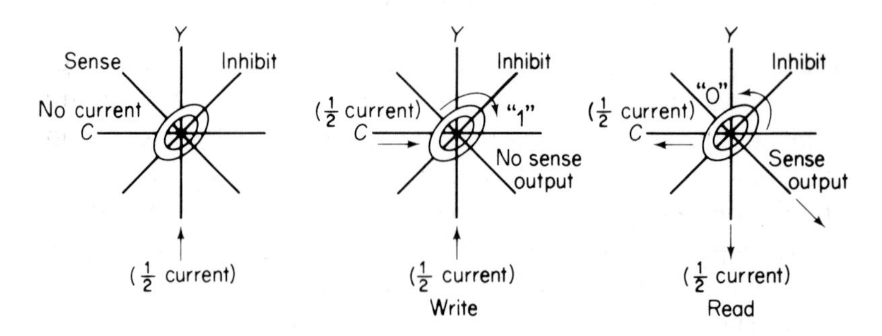

Fig. 8-4. Basic ferrite core memory matrix showing *write* and *read* functions.

The inhibit wire is positioned so that it will oppose the effect of the current through the address wires.

Note that there are 16 cores, one at each junction of the eight address wires. Thus a 0 or 1 bit can be stored at any of 16 locations or addresses. (In a typical computer, there are 4096 cores on a single matrix, each row and column having 64 cores. The actual ·physical arrangement of cores is illutrated further in Chapter 9.)

To *write* data into any address, current is applied to the corresponding address lines. For example, to write a 1 at address *YC*, a current is applied to both the *Y* and *C* lines simultaneously, in a direction that will magnetize the *YC* core to the 1 state. (Arbitrarily, this could be clockwise or counterclockwise. Likewise, a *write* command could be one that sets the core to 0 as long as the commands are consistent. For our example, we shall consider a write command as setting the core to a 1 state.)

Note that the individual *Y* and *C* currents are about one-half that required to set the core. Thus even though all the cores on the *Y* and *C* lines receive some current, only the *YC* core receives enough current to be set.

To *read* data from any address, current is again applied to the corresponding address lines but in a direction opposite to the write current. For example, to read the data at address *YC*, a current is applied to both the *Y* and *C* lines in a direction that sets the *YC* core to 0. Again, the individual *Y* and *C* currents are about one-half that required to set the core.

If the core is previously set to 1, the combined *YC* currents set it to 0. This changes the direction of magnetism (say from clockwise to counterclockwise), producing a voltage at the output of the sense lines. In practice, the sense voltage is amplified and is used to set a FF in a register. In our example, the presence of a sense line output is considered as a 1 and sets the FF to 1.

If the core is previously set to 0, the combined *YC* currents have no effect on the core, since it is already at 0. There is no change of magnetic direction and no voltage output from the sense line. The absence of sense-line output is considered as 0 and leaves the FF at 0. (The register FFs have previously been cleared to 0 by a timing pulse.)

If the core happens to be demagnetized and in some intermediate state (either 0 or 1), the read currents set the core to 0. However, the small change in magnetic state produces a small sense output voltage (not sufficient to set the register FF).

Note that the cores are arranged on the address wires at angles and that the sense wire passes through the core groups in opposite directions. This arrangement is to minimize the effect of noise produced by the address wire currents. Although these currents are insufficient to set the cores (unless there is coincidence of the two currents at a particular address), the currents can produce some change in the magnetic field and thus produce voltages (or noise) in the sense line. Using the arrangement of Figure 8-4, the voltages produced by one set of cores is of opposite polarity to the other set of cores, canceling any noise voltage in the sense line.

The read operation can be destructive. For example, if the core is in the 1 state, a read will set the core to 0. It is then necessary to write the 1 back into the memory at that address. This can be done by reading the register into which the memory is applied (output of the sense lines) and then writing the output of the register back into the memory (by applying currents to the appropriate address wires).

Keep in mind that the memory address may have originally been at a 0 when the read currents were applied. In this case, there is no output from the sense line, and the register remains at 0. For each bit where the register is at 0, the write current must be prevented from setting the memory core to 1. There are several methods for accomplishing this. The most common way is to apply a current through the inhibit line, canceling the effect of the write currents. The inhibit current is not sufficient to change the states of the cores but is sufficient to nullify a write command.

The inhibit current must be turned on during a write command only when the particular address is to remain at 0. Figure 8-5 shows a typical inhibit control circuit. The bit output from the memory register is connnected to an inverter. The output of the inverter is applied to an AND gate, along with an inhibit pulse. The inhibit pulse is present during the write command. The inhibit pulse output from the AND gate is amplified and applied to the inhibit line.

Fig. 8-5. Typical memory inhibit control circuit.

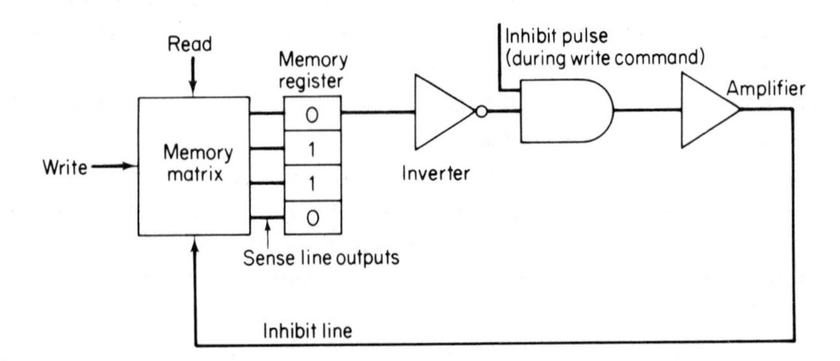

If the bit read out of the memory into the register is a 1, the 1 is inverted to 0 (false), keeping the AND gate closed. The inhibit pulse is not applied to the inhibit line, and the 1 is rewritten back into memory. If the original memory bit is 0, the 0 is inverted to a 1 (true), opening the AND gate. The inhibit pulse is then applied to the inhibit line, preventing the write command from setting the memory core to 1.

The driving currents required for the address lines of a typical ferrite core memory are on the order of 0.5–1 ampere (A). This amount of current requires amplifiers using power transistors. The amplifiers must be capable of reversing current flow, depending on the command (read or write).

Figure 8-6 shows typical ferrite memory drive circuits. There are two sets of power amplifiers—one for the *Y* address line and another

Fig. 8-6. Typical ferrite memory drive circuits.

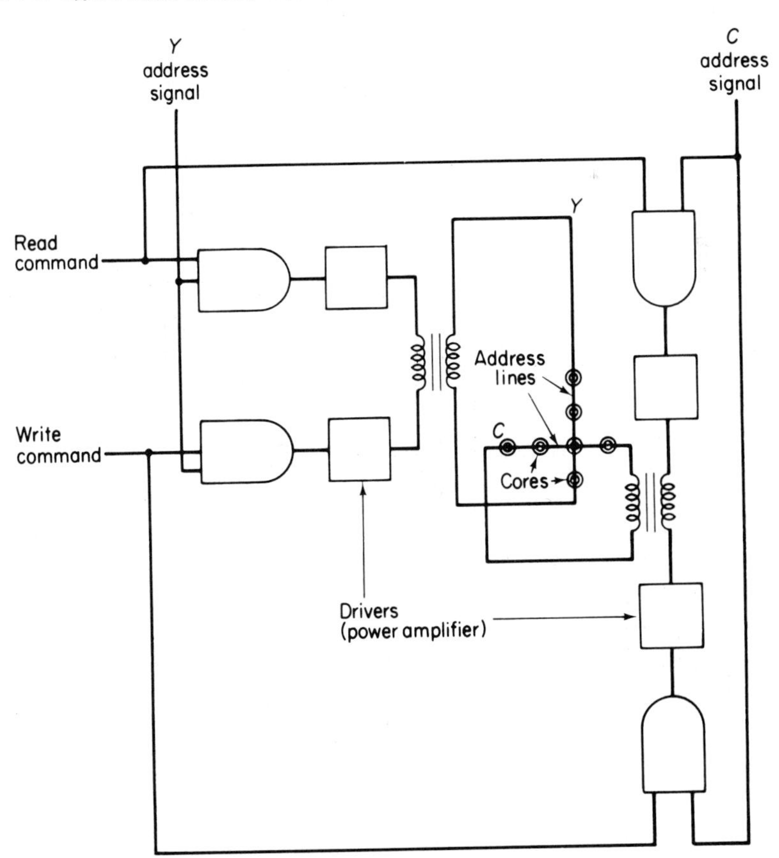

for the C line. The amplifiers (or drivers, as they are usually called) are placed in a condition to conduct only when both inputs to either AND gate are true. One set of AND gate inputs is made true by the Y and C address signals (as selected by the computer program control). The other sets of inputs receive read or write command pulses. During the write operation, both the Y and C signals are present, as are write pulses. Current flows through the Y and C address lines in a direction to set the YC core to 1. During read, the Y and C signals are still present, as is the read pulse. Current flows through the Y and C lines but in the opposite direction, setting the YC core to 0.

There are 16 possible addresses for each bit on the matrix of Figure 8-4. One matrix (or bit *plane*) is required for each bit used in computer words. That is, if computer words are three bits long, three bit planes are required. This is shown in Figure 8-7.

To read out a complete computer word into the register, the corresponding address of each bit plane must be read. In the example of Figure 8-7, the Y and C address lines of all three planes are driven at

Fig. 8-7. Typical ferrite core layout for three-bit computer word.

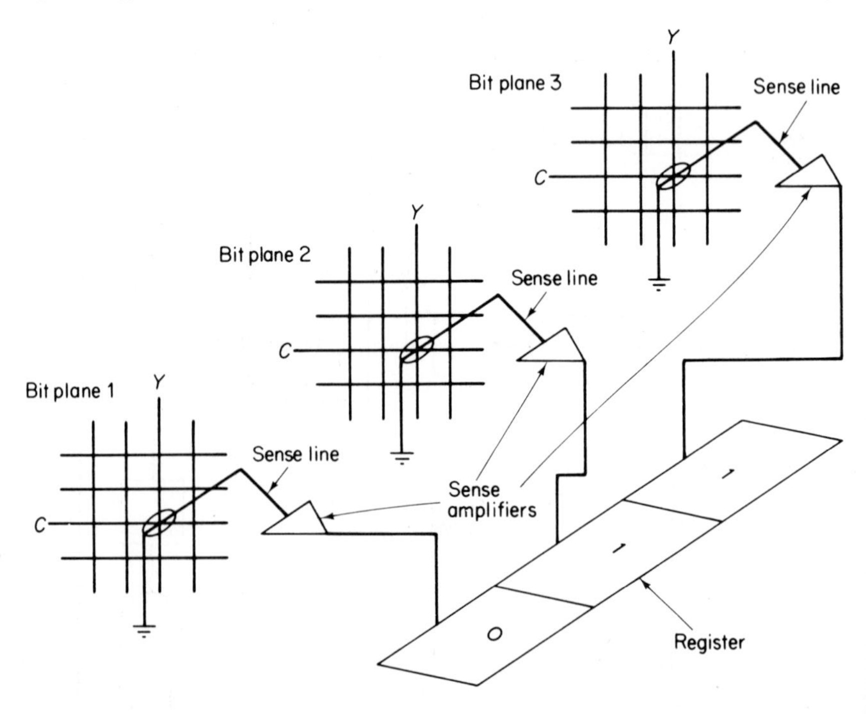

once. The *YC* core of the first bit plane is in the 0 state, producing no output from the first sense amplifier. Thus the first position of the register remains at 0. The *YC* cores of the second and third bit planes are in the 1 state, producing outputs on the corresponding sense amplifiers. Thus the second and third positions of the register are set to 1.

In a typical computer, each plane will contain 4096 cores or addresses. Sometimes dual planes are used, producing 8192 addresses. In expressing the storage capabity of a computer, both the number of addresses (rounded off to the nearest thousand) and the word length are given. For example, a typical unit is described as an 8K (8 thousand, actually 8192), 16-bit-word computer. In some computers, the memory is further divided into *pages*. These pages are not physical divisions but represent a system of how the addresses are arranged in relation to the registers. Although there is no standardization, a typical computer page is about 1000 addresses.

C. TAPE RECORDER STORAGE

Magnetic-tape recorders are often used with computers as an external storage device. These recorders provide high-speed read-in and read-out. The recorders used with computer systems are similar to those used in home entertainment units. Both systems have tape transports, record and playback heads (called write and read heads), and amplifiers. However, the detailed characteristics of the two systems are quite different.

1. Tape Amplifier Characteristics

The amplifiers used in computer recorders do not require the high fidelity of entertainment units, because computer recorders operate with digital information (bits of data) rather than voice or music. Digital information is recorded (written) and played back (read) on a *present* or *absent* basis. Often, a digital 1 is represented by the presence of a magnetic field on the tape (also known as a *magnetic spot*), while the absence of a field represents a 0. In other systems, the direction of the magnetic field (north or south, + or −) represents a 1 or 0.

Because of the on-off method of recording, computer recorders generally do not have the supersonic bias signal applied to the tape for linearity, as is the case in other recorders where high fidelity is required. However, computer recording systems often use a fixed d-c bias to place the tape in a condition to be magnetized by the binary information.

2. Tape Characteristics

The tapes used in computer recorders are generally longer than those of home units; 2400 or 3600 ft is standard. Although early magnetic tapes were made of metal, all popular tapes are now made of plastic, coated on one side with metal oxide. The oxide can easily be magnetized and retains its magnetism indefinitely. The bits of digital information are placed across the width of the tape on parallel tracks running along the entire length. Each track is assigned a read-write head for recording. In more expensive tape, a very thin coat of polyester on top of the oxide inhibits wear. Despite this added feature (of "sandwich tape") it is likely that the tape will have a certain amount of wear over a long period of time. Computer tapes are usually wider than entertainment tapes ($\frac{1}{2}$–1 in. is typical) so that several tracks or channels can be recorded simultaneously. Although the number of tracks on magnetic tape varies with its width, a seven- or nine-channel tape is used today with a tape width of $\frac{1}{2}$ in.

3. Tape-Coding System

The pattern of the magnetized spots across the width and along the length of the tape is a coded representation of the data stored on it. The BCD code is sometimes used. More often, an alphanumeric code is used. Typical seven-channel tape patterns are shown in Figure 8-8. Across the width of the tape, the seven tracks provide one column of data (one frame) or simply one character. The presence of a dash or a short line stands for one bit of information, which, combined with the 0 bits (the absence of a dash) in a seven-channel code, can represent a letter, a digit, or a special character.

Characters are recorded on tape serially, as shown in Figure 8-9. That is, the information is recorded one or more characters at a time,

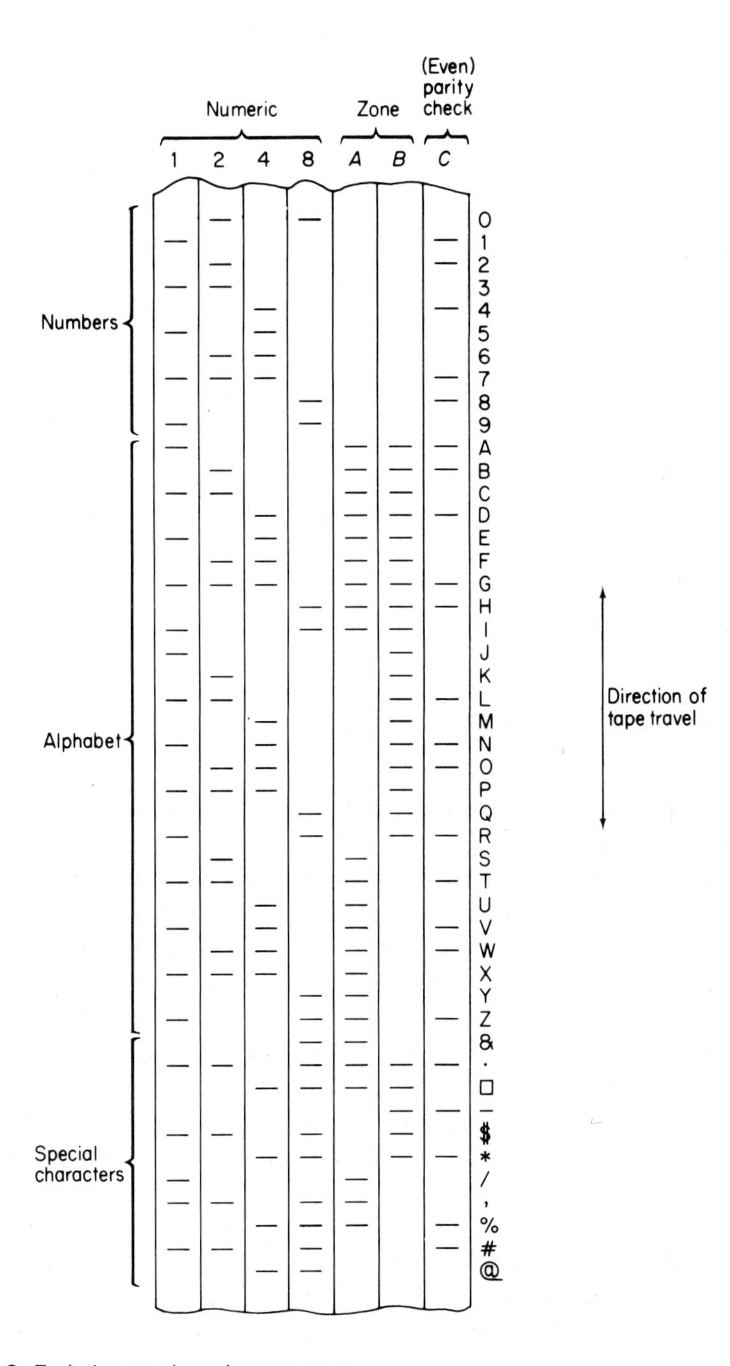

Fig. 8-8. Typical seven-channel tape patterns.

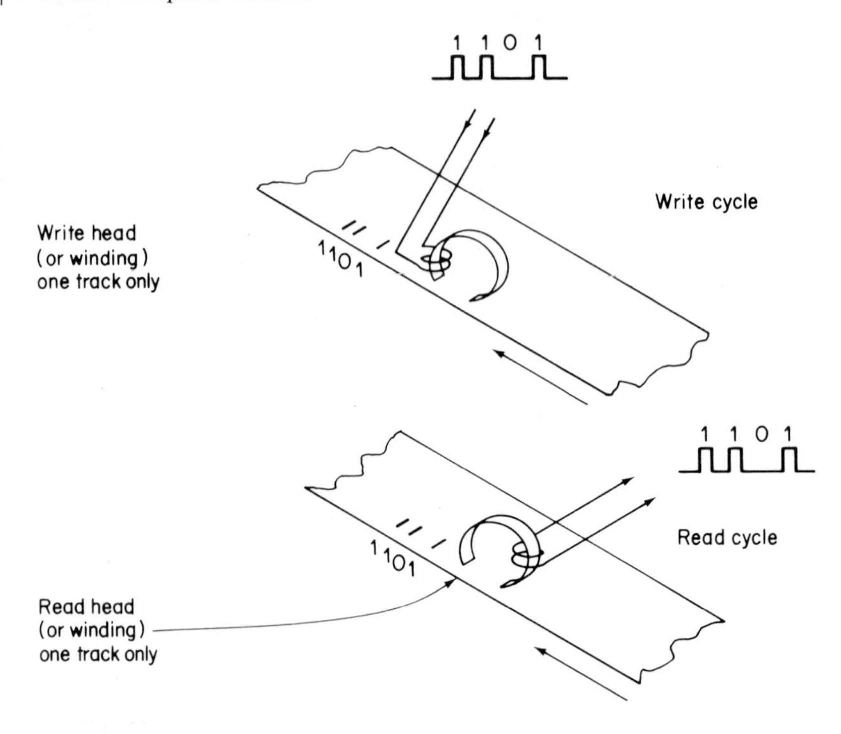

Fig. 8-9. Read and write cycles of magnetic tape.

as the tape passes by the read-write heads. (The actual number of characters is dependent on the coding format and the number of channels.) In the recording system of Figure 8-9, a magnetic field (or spot) is impressed across the tape (representing a binary 1) as current (in the form of pulses) passes through the "write" winding. (In some systems, one head is used for both read and write. In other recording systems, separate read and write heads are used.) In the absence of current, no spot is impressed on tape. During the read operation, as the tape is passed across the head by the tape transport, the presence of a moving magnetic spot produces current in the read head (binary 1). No current is produced when there is no spot on the tape passing the head (binary 0).

The system shown in Figure 8-9 is a return-to-zero (RZ) digital system. (Refer to Chapter 6, subdivision B, 1.) The RZ method is the least efficient for storing the most information on a given area of tape. That is, the RZ system provides the lowest amount of **pulse packing** or **packing density**. Pulse packing is a measure of how dense the pulse recording is (how close together the information is recorded). The higher the pulse density, the less amount of tape will be needed for storing data. With the RZ method, the pulse current returns to 0 between bits and remains at 0 for a 0 bit. (In some RZ systems, the pulse current returns to 0 between bits but changes direction for a 1 or 0 bit.)

Pulse density can be increased by use of the non-return-to-zero-level (NRZL) or non-return-to-zero-mark (NRZM) systems of Figure 8-10. In the NRZL system (Figure 8-10B), the direction of magnetization changes only when switching from a 0 to a 1 or from a 1 to a 0. In NRZM systems (Figure 8-10C) the magnetization changes direction only when it is necessary to store a 1.

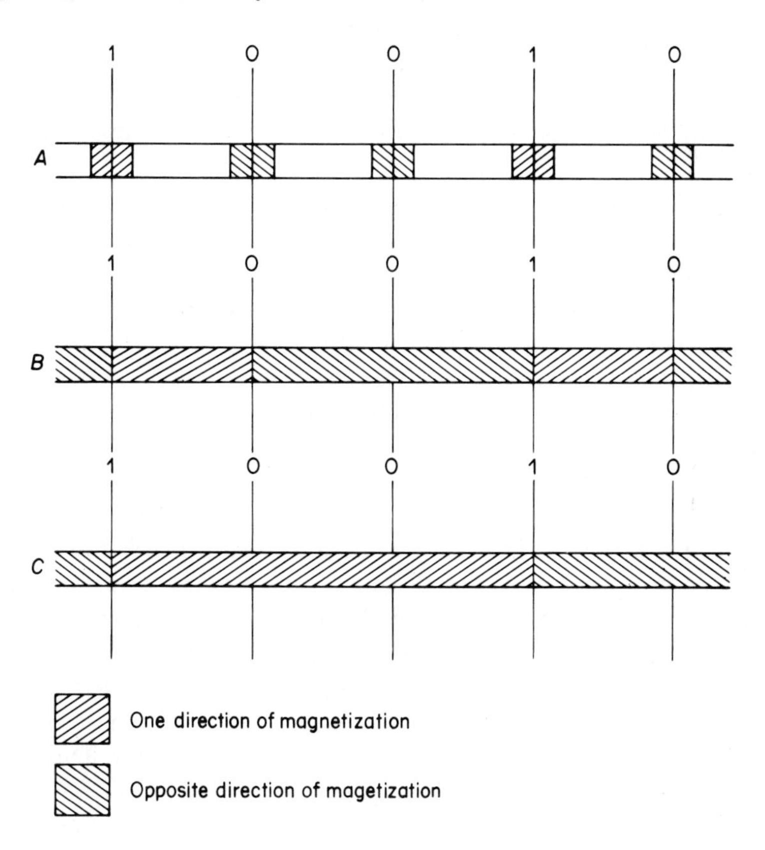

Fig. 8-10. Basic tape recording methods.

4. Tape Control Systems

Another difference between audio and computer tapes is the matter of starting and stopping. Unlike an audio tape that moves slowly and need not be stopped quickly, computer tape moves at a speed of 100 in. (or more) per second. Because the computer must pinpoint specific data (at a selected address or block on the tape), the computer tape control system must be able to stop the tape at the proper point with no lost motion.

Reading and writing on tape is performed on the tape unit at a constant speed. The **transfer rate** of information to and from tape depends largely on two factors: (1) the actual movement of tape across the read-write heads and (2) the number of characters that can be stored on an inch of tape (packing density). For example, assume a tape movement speed of 100 in./sec and a density of 400 characters/in. At these rates, the character transfer rate is 40,000 characters/sec. In typical systems, tape speed is about 90 in./sec, with a packing density of 800 characters/in., giving a transfer rate of approximately 72,000/sec.

Several methods are used to move tape across the read-write heads in a fast, yet synchronized manner to prevent breakage. The sudden burst of speed in starting a tape and the abrupt jolt when the tape stops have been "softened" by the provision of slack in the tape areas where breakage is likely to occur. Typical systems are shown in Figure 8-11 and 8-12.

The system of Figure 8-11 includes vacuum columns to house loops of tape on both sides of the read-write heads. The tape loops are suspended in vacuum columns, and a slight air pressure is applied to the top of the tape to provide some tension. The vacuum columns take up and give the required slack before and after recording is done.

The loop in each vacuum column acts as a buffer to prevent high-speed starts and stops from breaking the tape. Vacuum-actuated switches in the columns allow the file reel and takeup reel to act independently. The file reel feeds tape when the loop in the left chamber reaches a minimum point, and the takeup reel winds the tape when the loop in the right chamber reaches a maximum point. During the rewinding or backspacing of tape, the two reels simply reverse their roles. The vacuum action is the same, although rewinding speeds generally are faster than reading or writing speeds.

In the system of Figure 8-12, two columns are used, one for each reel. However, the switches are photoelectric cells that keep the tape loops above the lower switch and below the upper switch. Each tape reel has its own drive motor connected to a servomechanism. When a

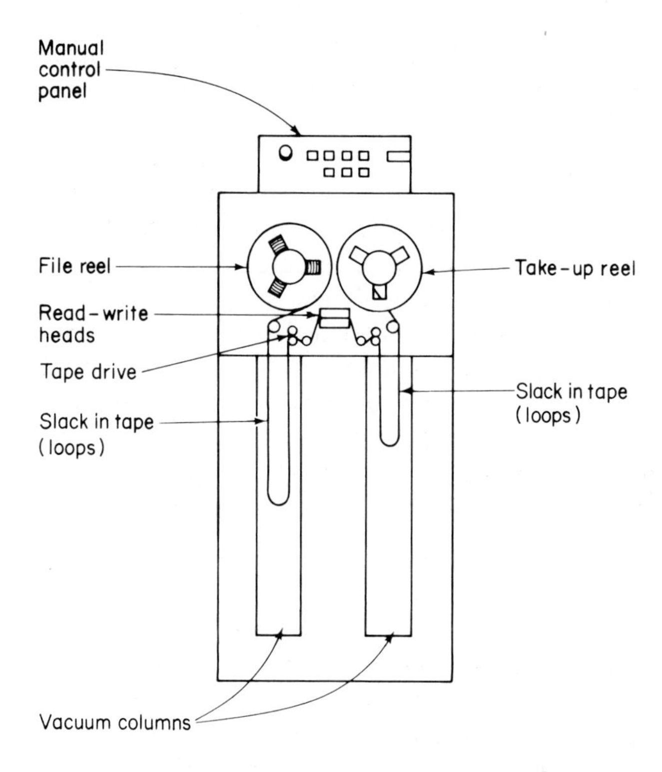

Fig. 8-11. Typical magnetic tape drive system with vacuum columns.

Fig. 8-12. Typical magnetic tape drive system with photoelectric switch control and tape bin.

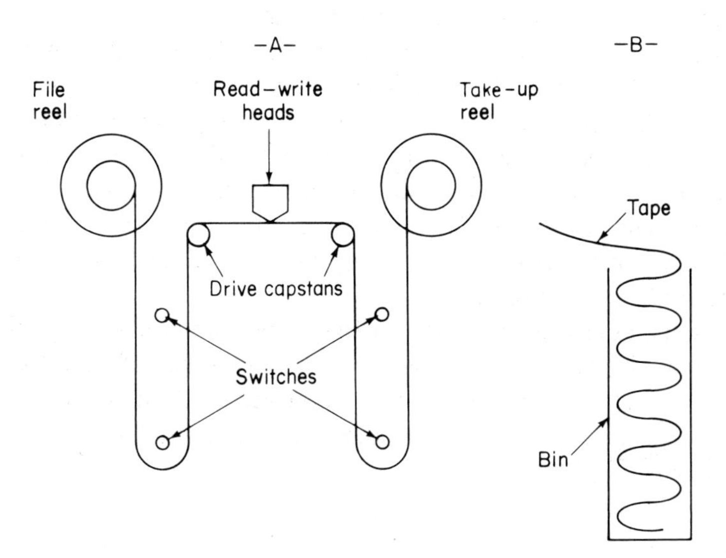

tape real starts, it has only to draw from the loop, not from the entire tape. The other reel and its motor move the tape to keep the loop at the proper size. In this way, quick stops and starts are possible without breaking the tape. In some high-speed systems, the tape reels are fed into bins where the tape lies in folds, as shown in Figure 8-12B. (Of course, the tape must be wound onto reels from the bins for future use.)

Only the basic tape control systems are shown here. There are many other tape control systems, and new systems are being developed. For example, some new tape systems have automatic tape threading, where tape cartridges are mounted on the tape drive mechanism for self-threading. Some tape control units use pinch rollers to move tape. Other units use suction only, with rotating capstans to pull the tape past the read-write heads. Some systems read tape in one direction only; others are capable of reading in the reverse direction as well.

5. Storing Data Records on Tape

Information is usually written on tape in groups (called **records**). In normal operation, information continues to be written on the tape until a flag or control signal is received from the computer. (Refer to Chapter 7, subdivision A.) This stops the tape drive. Some tape systems use a fixed block of characters in each record, but variable-length records are more common. Actual length is determined primarily by the storage capacity of the computer's main storage (usually a ferrite core matrix).

Figure 8-13 illustrates the physical arrangement of typical tape records. Note that there are **interrecord gaps** (IRGs) between records. Where one IRG is used between several record blocks (Figure 8-13B) considerable tape space is saved, thus increasing the amount of data that can be stored on a given length of tape. The IRGs are produced when the tape continues to be driven, but no information is written on the tape. The use of IRGs permits the tape drive to accelerate and decelerate when starting or stopping without failing to read or write the desired information.

In some tape systems, when an IRG is encountered during the read operation, the tape drive stops at about the center of the IRG. The remaining half of the IRG is used upon acceleration before the next record is read. A new read command from the computer starts the tape drive again.

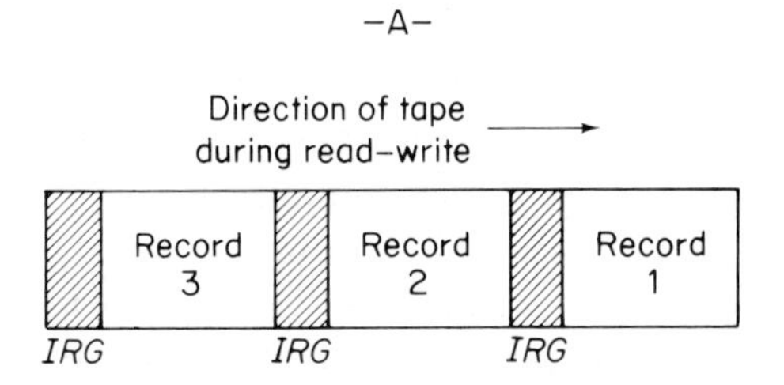

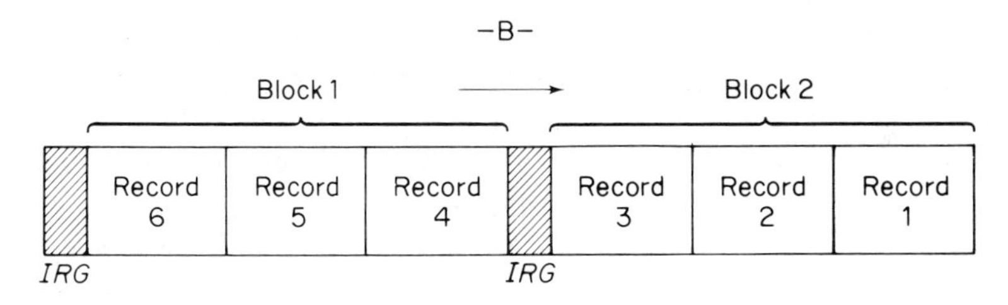

Fig. 8-13. Typical systems for storing data on magnetic tapes.

6. Safety and Accuracy of Tape Records

Many safeguards must be taken to preserve data stored on computer tapes. Obviously, the information can be destroyed if an erase signal is accidently applied to the tape unit heads or if new information is written on top of old information. A common safeguard to prevent accidental *overwriting* of tape is a safety indicator in the form of a plastic ring. When installed on a groove around the hub of a tape reel, the ring indicates that the tape may be used to store new information. The ring is removed when the writing of new information is to be prevented. This accounts for the term *no-ring, no-write* used by many computer operators and programmers.

Just as important, but perhaps not as obvious, there must be some system to ensure that the data are recorded accurately. There are three main concerns in recording digital data. First, all the bits must be recorded. Second, the information bits must be readable. Third, the bits must be recorded in the correct order, both horizontally and vertically on the tape.

The main causes of tape errors stem from physical and environmental factors (although there can be failures in the electronic circuits and components). Flaws in the tape itself due to faulty manufacturing processes probably are the most common causes of error. Also, tape normally wears out after a certain amount of use. This, plus a drastic change in temperature and/or humidity, may cause chipping of the oxide on which the magnetic spots are made. Dust particles or weakness in the magnetic field of the recorded bits often contribute to recording problems.

Dual recording systems are used where reliability is particularly important (such as when real-time digital data are being recorded on a one-time-only basis). In the dual recording systems, each character is written twice in each frame across the width of the tape by two sets of heads, amplifiers, etc. Of course, this requires twice the number of channels and twice the width of tape. When seven channels must be recorded, two sets of tracks (14 total) are recorded simultaneously with the same information. Generally, this requires a 1-in. (or wider) tape system.

Dual-gap read-write systems are used to provide a constant check (for readability) on data being recorded. All characters written on tape are immediately read by a read head (or separate read winding) immediately adjacent to the write head. Both readability and accuracy can be checked in this way. A basic dual-gap read-write circuit is shown in Figure 8-14. Here, information in a computer's output storage register is amplified and written onto the tape by a write head. Only one bit is shown in Figure 8-14. The circuit is repeated (amplifiers, heads, tracks, etc.) for each bit in the register. As the tape moves, the bit is read out immediately, amplified, and applied to another readout register. Each bit in the readout register is compared against the corresponding bits in the output storage register, using the comparator circuits described in Chapter 6 (subdivisions G and H, 1).

The recording operation continues as long as the recorded bits are readable and in agreement with the bits in the output register. If there is any inequality between the two registers, the comparison circuit stops the tape drive and sends a signal to the computer circuits (often an alarm light on the computer console). In some systems, the tape drive is reversed, and the bit is rewritten at the appropriate location on the tape.

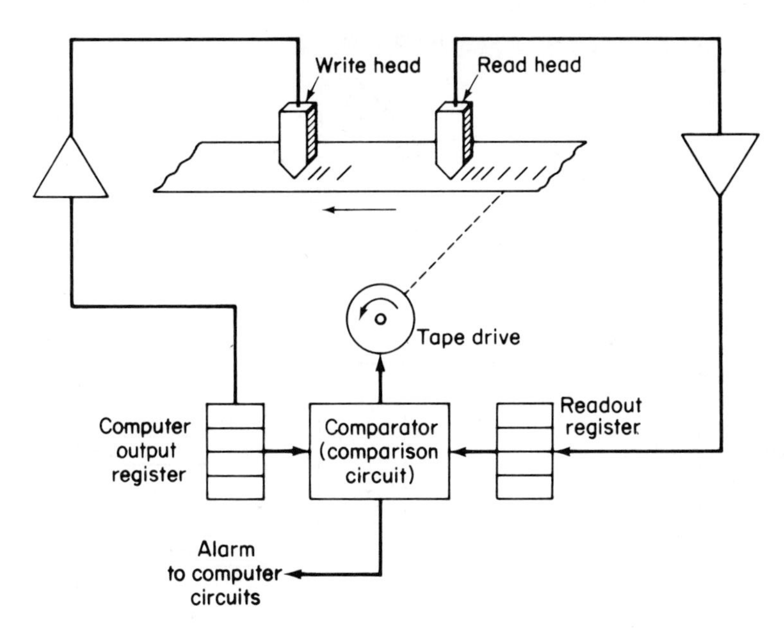

Fig. 8-14. Basic dual-gap read-write magnetic tape recording system.

Parity circuits are used to check the accuracy of the bits on tape. The parity circuits used are those discussed in Chapter 6 (subdivision H). Many computer tape systems provide both horizontal and vertical parity checks. The horizontal systems provide a check of complete words on each channel or track of the tape. Vertical systems check individual characters across all tracks simultaneously.

A basic vertical parity system is shown in Figure 8-15. Here, one channel of a seven-channel tape is reserved for vertical even parity check. A 1 bit is added to make an even number of 1 bits across the width of the tape.

In the case of characters J and K, both normally use an even number of 1 bits. Thus no parity bit is added. The character L and the number 7 use an odd number of 1s (three 1s). Thus a parity bit is added to both L and 7. The amplified output of the read heads applied to the computer input is also applied to the parity-checking circuit. If the input to the parity-checking circuit is even, operation continues as normal. If the parity checker receives an odd number of bits, an alarm is given and/or normal computer operation is stopped.

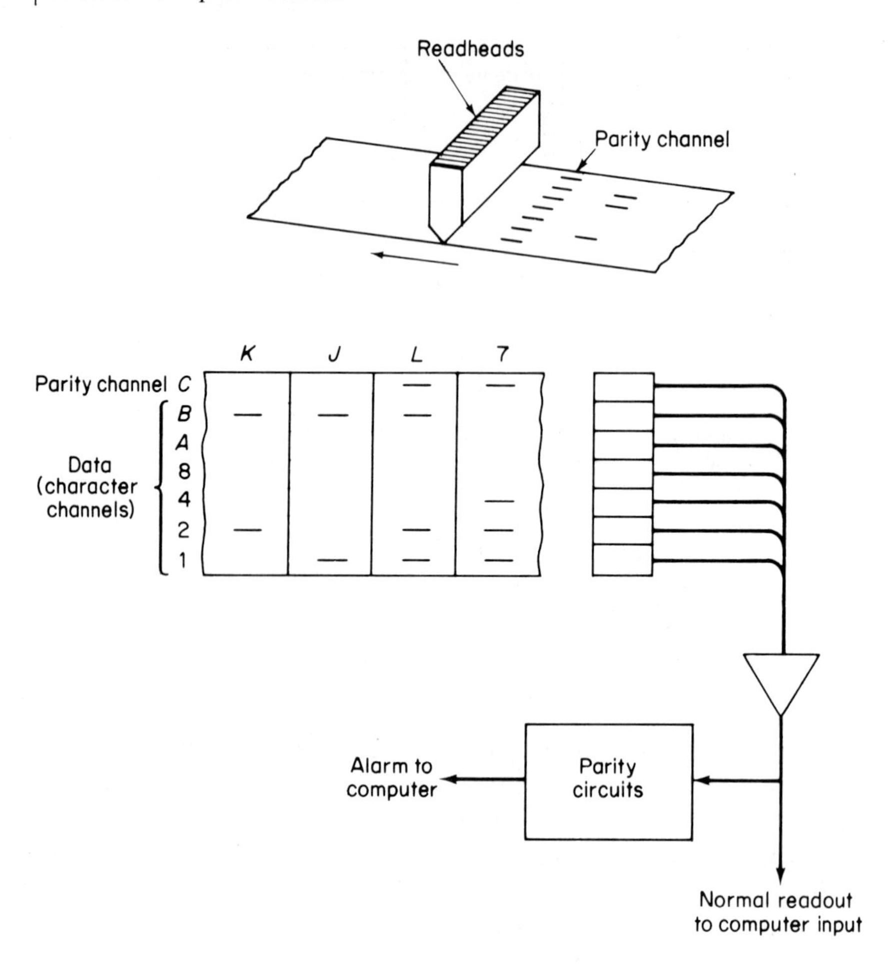

Fig. 8-15. Basic vertical parity system for magnetic tape recording control.

7. Locating Data on Tape Records

Since tape has no physical markings, some means must be used to locate data at a specific point on the tape. This is true for both read and write.

In some systems, reflective markers (such as silver-coated foil) are attached to the tape at the beginning and end of tape sections where a large block of information is recorded (or to be recorded). A photocell is mounted near the tape and picks up light from the reflective marker.

A change in light on the photocell stops the tape drive at the marker until a new read or write command is given.

Although physical markings can be used for the beginning and end of an information block, specific information at any point with the block is identified by means of an electronic *address*. Several addressing systems are used. In some cases, one or more of the tape tracks are reserved for bits that represent the address. In other cases, the first few characters or numbers in a particular record represent the address for that record. Such a system is illustrated in Figure 8-16.

As shown, each record is identified by three-digit decimal numbers (from 000 to 999). The read heads are connected through amplifiers and gates to the computer's internal or primary storage. When the gates are opened, the information being read is fed into the internal memory. The gates are opened upon command from the comparator network. This network compares the data in the address selection register with the data in the readout register. The address selection register is set to the desired address (record 733 in the illustration) by controls on the computer, and the tape drive is started. When the tape is at the desired address (record 733) the readout register indicates 733, and the comparator network opens the gates. As the tape continues to move, the information in the 733 record is read into the computer's internal

Fig. 8-16. Basic circuit for locating data on magnetic tape records.

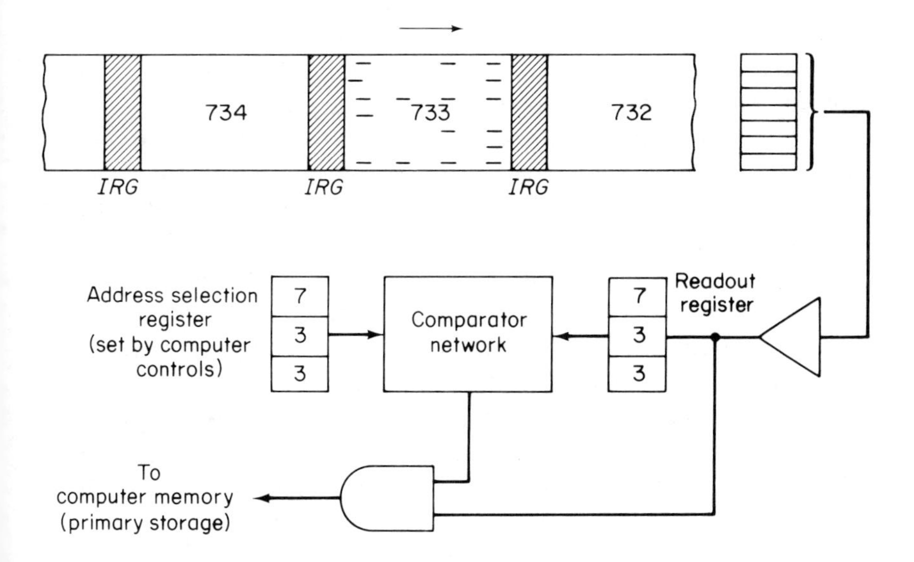

memory. The tape stops at the end of the record or goes to a new address, as determined by the address selection register.

Of course, the circuit of Figure 8-16 is oversimplified for illustration purposes. In practice, the tape drive and address selection circuits move the tape from address to address, stopping, reversing, and again moving forward at high speeds. In spite of the high speed, computer tape systems have a long access time. For example, in the extreme case where two addresses are located at the opposite ends of a 3600-ft reel, it could take several minutes to move from one address to the next. The magnetic drum discussed next has a much shorter access time.

D. MAGNETIC-DRUM STORAGE

As shown in Figure 8-17, the magnetic drum is a metal drum (often aluminum) coated with magnetically sensitive material on its outer surface. The surface is divided into a number of tracks or channels. Each track has single or multiple read-write heads, depending on whether data transfer is serial or parallel. The presence of one or more read-write heads for each track eliminates any access motion time (time required to get from one physical point to another). Since the only timing factors affecting drum operation are head selection time (which is negligible), rotational delay, and data transfer (to and from registers), the use of the magnetic drum as a storage device provides faster and more efficient operation than other direct access storage devices. (However, what the drum offers in terms of speed, it falls short of in storage capacity, when compared to the magnetic-tape devices.)

A magnetic drum usually rotates at 1200–15,000 revolutions/min (rpm), 3600 rpm being average. Information can always be located, on a single track, in less than one revolution. For example, in Figure 8-17B, if the head is at point *A* on the drum, the next desired spot of data could be at *C*, one-quarter turn away, or at *B*, still less than a full turn. The maximum access time for a drum rotating 3600 rpm is 8.3 mS (the time required for the drum to make one complete revolution). The average access time for a magnetic drum is about 4 μS. In most systems, the heads are staggered as shown in Figure 8-17C to make maximum use of the drum surface.

Switching is used for reading a word from its location on the drum or for writing a word in a certain place. Control circuits, similar to those

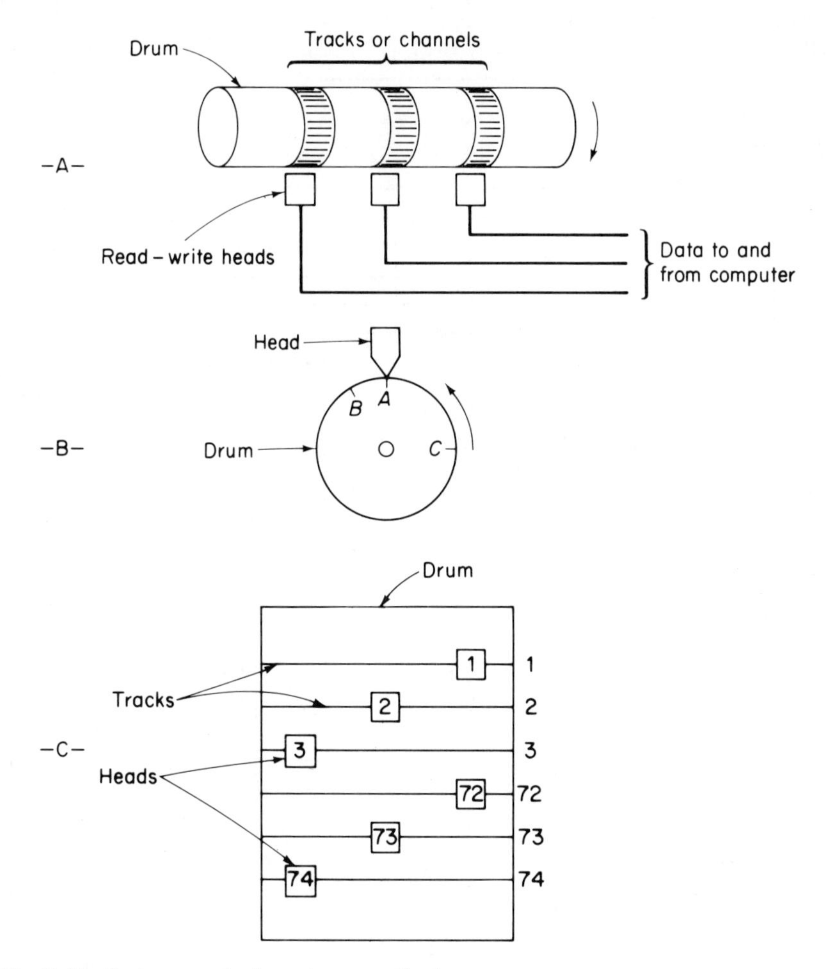

Fig. 8-17. Basic magnetic-drum storage methods.

shown in Figure 8-18, turn on the proper head at the beginning of a word to be read (or written) and turn it off at the end.

As shown, each track consists of a series of computer words separated by IRGs. For identification, a separate track (known as the timing track or address track) on the drum carries a series of prerecorded timing bits that produce timing pulses as the drum rotates past the timing head. The timing track output gives the precise location of any spot on the drum (at the corresponding point on all data tracks).

Assume that the instruction from the computer's control section is "Read word 77 on track 3." The address register is set for a count of

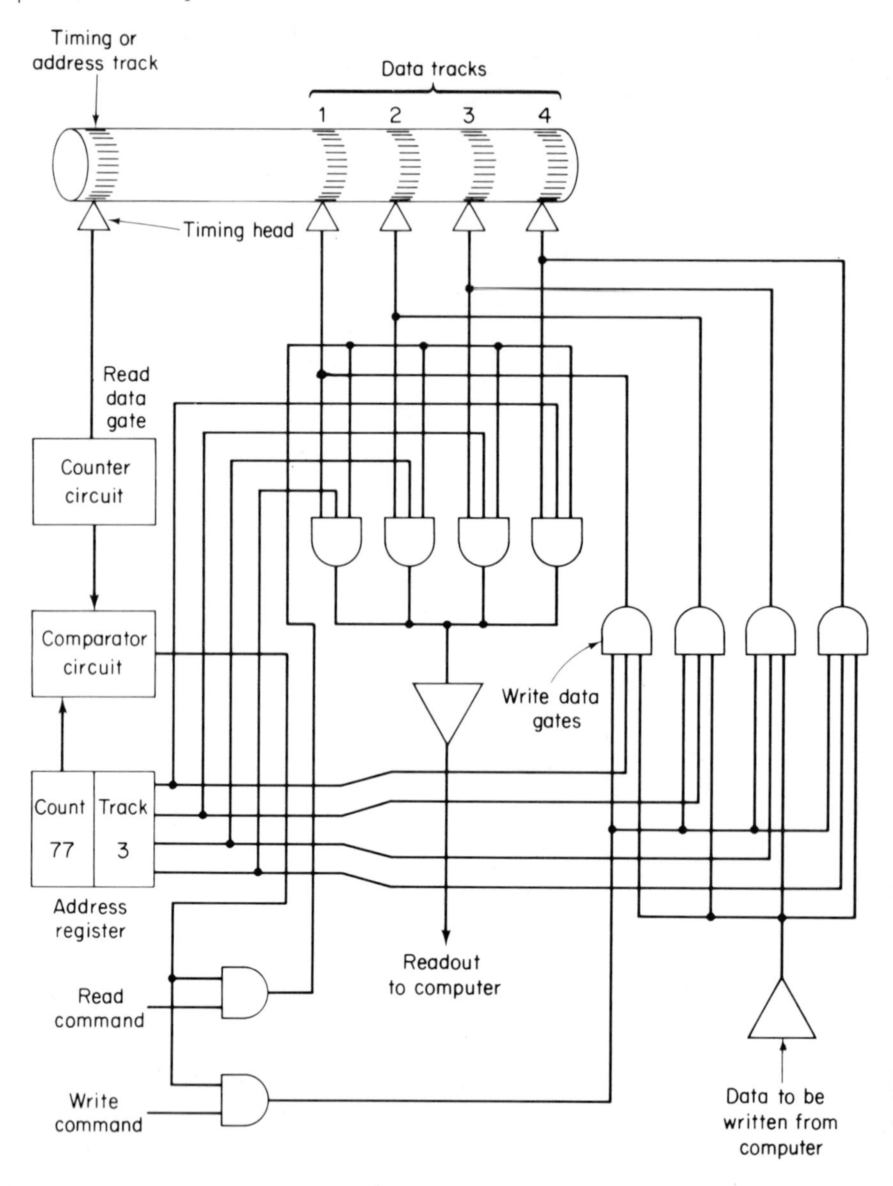

Fig. 8-18. Basic control circuits for magnetic-drum storage.

77 and for track 3. As the drum rotates, pulses from the timing track are read by the counter. When the count reaches 77, the comparison circuit provides an output that is applied to the read and write AND gates. With a read command present from the computer, the read AND

gate is opened, applying a command to the read data gates. These gates require three inputs (data, read, and address register) to open. Since the address register is set to 3, only the 3 data head output is passed to the common amplifier. This type of switching eliminates the need for separate amplifiers at each head. (However, some drum systems do use separate amplifiers, usually in IC form, for each channel.)

Writing on magnetic drum control circuits involves a similar operation. Assume that the instruction is "Write a word at position 88 of track 1." The address register is set for a count of 88 and for track 1. When the count reaches 88, a comparison circuit output is applied to the write AND gates and all write data track gates. However, with the address register at 1, only the 1 data head passes data from the computer to the drum.

Not all magnetic drums use the system shown in Figure 8-18. Several tracks can be used simultaneously to store the bits that make up a single character or number. In such systems, the use of tracks is similar to that described for magnetic tape. That is, the words are recorded serially along the tracks, with several tracks in parallel reserved for a single character (including parity bits and address bits).

E. MAGNETIC-DISC STORAGE

Magnetic-disc devices are general-purpose, random-access storage units and are normally used as input/output auxiliary devices in medium- to large-scale computer systems or for applications requiring large-volume data with immediate accessibility. As shown in Figure 8-19, the magnetic disc is similar to the 45 rpm "jukebox" record. (However, the typical magnetic disc rotation speed is about 1000 rpm.) The unit can consist of a single disc or a series of discs, arranged vertically on a spindle. Some disc models have permanently attached discs, while others use detachable sets of discs (called disc packs). The disc pack is popular because it permits the data in one file to be moved to another location for processing by other computers. Disc packs can be interchanged in about 1 minute.

As shown in Figure 8-19B, each disc face is divided into a number of concentric tracks or channels. Depending on the size of the disc, each track is capable of storing strings of characters serially or in parallel, as is the case with magnetic drums. Each track is divided into records separated by IRGs.

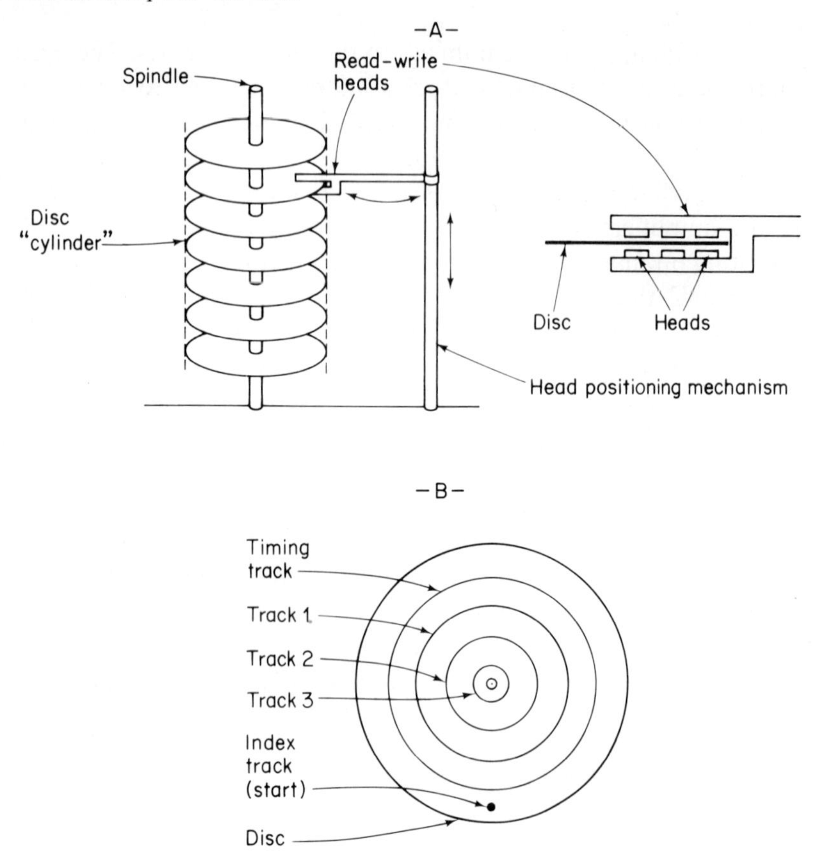

Fig. 8-19. Basic magnetic-disc storage methods.

Each disc is separated from adjacent discs to allow enough room for the movement of read-write heads. One head serves to read and write information on the top surface of the disc, while the other head reads and writes on the bottom surface, thus using both sides of the disc at all times. Since the discs are arranged vertically on a spindle, a given track is in the same relative position on all recording surfaces.

This positioning arrangement is important because once the read-write heads are positioned to read data from one track in a particular *cylinder*, all other tracks in the cylinder can be read without repositioning the read-write heads. This means that many tracks can be read or written with a single move of the read-write heads. Such a capability is of some importance since access time is the most significant factor in using magnetic discs.

Switching and control circuits for magnetic discs are very similar to those for magnetic drums. A separate timing or address track (usually on the outer edge of the disc) carries a series of identification bits that produce timing pulses as the drum rotates past the timing track head. Some magnetic discs also use an index track with a single bit of information to indicate the zero or starting position. As in the case of magnetic tape, several tracks on a disc (or group of discs) can be used for multiple-bit coding (such as for address and parity check).

F. OTHER STORAGE METHODS

There are many other storage methods used in computers. Likewise, new storage methods are being developed. A few of the other storage methods include woven-screen, grid-slot, optoelectric, laminated-ferrite, thin-film, twister, and transfluxer. Most of the newer storage techniques are similar to the basic storage systems described thus far. For example, the thin-film storage is essentially an IC version of the ferrite core memories. With thin-film storage, magnetic material is deposited on semiconductor chips. With woven-screen storage, no ferrite cores are used at the junction of the intersecting wire matrix. Instead, the wires themselves are coated with magnetic material.

From a practical standpoint, if technicians understand the basic storage methods described thus far, they should have no difficulty in understanding the circuit requirements for any new storage method.

G. SUMMARY OF STORAGE CLASSIFICATIONS

As discussed at the beginning of this chapter, computer storage systems are often classified according to type of access. Core memories may be written or read out at any point in time or in any sequence of operation. Thus core memories are true **random-access** (or **direct-access**, depending on which service literature you read) units. A computer tape unit requires reading along the entire length or until the required information is found. Thus tape units are **serial-access** storage forms. Both drums and discs require random (direct) location of the track and then a series search for the specific data—thus the name **random-serial**.

9 OPERATING PRINCIPLES OF A WORKING COMPUTER

This chapter describes operating fundamentals of a Hewlett-Packard 2116 Computer (which we shall refer to as the HP2116, or the computer, in the following discussions). The machine in question is a small, general-purpose digital computer, typical of those found in industrial applications such as data acquisition systems. The computer's physical arrangement is shown in Figure 9-1, with details of the front panel (or operating console) shown in Figure 9-2.

The readers should note that even though these principles and operating steps apply specifically to the HP2116 computer, they are representative of similar steps and principles common to most digital computers.

In this chapter, we shall concentrate on how the HP2116 manipulates information internally to execute the basic instructions for which the computer was designed. In the interest of readers without previous computer experience of any kind, the material in this chapter and in Chapter 10 is organized to begin at an elementary level and to progress

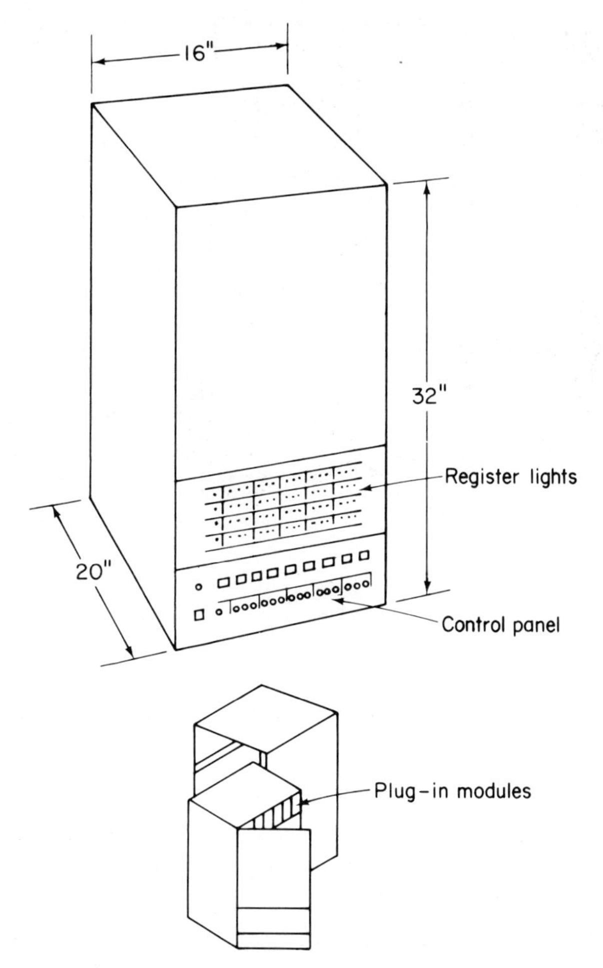

Fig. 9-1. Physical arrangements of the Hewlett-Packard computer.

on the basis of previously given information, in the form of a training course.

Some of the material supplements (and may duplicate) the discussions in previous chapters. However, unless the reader is already thoroughly familiar with computer number systems, basic computer circuits, and computer fundamentals, it is recommended that he study Chapters 1–8 before attempting to understand the following descriptions.

The fundamental operations described in this chapter (and in Chapter 10) are, in practice, nearly always accomplished with the aid of input/

Fig. 9-1a. Hewlett-Packard 2116 computer (top of center rack) shown in typical arrangement with accessories.

output devices and the manufacturer's software. For example, even in the most basic systems, the HP2116 is operated with a keyboard teleprinter for read-in and read-out of data. The computer generally uses one or more of the programs supplied by the manufacturer (possibly in the form of punched paper tape). Likewise, the technician will probably use one or more of the manufacturer's diagnostic programs when testing and troubleshooting the computer.

However, for simplicity, it is assumed in the following discussion that the computer is an independent instrument, operated only by front-panel controls. Also, it is assumed for descriptive purposes that the HP2116 runs slowly enough to observe the operations step by step. When running, the HP2116 reads and executes each instruction usually in 1.6 or 3.2 μS. Thus only the beginning and ending conditions are normally readable on the front-panel display. (Note that it is possible to single-step the HP2116 through each instruction, one phase at a time, by using the *single cycle* pushbutton, Figure 9-2.)

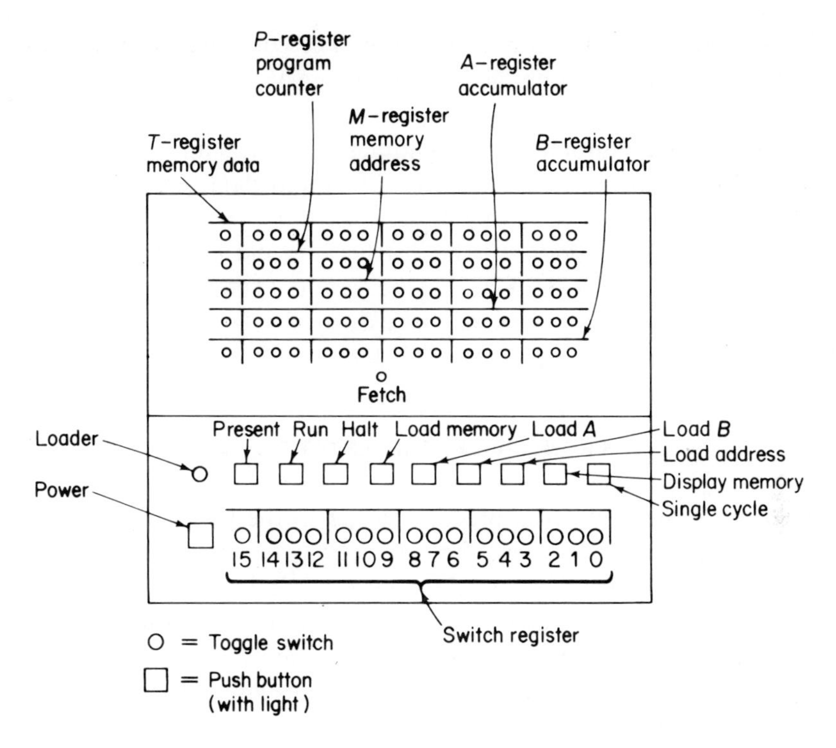

Fig. 9-2. Operating console (front panel) of the Hewlett-Packard computer.

A. OUTLINE OF COMPUTER OPERATION

The computer performs its operations solely by instructions inserted into its memory by the user. The front-panel controls thus do not *operate* the computer but rather are used for entering instructions and data into the memory and for initiating operation of the starting instruction. Very basically, the overall operation is as follows.

The user enters instructions and data (all manually set in binary coded numbers on the 16 switches of the switch registers, Figure 9-2) into the computer's memory, using the load address and load memory push buttons.

When the program of instructions is complete in the memory and is ready to be run, the user enters the address of the starting instruction, which points the computer to the location in the memory where the first instruction has been stored. The switch register and load address switches are used for this purpose.

The user presses the run pushbutton. The computer reads and executes the instruction contained in the memory cell designated by the starting address.

The computer automatically continues to the next and all succeeding instructions, operating on the internally stored data, until reaching a halt instruction.

The user, having prepared the instructions and knowing where the computer answer is stored, reads the result. (The load address and display memory pushbuttons may be used to display the answer on the front panel.)

B. FRONT-PANEL PRESENTATION

To present the material of this chapter in the most practical form from the user's point of view, the descriptions relate to the front-panel view of the computer (Figure 9-2). Figure 9-3 is a simplified block diagram of the HP2116, showing the relationship of the display registers. The block diagram, which corresponds to the physical layout of the panel (shaded areas), is used for descriptions of register operations later in this chapter.

As shown in Figure 9-2, information is displayed in rows of 16 lights, numbered 0–15. The lights indicate the state (0 or 1) of corresponding FFs in the computer registers. The switch register consists of 16 switches, numbered in an identical fashion to the register lights.

Each light or switch represents a bit in the binary numbering system, where a light off or a switch down is a 0 and a light on or a switch up is a 1. As discussed, in the binary system there are only two digits (0 and 1), which are easily stored and manipulated by a computer using bistable devices (FFs). Thus input information that is applied to the computer in binary form (such as by the switch register) is said to be in machine language since the computer can handle these numbers directly without conversions of any kind. For the user, however, binary numbers (such as 1011010011101000) are difficult to read and use, so the bits are grouped in threes for convenient notation in the octal numbering system.

For a full discussion of the octal and binary number systems, as well as conversions to and from the decimal system, refer to Chapter 3. The following paragraphs describe how the octal and binary number systems relate to the computer front-panel presentation.

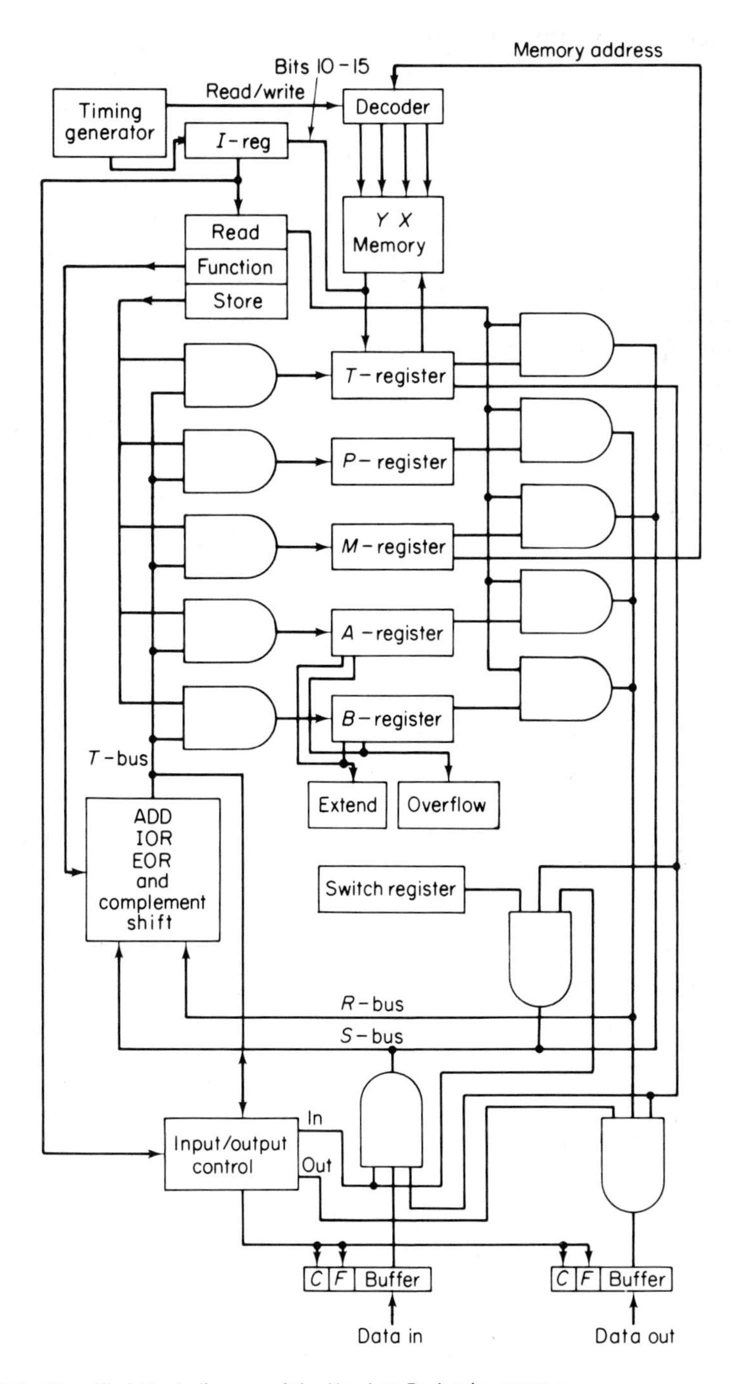

Fig. 9-3. Simplified block diagram of the Hewlett-Packard computer

There are five three-bit groups in each row of panel lights and the switch register, with one bit remaining at the left end. Since this last bit (bit 15) is normally used for special purposes (typically, to indicate direct/indirect addressing or +/− numbers), the following paragraphs disregard this bit and deal only with the 15 bits numbered 0–14. The concept of using bit 15 for signed numbers is introduced later.

In converting any group of three bits to an octal digit, the binary significance of each bit is converted to its absolute value, which is then considered to be absent or present, depending on whether the bit is a 0 (light off) or a 1 (light on), respectively. This arrangement is shown in Figure 9-4.

By various combinations of on and off states, eight digits are possible, 0–7. The digits 8 and 9 never appear in the octal numbering system. Figure 9-5 lists all eight binary-octal equivalents, along with some examples of numbers that might be read from an HP2116 display register.

As can be seen in the last example of Figure 9-5, the largest possible number that can be displayed by a register is 77777 (all lights on). Since there are no 8s or 9s in the octal system, this number must correspond to some lower falue in the decimal system (specifically 32767).

To avoid confusion when numbers are written in more than one numbering system, a subscripted digit is attached to the number to identify the system used. Thus

$$111111111111111_2 = 77777_8 = 32767_{10}.$$

The following chapters use these subscripts or the word binary, octal, or decimal whenever such confusion may occur.

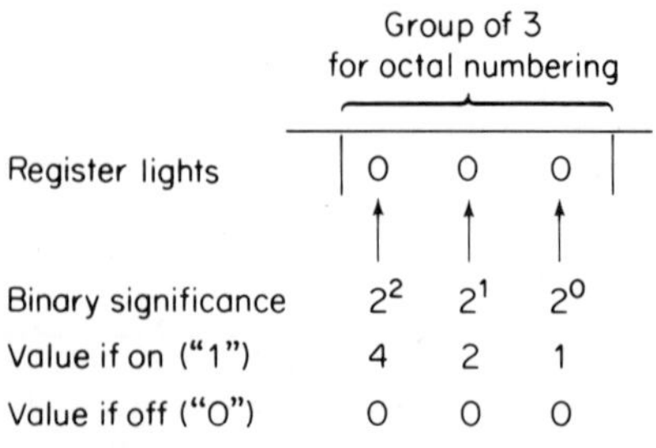

	Group of 3 for octal numbering		
Register lights	O	O	O
Binary significance	2^2	2^1	2^0
Value if on ("1")	4	2	1
Value if off ("0")	0	0	0

Fig. 9-4. Composition of octal digits on computer registers.

Binary		Octal Interpretation	Octal
000	=	0	= 0
001	=	1	= 1
010	=	2	= 2
011	=	2+1	= 3
100	=	4	= 4
101	=	4+1	= 5
110	=	4+2	= 6
111	=	4+2+1	= 7

Examples

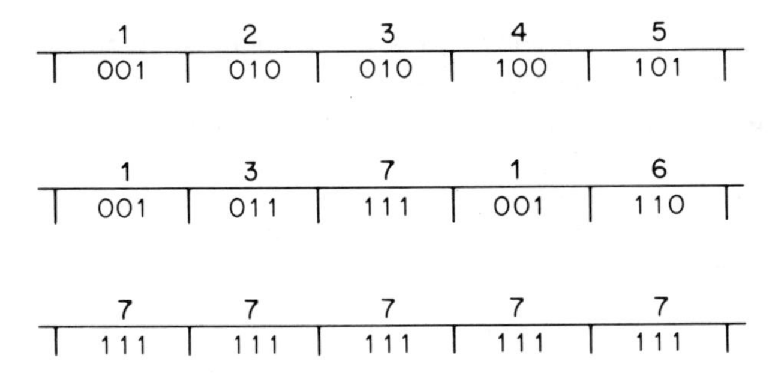

Fig. 9-5. Binary-octal conversions as they appear on computer registers (switches or register lights).

C. BASIC COMPUTER ARITHMETIC

In the basic instructions of the HP2116, there is an add instruction but no subtract, multiply, or divide. Thus the last three operations must be constructed from the add instruction or by some other method. Although it is possible to perform multiplication and division by successive addition or subtraction, respectively, the more efficient method is by register manipulation available through special computer programming. (Refer to Chapter 6.)

To subtract, the operation is to convert the subtrahend (negative number) to its *true complement* value and then to add as if both numbers were positive. The result is the true difference between the two numbers when the last carry digit is removed. Simple logic in the computer drops the excess carry, so that the user need not be aware of it.

The true complement of a number in any system is obtained by subtracting the number from any power of the base large enough to allow the arithmetic to bc performed. That is, five digits are required if four-digit numbers are involved:

Decimal	Octal	Binary	
10000	10000	10000	
− 798	− 567	− 101	(subtrahend)
9202	7211	1011	(true complement)

Once the true complement has been obtained, it is added to the number from which the subtrahend is to be subtracted. For example, assume that the computer is to perform the following subtraction:

Decimal	Octal	Binary	
9123	7123	1010	
− 798	− 567	− 101	(subtrahend)
8325	6334	101	

Using the true complement method, the answers are

Decimal	Octal	Binary	
9123	7123	1010	
+9202	+7211	+1011	(true complement)
18325	16334	10101	
Or 8325	Or 6334	Or 101	(with carry dropped)

The true complement method of subtraction may appear to be extra work when the problems are done on paper. However, the process is much simpler for the computer. In computers such as the HP2116, it is even more simple to use the one's complement (subtracting from 1s instead of 0s) where all 1s are switched to 0s and vice versa. Adding 1 to the result produces the true two's complement. (Note that the one's complement in binary corresponds to the nine's complement in decimal and the seven's complement in octal.) Using the same examples,

	Decimal	Octal	Binary	
	9999	7777	1111	
	− 798	− 567	− 101	(subtrahend)
	9201	7210	1010	
Add:	1	1	1	
	9202	7211	1011	(true complement)

Negative numbers are constructed and used in the HP2116 in exactly this way. For example, if the negative number 07000_8 is wanted for some later arithmetic, this number is taken in positive form, one's complemented and incremented, and is then ready for use as a two's complement negative number. However, it is necessary to identify the number as negative. This is done by a 1 bit in the bit-15 position (extreme left-hand digit of each register). Using the binary-octal register arrangement as it appears on the front panel, the operation is

	Bit 15 sign	0	7	0	0	0	Octal
Positive:	0	000	111	000	000	000	
Complement:	1	111	000	111	111	111	
Increment:						+1	
Negative: (two's complement representation)	1	111	001	000	000	000	equals (171000_8).

If it is now desired to perform a subtraction (say, $60000_8 - 07000_8 = 51000_8$), the computer adds the positive number and the two's complement representation as shown below. (For comparison, a subtraction producing a negative answer is also shown.) Note that bit 15 is treated as part of the negative number in all arithmetic operations, and unless overflow occurs (registers are too full to handle an additional bit), bit 15 will always appear as a 0 for computed answers that are positive or as a 1 for negative answers. Since there are only 16 bit places available to represent the total in any register, the final carry (seventeenth bit, carried to the extend register) is disregarded, and the displayed result is the true difference.

	Binary	Octal
Positive answer:		
	0 110 000 000 000 000	(+60000)
	1 111 001 000 000 000	(−70000)
(1)	0 101 001 000 000 000	(+51000)
Negative answer:		
	1 010 000 000 000 000	(−60000)
	1 000 111 000 000 000	(+07000)
	1 010 111 000 000 000	(−51000)

The basic instructions of the HP2116 include a positive-to-negative conversion (one's complement and increment). Thus it is usually not necessary for the operator to figure the complements before entering them into the computer. The reverse conversion (from negative to positive) is done in exactly the same way (one's complement, then increment). Thus, if the negative number 07000_8 is present in the computer memory (stored as 171000_8, or $1\,111\,001\,000\,000\,000_2$), conversion back to positive is

Negative:	1 111 001 000 000 000	
Complement:	0 000 110 111 111 111	
Increment:	+1	
Positive:	0 000 111 000 000 000	(equals 007000_8).

As a negative number grows larger, its representation in two's complement form grows smaller. The largest negative number that can be represented in a display register is therefore a 1 with 15 0s. This is equivalent to a positive number of

Negative:	1 000 000 000 000 000	
Complement:	0 111 111 111 111 111	
Increment:	+1	
Positive:	1 000 000 000 000 000	(or 100000_8 or 32768_{10}).

D. COMPUTER CIRCUIT STRUCTURE

The simplified block diagram of the computer, Figure 9-3, is the basis for the partial versions used to illustrate descriptions in the

the following paragraphs. Figure 9-3 is reconstructed step by step as explanations progress.

The first step is Figure 9-6, which outlines the blocks and signal routes mentioned in the following discussion of the memory. The block diagrams make use of several AND gate symbols in addition to circuit blocks. These gates can produce an output only when all inputs are present (or true). For example, referring to Figure 9-3, data on the T bus can enter the T register only if a store signal is also present at the gate leading to the T-register input. Since the store signal is selective (although it is not indicated on the diagram), only this one gate is enabled, while the remaining four are disabled. Thus the data enter only the selected register.

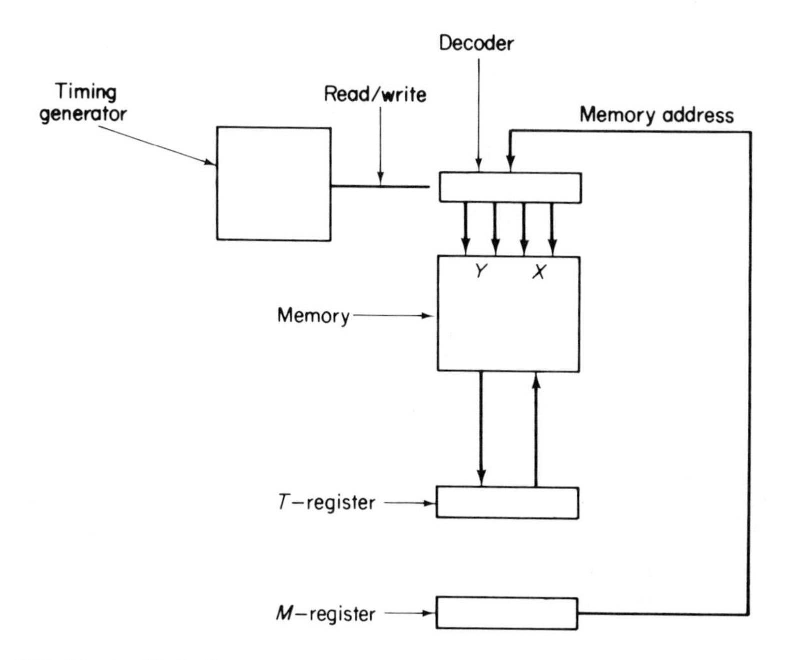

Fig. 9-6. Memory block diagram.

E. MEMORY MODULE

As discussed in Chapter 8, the memory of any computer is the storage area. The primary storage area of the HP2116 computer is a core memory, inside the computer. Auxiliary storage for the HP2116 is available in the form of disc storage and magnetic tape. The auxiliary storage units are accessed through the computer's input/output system and are not treated as an extension of memory in this discussion.

Figure 9-7 shows the physical structure of the memory module, and the following paragraphs describe each of the four components that make up the module.

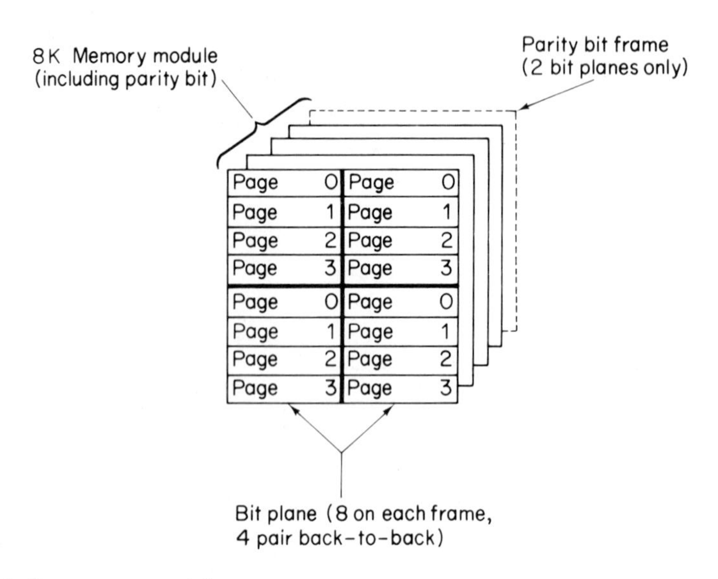

Fig. 9-7. Core memory module.

1. *Core.* As discussed in Chapter 8, the ferrite core (a small ring of magnetic material) has the ability to store binary information in that clockwise and counterclockwise magnetization can be assigned digital values of 1 and 0. By threading a current-carrying wire through the core, the core's direction of magnetization can be reversed simply by changing direction of the current. Since the mass of the core is very small (0.03-in. diameter), little magnetizing force is required to switch the binary state, thus permitting fast switching speeds (about 400 nS in the HP2116). The magnetic state remains indefinitely after the current is removed, so that switching can be accomplished by bidirectional current pulses. This is shown in Figure 9-8.

Since it is necessary to be able to select desired uses of information in the memory module, four wires are threaded through each core, as

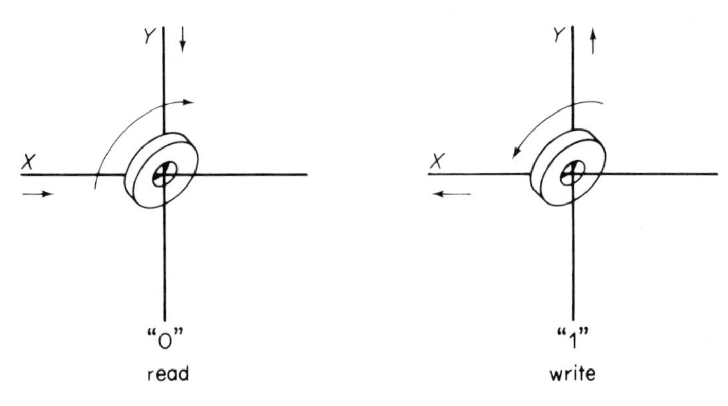

Fig. 9-8. Binary storage in a magnetic core.

shown in Figure 9-9. In practice, the wires do not *loop* through the core, as shown for clarity in the figure, but simply pass through the center of a series of cores. Figure 9-9 shows how one bit of information is addressed and transferred to and from the T register. Operation is as follows:

a. Assume that the computer is running and that the program has set the M register to a memory location number (address) desiring access to that location.

b. The address from the M register, consisting of 12 binary bits, is applied to a binary-to-octal decoder, which reduces the 12 binary address lines to four octal lines that thread, in pairs, through the selected core. For purposes of illustration, the diode decoding matrix is shown as four switches. Note that each of these switches can select one of eight ends of the X and Y wires, thus making possible $8 \times 8 \times 8 \times 8 = 4096$ combinations to address 4096 core locations.

c. At a specific time in the computer's timing sequence (start of each memory cycle), all 16 bits of the T register are reset to zero.

d. A read pulse is then applied to the decoder. Many cores will receive either a Y-current or X-current pulse, neither of which alone is sufficient to switch the state of the core, but only one core out of 4096 on a plane receives both Y-current and X-current pulses. The read current is always in the direction that will magnetize the core in the 0 direction. (If more than one module is present, module selection is accomplished simply by routing the read pulse to the appropriate module, as determined by bits 12, 13, and 14 of the M register.)

e. If the core was previously magnetized in the 1 direction, the read

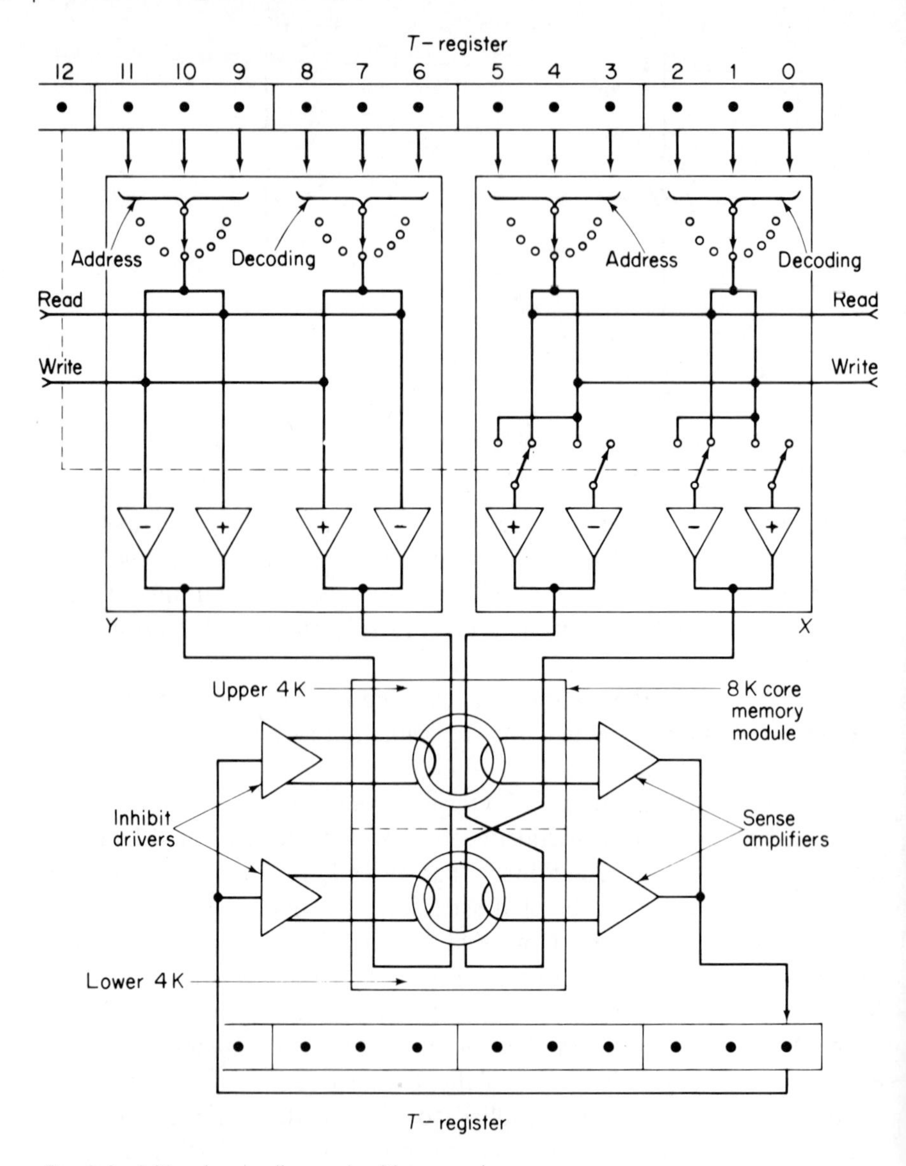

Fig. 9-9. Addressing, reading, and writing cores in memory.

current, in switching the core, causes a flux change that induces a current into the sense output line. This output is amplified and used to set the corresponding bit FF of the T register (assumed to be bit 0 in Figure 9-9). If the core was in the 0 state, there is no flux change and the *T*-register bit remains 0 (as reset in step c).

f. Since steps d and e destroyed the stored information, it is necessary to write the information back. This information, which is now in the T register, is connected back to the core via the inhibit line. Then the *X* and *Y* lines are pulsed with a write current pulse, which is of opposite polarity to the read pulse (that is, tending to magnetize in the 1 direction).

g. If the inhibit current is not turned on, the core switches back to the 1 state. If the inhibit current is turned on, it cancels part of the write magnetizing force, so that the core cannot switch, and the core remains in the 0 state.

The sequence of events in the preceding paragraphs briefly describes the HP2116's *memory cycle*. There are two exceptions that modify the memory slightly: (1) during the execute phase of the store instructions, the output of the sense amplifier is inhibited, and instead the data to be stored are transferred into the T register from the A or B register during the read time period; (2) during the execute phase of the increment-skip-if-zero instruction, the T register is incremented between the read and write time periods

2. *Memory location*. The word length of the HP2116 is 16 bits, only one of which is shown in Figure 9-9. To store one 16-bit word, 16 cores are required, as indicated in Figure 9-7. These 16 cores comprise a *memory location*, sometimes referred to as a *memory cell*. When information is transferred into or out of a memory location, the information in all 16 bits must be transferred simultaneously. Thus the *X* and *Y* selection lines are strung through the 16 cores, causing the reading and writing of all 16 cores simultaneously. Figure 9-10 illustrates this condition, showing only three cores for simplicity. Note that each of these cores is on a different plane.

3. *Bit plane*. Cores are strung on a grid of wires as shown in Figure 9-11. There are 4096 cores on this grid, called a bit plane. An 8K module consists of five frames with each of the first four frames having eight bit planes each, four on each side back to back (Figure 9-7), and the fifth frame having only two bit planes (for the parity bit). Thus there are two bit planes for each of the 16 bits (32 planes) plus two planes for the parity bit (making a total of 34 planes).

Each bit position of the T register is wired by the sense and inhibit lines through all 8192 cores on the corresponding bit plane. Since only one core on an individual bit plane is sensed (addressed) at a given time, the sense line needs only to detect a flux change anywhere on the

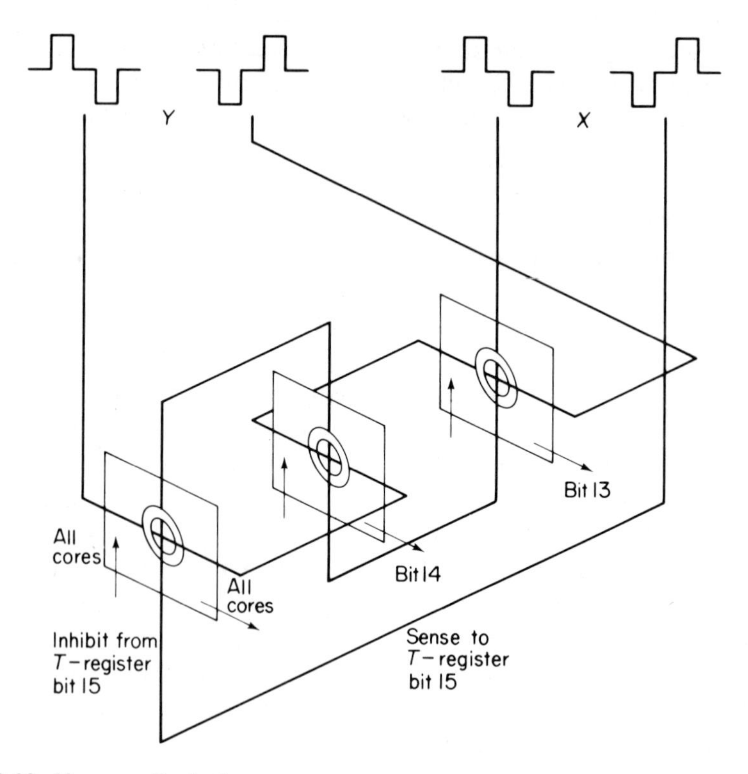

Fig. 9-10. Memory cell selection.

bit plane. Similarly, the inhibit signal is applied to the entire bit plane when writing but actually affects only the selected core.

4. *Page.* Pages of a memory are not physical divisions of the module. Wiring of the bit planes is symmetrical and does not account for page boundries. The page boundries are determined only by the bit format of memory reference instructions and are shown as broken lines in Figure 9-7 for visualizing the physical placement of memory pages.

5. *Memory layout.* The 8192-word memory module is logically divided into eight pages of 1024 words each. A page is defined as the largest block of memory that can be addressed by the memory address bits of a memory reference instruction (excluding the zero/current page bit, discussed in the following paragraphs). In the HP2116, memory reference instructions have ten bits to specify a memory address, and in this the page size is 1024 locations (2000 in octal notation). Octal addresses of the four pages of the basic module and also a second module are therefore

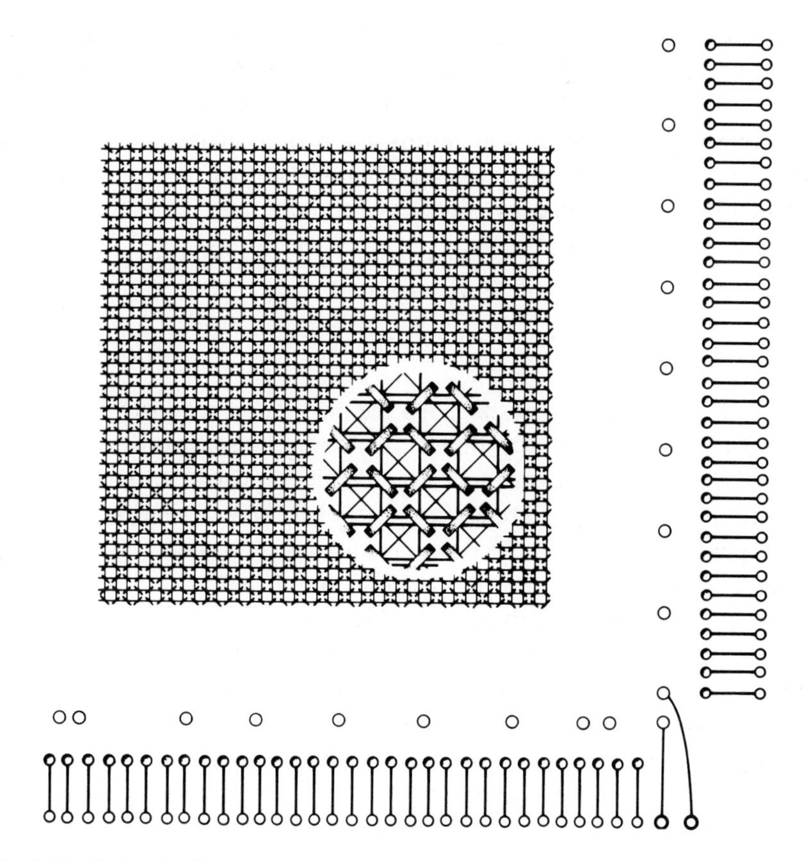

Fig. 9-11. Typical ferrite core plane (bit plane) arrangement.

Basic module:

	00000 to 01777
	02000 to 03777
	04000 to 05777
Lower 4K	06000 to 07777
Upper 4K	10000 to 11777
	12000 to 13777
	14000 to 15777
	16000 to 17777.

6. *Zero/current page addressing.* For direct addressing purposes, generally only two memory pages are of interest: page zero (the base

page, consisting of locations 00000–01777) and the current page (the page in which the instruction itself is located). All memory reference instructions include a bit (bit 10) reserved to specify one or the other of these two pages. To address locations in any other page, *indirect addressing* is used. Page references for direct addressing of memory reference instructions are specified by bit 10 as follows:

0 = page zero (Z)

1 = current page (C).

7. *Direct/indirect addressing.* All memory reference instructions use bit 15 to specify direct or indirect addressing. Direct addressing combines the instruction code and the effective address into one word, permitting a memory reference instruction to be executed in two machine phases (fetch and execute, as discussed in later paragraphs). Indirect addressing uses the address portion of the instruction word to access another word in memory, which is taken as a new memory reference for the same instruction. This new address is a full 16 bits long, 15 bits of address plus another direct/indirect bit.

The 15-bit length of the address permits access to any location in any module. If bit 15 again specifies indirect addressing, still another address is obtained. This multiple-step indirect addressing may be done to any number of levels. The first address obtained in the indirect phase, which does not specify another indirect level, becomes the effective address for the instruction. Instructions with indirect addresses are thus executed in a minimum of three machine phases (fetch, indirect, execute). Direct or indirect addressing is specified by bit 15 as follows:

0 = direct

1 = indirect.

8. *Reserved locations.* Note that the first 64 memory locations of the base page (octal addresses 00000–00077) as well as the last 64 locations of the memory (octal addresses 17700–17777) are reserved for special purposes. The last 64 memory locations are reserved for a special program (supplied by the manufacturer). The first 64 locations are used as follows:

00000	address of A register
00001	address of B register
00002 } 00003 }	for exit sequence if A and B contents are used as executable words
00004	Interrupt location, highest priority (reserved for power fail interrupt)
00005	reserved for memory parity interrupt and memory protect interrupt
00006 } 00007 }	reserved for direct memory address interrupt
00010 } 00017 }	interrupt locations in decreasing order of priority.

F. THE REGISTERS

Figure 9-12 shows the seven working registers of the HP2116. The five principal registers (T, P, M, A, and B) are purposely shown as being independent of each other since, in fact, information is not transferred directly from register to register. Rather, information is transmitted via the bus system (described in subdivision G of this chapter) under command of the instruction logic (described in subdivision H of this chapter). The following paragraphs explain what the registers do and why they are needed. In essence the registers are short-term information storage devices consisting of FF circuits, with front-panel indicator lamps to indicate the status of each bit (by indicating the state of the corresponding FF).

1. *T register*. All data transferred into or out of the memory are routed through the 16-bit T register (*transfer register*). The T register is the *memory data* register and indicates what went into or out of a memory cell during the preceding memory cycle. For the majority of operations when a computer is running, the principal concern is with the data readout of a memory cell. Once a word of information is in the T register, it is accessible for arithmetic operations and for transfers to other registers via the bus system. For the reverse (write) operation, the T register is loaded by transfers from other registers, and the information is stored in the memory during the latter half of the memory cycle.

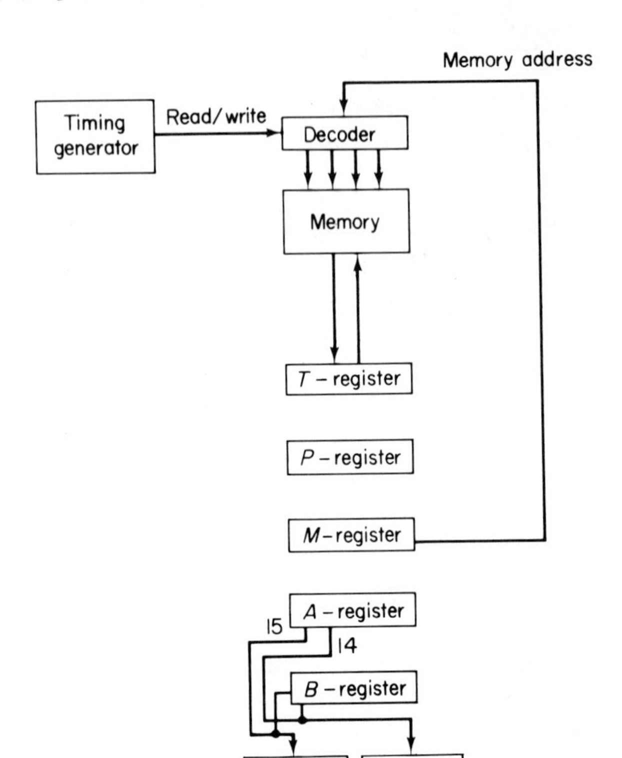

Fig. 9-12. Register block diagram.

2. *P register.* The P register is the computer's program counter. Upon completion of each instruction, the P register indicates the address of the next instruction to be fetched out of memory. The P register automatically increments by 1 (or 2, when executing a skip instruction) after the execution of each instruction. A jump instruction can set the P register to any core location number.

In effect, the P register goes through a step-by-step counting sequence and causes the computer to read successive memory locations, corresponding to the existing count. In the simplest case, the P register will start at zero when the run pushbutton is pressed, causing memory location 00000 to be read into the T register; the computer acts on the instruction code in the readout data and then advances the P register to 1 (memory location 00001_8). This process of stepping through memory locations (at a rate of 1.6 or 3.2 μS/step for most instructions) continues until one of the instructions read out is a halt, which terminates the program.

Of necessity, this simple case is not typical. First, programs do not normally begin at locations lower than 00077_8, since these locations are reserved for special purposes. Thus the starting address of a program must be manually set into the P register before pressing the run pushbutton. Second, the strict sequential stepping can be altered in the course of a program, either by a skip instruction (which causes the P register to increment by 2 instead of 1, thus skipping one memory location) or by a jump instruction (which transfers numbers from another register into the P register, thus causing the program to continue at a different point in memory).

3. *M register*. The M register is the computer's memory address register and holds the address of the memory cell being read or written into. The M register indication differs from the P register indication when multiphase instructions are being processed, since the M register will be changed by memory references in the instructions (which may be several in the case of indirect addressing) or by an interrupt, whereas the P register remains constant until completion of the instruction.

The setting of the M register can occur from any of the other registers, depending on the effects of instructions. It could be assumed that the P register directly addresses memory. In actual fact, however, the computer must transfer the desired address from the P register to the M register, which in turn addresses the desired memory location. Thus it is seen that these two registers (P and M) frequently contain the same number. The reason both registers are needed is that it is necessary for one register (P) to keep track of the location of the current instruction in case the instruction is a multiple-phase type. In this case, the M register may have to be changed several times in the course of executing an instruction.

A common example is when the instruction is "Add the contents of location 100_8 to the A register" (ADA 100). The P and M registers are identical while reading this instruction out of memory (say the instruction is in location 500_8; both registers indicate this value). Then the M register must change to 100 to get the contents of this location for the addition. After the addition has been executed, the contents of the P register are incremented by 1 (501_8). The P and M registers are then both set to this new value, and the computer is ready to read out the next instruction.

4. *A register*. The A register is an accumulator, holding the results of arithmetic and logical operations performed by programmed instructions. The A register may be addressed to any memory reference instruction, such as location 00000, thus permitting interregister operations such as "Add B to A," "Compare B with A," etc., using a single-word instruction.

As discussed, an accumulator in a computer accumulates the results of arithmetic operations. A simple example is given in the preceding paragraph, where one number from memory is added to the existing contents of the A register. Assuming that the A register previously held the number 1000_8 and the number in location 100 is 22_8, the number left in the A register after execution is 1022_8.

Other types of operation which may be done with the A register are Boolean logic operations (AND, EXCLUSIVE OR, INCLUSIVE OR), comparison for equality with a memory word, shifting or rotating bits left or right, testing the status of individual bits, complementing bits, and accepting or holding data for transfer to and from external devices. All these functions are accomplished by the instruction logic (described in subdivision H of this chapter).

5. *B register*. The B register is a second accumulator, which can hold the results of arithmetic and logical operations completely independent of the A register. The B register may be addressed by any memory reference instruction, such as location 00001, for interregister operations with the A register.

The B register has the same capabilities as the A register, except that the three Boolean logic instructions of AND, EXCLUSIVE OR (listed as XOR), and INCLUSIVE OR (listed as IOR) can apply only to the A register. The main reason for having two accumulators is to provide faster, more flexible arithmetic than can be accomplished with one accumulator.

6. *E register*. The E register (extend register) is a one-bit register, used to link the A and B registers by rotate instructions or to include a carry from bit 15 of the A or B register by an add or increment instruction. This is of significance primarily where arithmetic functions must be carried out several places. The E-register bit (known as the extend bit or E bit) is not complemented by a carry if already set. The E bit can be cleared, complemented, or tested by program instructions. The E bit is set when the EXTEND panel light is on (1) and clear when off (0).

The E register is shown connected to bit 15 of both the A and B registers. This is to indicate that the one-bit E register becomes set whenever there is a carry out of bit 15 of either accumulator (that is, whenever the quantity accumulated exceeds 16 ones). This fact is frequently of considerable significance. For example, if the quantity in an accumulator is 16 ones and an ADD instruction adds 1, the result in the accumulator is 16 zeros. This answer is obviously incorrect; it is correct if the E bit, which is now in the set state (1), is temporarily assumed to be "bit 16." The program can be written to make this assumption, and it can proceed without error on the basis of the resulting information. To be certain that the extend information is valid, the E register is normally cleared by an instruction before the addition is done.

Another valuable feature of the E register is the ability to link the two accumulators (A and B registers), effectively providing a single 32-bit accumulator.

7. *Overflow register.* The overflow register is a one-bit register that (when in the on or set state) indicates that an add or increment instruction referencing the A or B register has caused one of these accumulators to exceed the maximum positive or negative number that can be contained (+32767 or −32768, decimal). This condition is implied by a carry (or lack of carry) from bit 14 to bit 15. By program instructions, the overflow bit may be cleared, set, or tested. The overflow panel light remains on until the bit is cleared by an instruction and is not complemented if a second overflow occurs before being cleared. It will not be set by shift or rotate instructions.

The overflow register is similar in purpose to the E register. However, there is a difference: whereas the E register indicates that the largest 16-bit quantity has been exceeded, the overflow register indicates that the largest *signed* (+ or −) quantity has been exceeded. (A program may work with both signed and unsigned numbers.)

Since bit 15 is the sign bit, bit 14 (as shown in Figure 9-12) is the source of the significant carry. Having two possible signs (+ and −) means that detection of overflow requires two different sets of conditions. For the addition of two positive numbers, overflow occurs if there is a carry from bit 14 to bit 15 in one of the accumulators. For addition of two negative numbers (which are represented in two's complement form), overflow occurs if there is not a carry from bit 14 to bit 15. Obviously overflow cannot occur when adding numbers of opposite signs, since the resulting quantity cannot be greater than the larger of the two numbers. As with the E register, the overflow register should be cleared before an addition.

G. THE BUS SYSTEM

Figure 9-13 outlines the routes by which data travel internally from one register to another. Although the buses are represented by a

Fig. 9-13. Bus system block diagram.

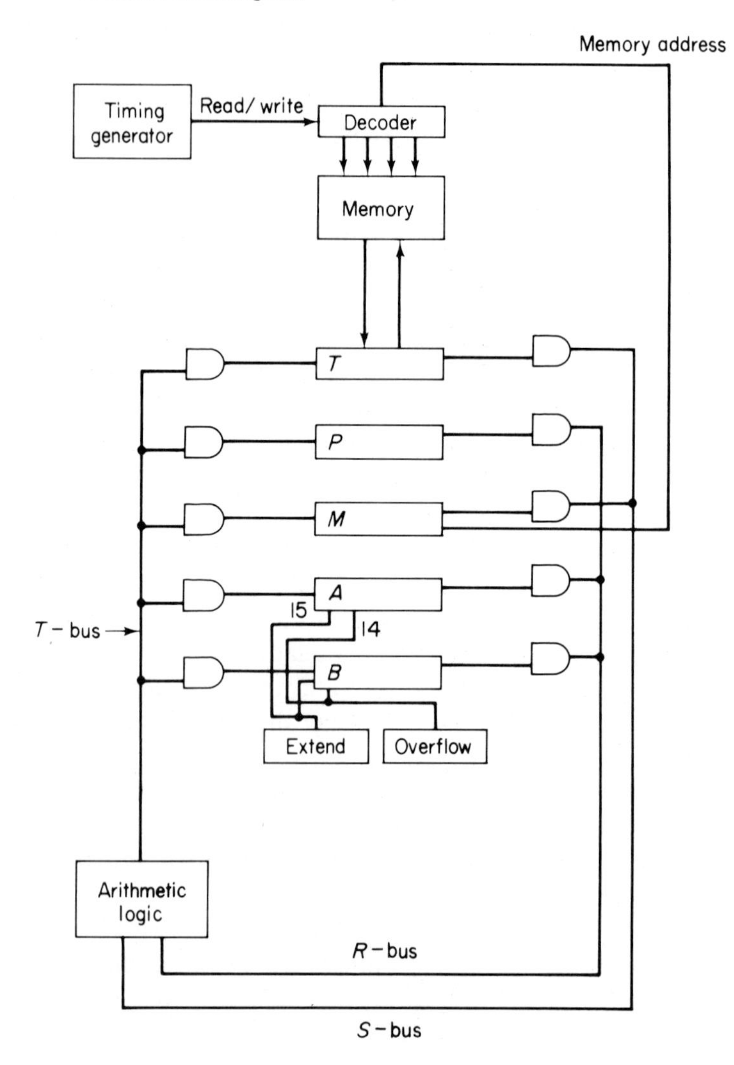

single line in this figure, assume each line to be composed of 16 individual lines, one for each register bit. Included in Figure 9-13 is an *arithmetic logic* block, which has not previously been discussed. It is shown here mainly to illustrate the linkage between buses.

The HP2116 uses an R-S-T bus configuration. This is a conventional notation designating a three-bus system that applies two input buses (R and S) to an arithmetic unit with an output on the third bus (T). The use of two input buses permits arithmetic operations combining the contents of two registers. A common example is the execution of the ADA 100 instruction previously used (in the M register). In this example, the contents of location 100 is the number 22_8. During execution of the instruction, the number (22_8) is read into the T register. The other number (1000_8) is in the A register. Simultaneously, both the T register and the A register are read into their respective buses (S and R). The two numbers are added in the arithmetic logic circuits, and the result (1022_8) is stored via the T bus back into the A register as the accumulator sum.

Note that several register combinations are possible as inputs to the arithmetic logic. One point worth noting is that since the A and B registers are addressable as memory locations, the contents of these registers can be transferred via the R and T buses into the T register. From this point, the contents can be combined with either accumulator (including combining the number with itself; that is, "add A to A"). This is all accomplished in one instruction.

H. THE INSTRUCTION LOGIC

Figure 9-14 shows the elements of the instruction logic in the HP2116. As indicated, timing is essential to operation of the instruction logic. The following descriptions do not detail all timing relationships since these vary with instructions, but it should be understood that timing pulses are gated with each operation to make it occur in proper sequence. Machine timing is discussed in detail throughout the remainder of this chapter.

As shown in Figure 9-14, the six most significant bits read out of memory (bits 10–15) during each memory cycle are applied to the 6-bit instruction register (I reg), which decodes the instruction. (Actually, the instruction register receives its information via the T register; for simplicity, Figure 9-14 shows a direct connection to the memory.)

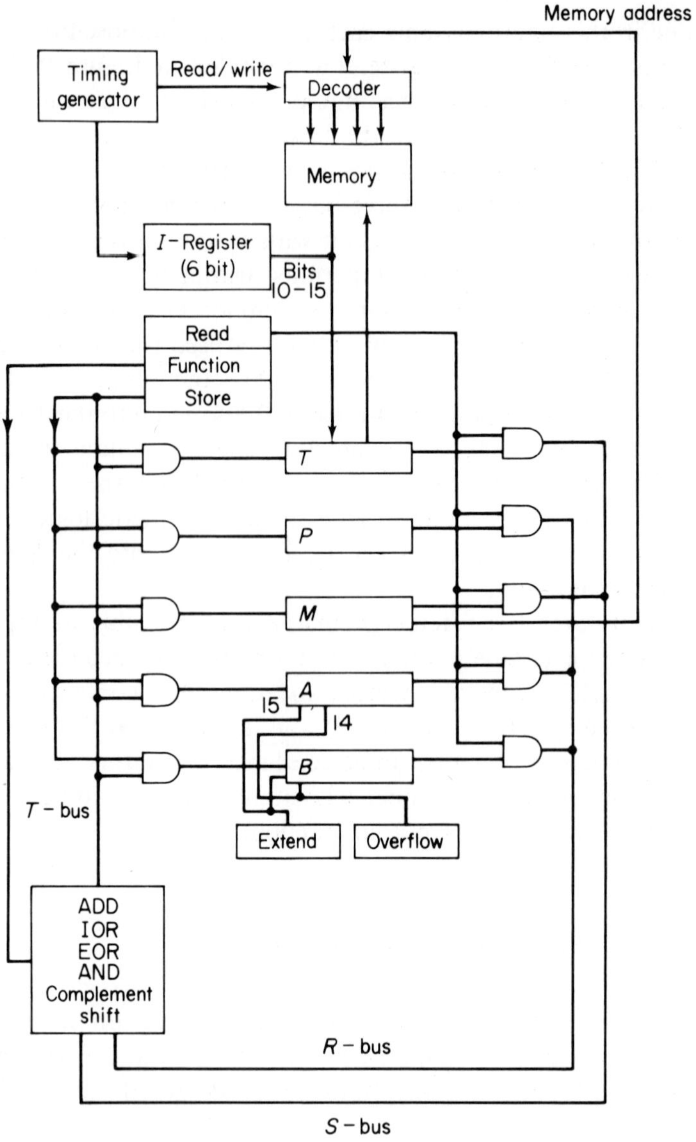

Fig. 9-14. Instruction logic block diagram.

Only during the fetch phase (described in subdivision J of this chapter), however, are these bits recognized as an instruction code. At this time, the decoded instruction enables three functional operations, which, in turn, will become active at a specific time, depending on the instruction. These operations are described in the next three paragraphs.

1. *Read.* The read signal, shown connected to the output gate of all five working registers, strobes the data of one or two registers onto their corresponding buses (R and S). This places the data at the inputs of the arithemtic logic circuits.

2. *Function.* The function signal activates one of the six listed arithemtic functions. The selected function alters or combines the data on the R and/or S buses and routes the resulting data out on the T bus.

3. *Store.* The store signal, shown connected to the input gate of all five working registers, effectively opens the input of one or more of these registers to accept the data that appears on the T bus. In many cases, depending on the instruction, only part of the information on the T bus is stored into a register.

I. THE INPUT/OUTPUT SYSTEM

Figure 9-15 shows the means by which data are transferred in and out of the computer. This is the input/output system; all elements shown are contained within the main frame. Interface arrangements are shown for only two external devices, one input and one output. Actually, the computer has provisions for interfacing with many units simultaneously. The switch register is shown as part of the input/output system and is considered as an input device (since data can be entered into the computer, depending on the switch positions).

As indicated by Figure 9-15, the input/output control logic is used to process all input/output operations. Input/output control operates in two ways:

1. Processes input/output instructions.
2. Processes service requests by peripheral devices.

These two types of operations are discussed separately in the following paragraphs.

Processing input/output instructions

Input/output instructions decoded by the instruction register are routed to input/output control, which translates the instruction into

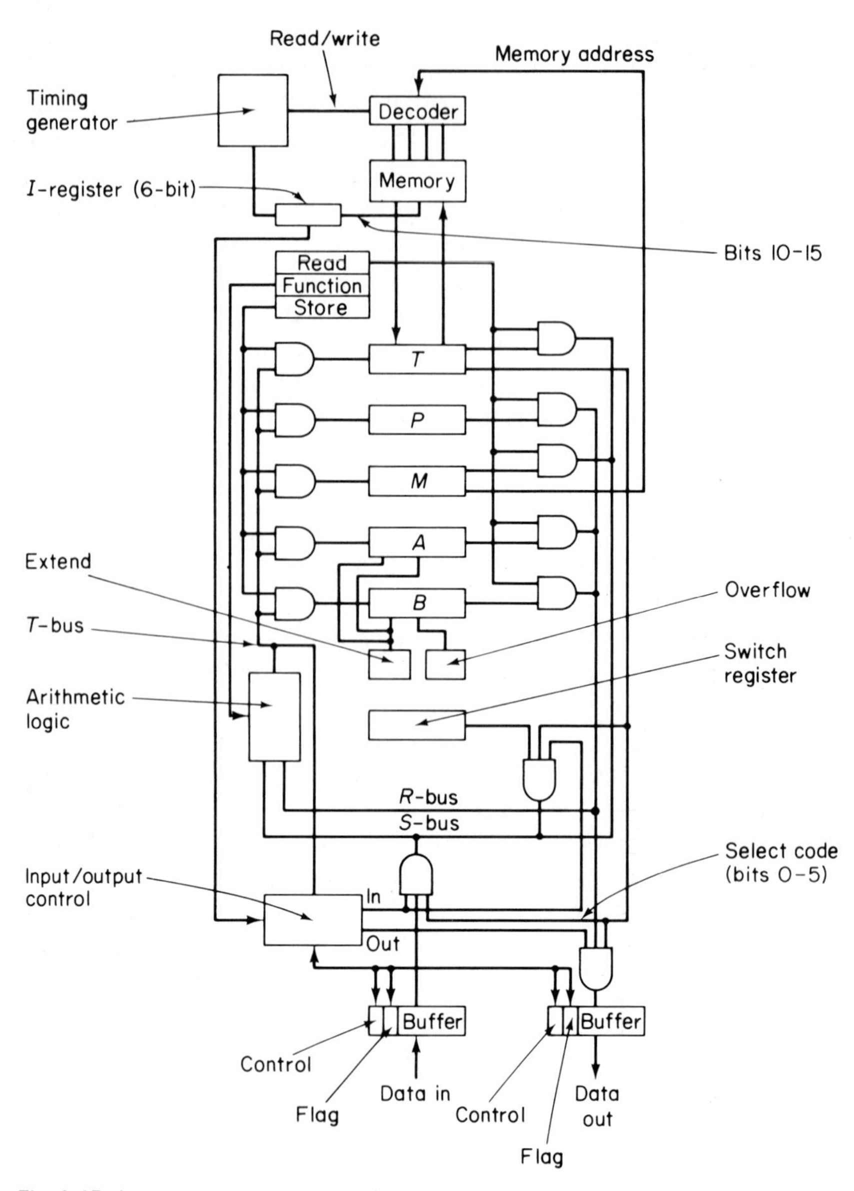

Fig. 9-15. Input/output system block diagram.

appropriate driving signals. One such signal is an *in* signal, which strobes all interface positions for input (represented by two AND gates in Figure 9-15, one accepting data from a buffer register and one accepting data from the switch register). One of these interface positions can be enabled, according to the select code (bits 0–5 from the T register), and the corresponding data are strobed by the in pulse onto the S bus. From there, the data are transferred via the T bus into the A or B register (as enabled by a store signal at the A or B input gate).

Another driving signal is the *out* signal. This signal strobes all interface positions for output (one shown in Figure 9-15). The select code from the T register enables one interface position and permits the out signal to strobe the data on the R bus into the corresponding output buffer. (The data on the R bus are read out of the A or B registers by a read signal.)

In addition to transferring data, input/output control can (according to instruction) send out signals to test the state of the control and flag bits (C and F bits) or to set or reset these bits. The select code determines which interface will receive the signal from input/output control. The control and flag bits are command signals for transferring data between the buffer and the peripheral device (not shown).

Processing input/output service requests

If a specific instruction has at some previous time enabled the interrupt system (considered to be part of the input/output control block in Figure 9-15), a peripheral device may request new data from the computer (if output) or may request to feed new data to the computer (if input). This request for service is done by setting the interface flag bit.

The flag signal, via input/output control, interrupts the computer's operations by forcing the M register to be set (via the T bus) to a memory address specified by the flag. At the same time, the fetch phase is set so that the computer must execute the instruction contained in the specified memory cell. Generally, this instruction will be a jump to a service subroutine. This subroutine consists of instructions that will prepare or accept the new data. On completion of service, it is the subroutine's responsibility to return the P and M registers to the values they contained before being interrupted.

J. COMPUTER INSTRUCTIONS

Before going into how the various instructions are executed, let us consider what instructions are available to the computer.

The HP2116 has 70 basic one-word instructions, all executable in 1.6 or 3.2 μS (except for ISZ, which is executable in 3.6 μS). These instructions are grouped into three types: memory reference, register reference, and input/output instructions. A comparison of the three formats is included in Figure 9-16.

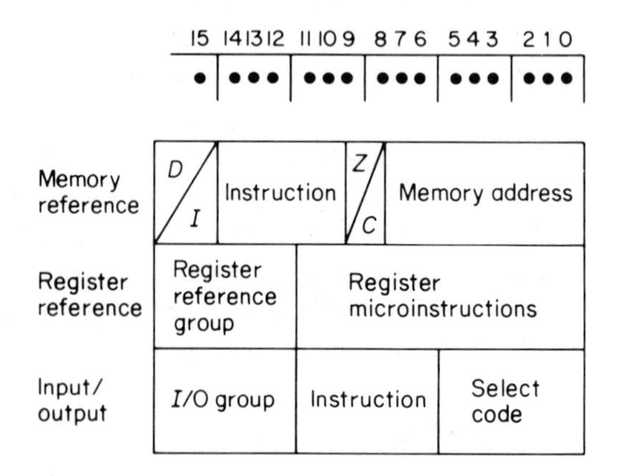

Fig. 9-16. Basic instruction formats.

Memory reference instructions use ten bits (0–9) for a memory address, bit 10 to specify zero or current page and bit 15 for direct or indirect addressing. This leaves four bits (14, 13, 12, and 11) to encode the 14 instruction commands in this group.

The other two types of instructions use four bits (15, 14, 13, and 12) to distinguish the register reference and input/output instructions. The register reference type uses bits 11–0 to combine up to eight **microinstructions** (that is, instructions formed by only one, two, or three bits), with the resulting multiple instruction operating on the A, B, or E register as a single-word instruction. The input/output type uses bits 11–6 for a variety of input/output instructions and bits 5–0 to make the instructions apply directly to one of 64 possible input/output devices or functions.

The following paragraphs describe in detail each of the instructions in the three type groups. Virtually all computers of this type have similar (although not identical) instructions.

Note that in the following paragraphs the functions of bits appearing in the form A/B, D/I, D/E, Z/C, or H/C are obtained by coding a

0 or 1, respectively (0/1). Thus, for example, A is specified by a 0 bit and B by a 1 bit.

1. Memory Reference Instructions

The 14 memory reference instructions execute some operations involving memory locations, such as transferring information in or out of a memory cell or checking the memory cell contents. The cell referenced (that is, the absolute address) is determined by combination of the ten memory/address bits in the instruction word (0–9) and the five bits (10–14) assumed from the existing indication of the P register. This means that memory reference instructions can directly address any word in the current page; also, if the instruction is in some location other than the base page (page zero), bit 10 of the instruction word doubles the addressing range to 2048 words by allowing selection of either page zero or current page (that is, bits 10–14 of the address in the M register can be reset to zero instead of assuming the existing indication of the P register). This feature provides a convenient linkage between all pages of memory, since page zero can be reached directly from any other page.

Note that since the A and B registers can be addressed, any memory reference instruction can apply to either of these registers, as well as to memory cells. For example, ADA 0001 means "add the contents of the B register (its address being 0001) to the A register."

Figure 9-17 gives instruction codes and mnemonics for all 14 memory reference instructions. All memory reference instructions take a minimum of two machine phases (discussed in later paragraphs of this chapter). One phase is required to read the instruction word, and the second phase is used to read the referenced memory cell. An exception is the instruction JMP, which is a one-phase instruction.

Logic truth tables, relating to the first three memory reference instructions, are given in Figure 9-18. Note that logic operations are performed on a bit-for-bit basis (that is, no carries).

AND: AND to A

The contents of the addressed location are logically ANDed to the contents of the A register. The contents of the memory cell are left unaltered.

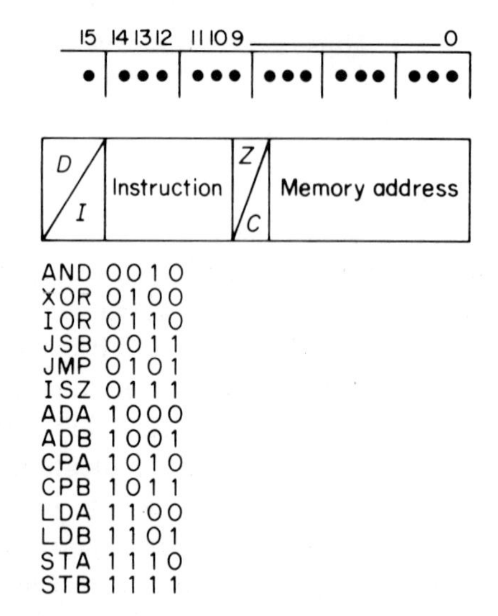

Fig. 9-17. Memory reference instruction formats.

	AND	XOR	IOR
A contents memory	0 0 1 1 0 1 0 1	0 0 1 1 0 1 0 1	0 0 1 1 0 1 0 1
Result (in *A*)	0 0 0 1	0 1 1 0	0 1 1 1

Fig. 9-18. Logic truth tables for memory reference instructions AND, XOR, and IOR.

XOR: EXCLUSIVE OR to A

The contents of the addressed location are combined with the contents of the A register as an EXCLUSIVE OR logic operation. The contents of the memory cell are left unaltered.

IOR: INCLUSIVE OR to A

The contents of the addressed location are combined with the contents of the A register as an INCLUSIVE OR logic operation. The contents of the memory cell are left unaltered.

JSB: Jump to Subroutine

This instruction, executed in location P, causes computer control to jump unconditionally to the memory location (X) specified in the address portion of the JSB instruction word. The contents of the P register plus 1 (return address) are stored in location X, and the next instruction to be executed will be that contained in the next location (X + 1). A return to the main program sequence at P + 1 may be effected by a jump to indirect location X.

JMP: Jump

This instruction transfers control to the contents of the addressed location. That is, JMP causes the P and M registers to be set according to the memory address portion of the instruction word, thus addressing memory cell X, so that the next instruction will be read from location X.

ISZ: Increment and Skip if Zero

An ISZ instruction adds 1 to the contents of the addressed memory location. If the result of this operation is zero, the next instruction is skipped (that is, the P and M registers are advanced by 2 instead of 1). Otherwise, the program proceeds normally to the next instruction in sequence. The incremented value is written back into the memory cell in either case. An ISZ instruction referencing locations 0 or 1 (A or B registers) cannot cause the setting of the extend or overflow bits (unlike INA or INB, which are register reference instructions described in later paragraphs).

ADA: Add to A

The contents of the addressed memory location are added to the contents of the A register, and the sum remains in the A register. The result of the addition may set the extend or overflow bits. The contents of the memory cell are unaltered.

ADB: Add to B.

The contents of the addressed memory location are added to the contents of the B register, and the sum remains in the B register. Extend or overflow bits may be set, as for ADA. The contents of the memory cell are unaltered.

CPA: Compare to A, Skip if Unequal

The contents of the addressed location are compared with the contents of the A register. If the two 16-bit words are different, the next instruction is skipped (that is, the P and M registers are advanced by 2 instead of 1). If the words are identical, the program proceeds normally to the next instruction in sequence. The contents of neither the A register nor the memory cells are altered.

CPB: Compare to B and Skip if Unequal

Same as CPA, except that comparison is made with the B register.

LDA: Load into A

The A register is cleared and loaded with the contents of the addressed location. The contents of the memory cell are unaltered.

LDB: Load into B

The B register is cleared and loaded with the contents of the addressed location. The contents of the memory cell are unaltered.

STA: Store A

The contents of the A register are stored in the addressed location. The previous contents of the memory cell are lost; the A register is unaltered.

STB: Store B

The contents of the B register are stored in the address location. The previous contents of the memory cell are lost; the B register is unaltered.

2. Register Reference Instructions

The register reference instructions, in general, manipulate bits in the A, B, and E registers. There is no reference to memory; thus these instructions are executed in only one machine phase. There are 39 basic register reference instructions, which are combinable to form a one-word multiple instruction that can operate in various ways on the contents of the A, B, or E registers. These microinstructions are divided into two subgroups, the shift-rotate group (SRG) and the alter-skip group (ASG). Three instructions (SLA, SLB, and CLE) appear in both groups.

Register reference microinstructions can be combined under the following general rules:

1. Instructions from the two groups cannot be mixed.
2. References to both A and B registers cannot be mixed.
3. Only one microinstruction can be chosen from each column of the selection tables in Figures 9-19 and 9-20.
4. Use 0 to exclude unwanted microinstruction bits.
5. The sequence of execution is left to right in the selection tables (column 1, then column 2, etc.).
6. If two (or more) skip functions are combined, the skip will occur if either or both conditions are met. One exception is the RSS instruction (described later).

Register reference instructions are recognized by the computer when the four most significant bits of the instruction word are 0s; the general format for this type of instruction (the dots representing variable microinstruction bits) is thus

0 000 ··· ··· ··· ···.

Shift-rotate group

The SRG instructions are specified by a 0 for bit 10 (compare Figures 9-19 and 9-20). Figure 9-19 gives both the bit format and the selection table for using these instructions. Definitions for the mnemonics used are as follows:

NOP	no operation; memory cycle only
CLE	clear E register
SLA	skip next instruction if least significant bit of A register is 0 (that is, skip if an even number is in A)

	15	14	13	12	11	10	9	8	7	6	5	4	3	2	1	0
	Type 2				A/B	0	D/E	Col. 1			2	D/E	3	Col. 4		
NOP	0	0	0	0	0	0	0	0	0	0	0	0	0	0	0	0
CLE	0	0	0	0		0					1					
SLA	0	0	0	0	0	0					1					
SLB	0	0	0	0	1	0					1					
ALS	0	0	0	0	0	0	1	0	0	0		X		X	X	X
BLS	0	0	0	0	1	0	1	0	0	0		X		X	X	X
ARS	0	0	0	0	0	0	1	0	0	1		X		X	X	X
BRS	0	0	0	0	1	0	1	0	0	1		X		X	X	X
RAL	0	0	0	0	0	0	1	0	1	0		X		X	X	X
RBL	0	0	0	0	1	0	1	0	1	0		X		X	X	X
RAR	0	0	0	0	0	0	1	0	1	1		X		X	X	X
RBR	0	0	0	0	1	0	1	0	1	1		X		X	X	X
ALR	0	0	0	0	0	0	1	1	0	0		X		X	X	X
BLR	0	0	0	0	1	0	1	1	0	1		X		X	X	X
ERA	0	0	0	0	0	0	1	1	0	1		X		X	X	X
ERB	0	0	0	0	1	0	1	1	0	1		X		X	X	X
ELA	0	0	0	0	0	0	1	1	1	0		X		X	X	X
ELB	0	0	0	0	1	0	1	1	1	0		X		X	X	X
ALF	0	0	0	0	0	0	1	1	1	1		X		X	X	X
BLF	0	0	0	0	1	0	1	1	1	1		X		X	X	X

Selection table

1	2	3	4
ALS ARS RAL RAR ALR ERA ELA ALF	CLE	SLA	ALS ARS RAL RAR ALR ERA ELA ALF
BLS BRS RBL RBR BLR ERB ELB BLF	CLE	SLB	BLS BRS RBL RBR BLR ERB ELB BLF

Combining guide

1. Choose up to 4 instructions, one from each column of the selection table.
2. Use a one-bit for bit 9 to enable column 1 instructions, and a one bit for bit 4 to enable column 4 instructions. Examples above shows column 1 enabled (executed first) with duplicate column 4 pattern (executed last) indicated by X's.
3. Use a one-bit for bit 5 to select column 2 (CLE), or a zero-bit to exclude CLE.
4. Use a one-bit for bit 3 to select column 3 (SLA/B), or a zero-bit to exclude SLA/B.

Fig. 9-19. Shift-rotate instructions.

SLB skip next instruction if least significant bit of B register is 0 (that is, skip if an even number is in B)

ALS left-shift A register one place, arithmetically (15 bits only); a 0 replaces vacated bit 0; the bit shifted out of bit 14 is lost; bit 15 (sign bit) is not affected

BLS left-shift B register one place, arithmetically (15 bits only); a 0 replaces vacated bit 0; the bit shifted out of bit 14 is lost; bit 15 (sign bit) is not affected

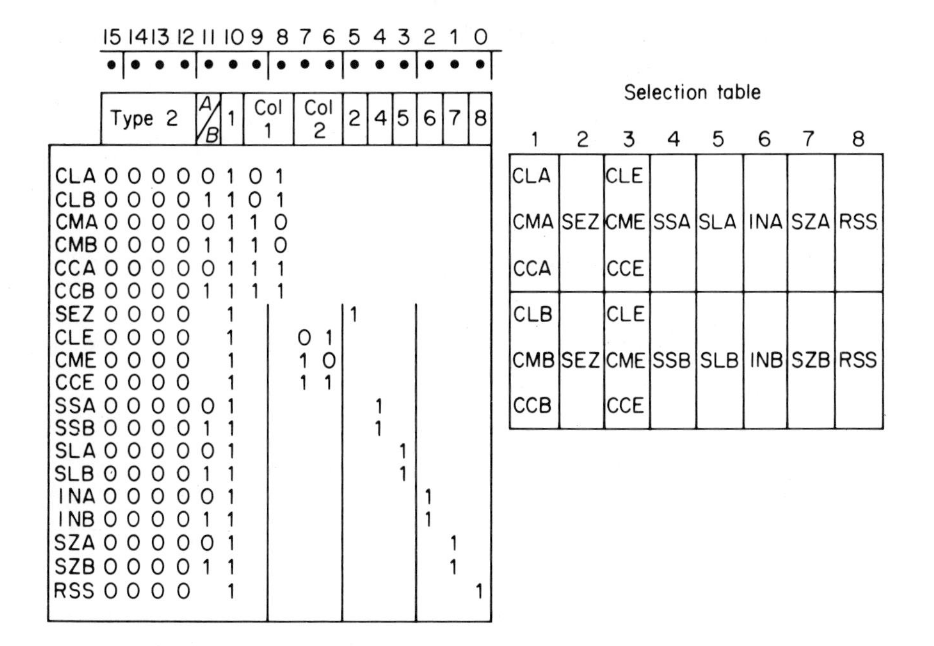

15 14 13 12 11 10 9 8 7 6 5 4 3 2 1 0
Type 2
A/B
1
Col 1
Col 2
2 4 5 6 7 8
CLA 0 0 0 0 0 1 0 1
CLB 0 0 0 0 1 1 0 1
CMA 0 0 0 0 0 1 1 0
CMB 0 0 0 0 1 1 1 0
CCA 0 0 0 0 0 1 1 1
CCB 0 0 0 0 1 1 1 1
SEZ 0 0 0 0 1 1
CLE 0 0 0 0 1 0 1
CME 0 0 0 0 1 1 0
CCE 0 0 0 0 1 1 1
SSA 0 0 0 0 0 1 1
SSB 0 0 0 0 1 1 1
SLA 0 0 0 0 0 1 1
SLB 0 0 0 0 1 1 1
INA 0 0 0 0 0 1 1
INB 0 0 0 0 1 1 1
SZA 0 0 0 0 0 1 1
SZB 0 0 0 0 1 1 1
RSS 0 0 0 0 1 1
Selection table
1 2 3 4 5 6 7 8
CLA CLE
CMA SEZ CME SSA SLA INA SZA RSS
CCA CCE
CLB CLE
CMB SEZ CME SSB SLB INB SZB RSS
CCB CCE

Combining guide

1. Choose up to 8 instructions, one from each column of selection table
2. Use the specified two-bit combinations of bits 8 and 9, plus *A/B* bit 11, to encode column 1 instructions.
3. Use the specified two-bit combinations of bits 7 and 6, to encode column 3 instructions.
4. Use a one-bit in bits 5,4,3,2,1, plus *A/B* bit 11, to encode column 2,4,5,6,7 instructions respectively.
5. Use a one-bit for bit 0 to encode column 8.

Fig. 9-20. Alter-skip instructions.

ARS — right-shift A register one place, arithmetically; the bit shifted out of bit 0 is lost; a copy of the sign bit (bit 15) is shifted into bit 14; bit 15 is not affected

BRS — right-shift B register one place, arithmetically; the bit shifted out of bit 0 is lost; a copy of the sign bit (bit 15) is shifted into bit 14; bit 15 is not affected

RAL rotate A register left one place, all 16 bits; bit 15 is rotated around to bit 0

RBL rotate B register left one place, all 16 bits; bit 15 is rotated around to bit 0

RAR rotate A register right one place, all 16 bits; bit 0 is rotated around to bit 15

RBR rotatc B register right one place, all 16 bits; bit 0 is rotated around to bit 15

ALR left-shift a register one place, same as ALS, but clear sign bit after shift

BLR left-shift B register one place, same as BLS, but clear sign bit after shift

ERA rotate E register right with A register one place (17 bits); bit 0 is rotated into E register; extend contents are rotated into bit 15

ERB rotate E register right with B register one place (17 bits); bit 0 is rotated into E register; extend contents are rotated into bit 15

ELA rotate E register left with A register one place (17 bits), bit 15 is rotated into E register; extend contents are rotated into bit 0

ELB rotate E register left with B register one place (17 bits); bit 15 is rotated into E register; extend contents are rotated into bit 0

ALF rotate A register left four places, all 16 bits; bits 15, 14, 13, and 12 are rotated around to bits 3, 2, 1, and 0, respectively; equivalent to four successive RAL instructions

RLF rotate B register left four places, all 16 bits; bits 15, 14, 13, and 12 are rotated around to bits 3, 2, 1, and 0, respectively; equivalent to four successive RBL instructions.

Alter-skip group

The ASG instructions are specified by a 1 in bit 10. Figure 9-20 gives both the bit format and the selection table for using these instructions. Definitions for the mnemonics used are as follows:

CLA	clear A register
CLB	clear B register
CMA	complement A register, one's complement, reversing the state of all 16 bits
CMB	complement B register; reverse state of all 16 bits
CCA	clear, then complement A register; puts 16 1s in the A register; this is the two's complement form of −1
CCB	clear, then complement B register; puts 16 1s in the B register; this is the two's complement form of −1
CLE	clear E register
CME	complement E register, reverses state of the extend bit
CCE	clear, then complement E register; sets the extend bit
SEZ	skip the next instruction if E register is 0
SSA	skip next instruction if sign bit (bit 15) of A register is 0 (that is, skip if the contents of A are positive)
SSB	skip next instruction if sign bit (bit 15) of B register is 0 (that is, skip if the contents of B are positive)
SLA	skip next instruction if least significant bit of A register is 0 (that is, skip if an even number is in A)
SLB	skip next instruction if least significant bit of B register is zero (that is, skip if an even number is in B)
INA	increment A register by 1; can cause setting of extend or overflow bits
INB	increment B register by 1; can cause setting of extend or overflow bits
SZA	skip next instruction if A register is 0 (16 zeros)
SZB	skip next instruction of B register is 0 (16 zeros)
RSS	reverse skip sense; skip occurs for any of the preceding skip instructions, if present, when the nonzero condition is met; RSS without a skip instruction in the word causes an unconditional skip; if a word with RSS also includes both SSA/B and SLA/B, both bits 15 and 0) must be 1 for skip to occur; in all other cases the skip occurs if either or both conditions are met.

Input/output instructions

The HP2116 has 17 basic input/output instructions, which provide the following general capabilities:

1. Fix the state of the flag, control, and overflow bits.
2. Test the state of the flag and overflow bits (that is, skip if set or clear, as specified).
3. Enter data from a specific device into the A or B registers.
4. Output data to a specific device into the A or B registers.
5. Halt the program.

Input/output instructions are recognized by the computer when the four most significant bits of the instruction word are 1000 and bit 10 is a 1. The codes and mnemonics for all 17 instructions are given in Figure 9-21. (Note that the MAC instruction is not counted as a basic instruction, as is discussed in later paragraphs.) All input/output instructions are executed in one phase.

Note that bit 11, where relevant, specifies the A or B register; otherwise bit 11 may be 1 or 0 without affecting the instruction. Bit 9, where not specified, offers the choice of holding (0) or clearing (1) the device flag after execution of the instruction. (*Exception:* The H/C bit associated with the SOC or SOS instructions holds or clears the overflow bit instead of the flag bit.)

Bits 8, 7, and 6 identify the instruction; some of the instructions, however, require additional specific bits for the complete code. Bits 5–0 form select codes to make the instruction apply to one of up to 64 input/output devices for functions.

The MAC instruction listed in Figure 9-21 is available to provide up to 2048 entries for various subroutines. Since it is used only by special options and special software, MAC is not counted as one of the 70 basic machine instructions. The basic HP2116 will treat MAC as a no-operation (NOP) instruction.

HLT: Halt

HLT stops the computer and holds or clears the flag (according to bit 9) of any desired input/output device (as selected by bits 5–0). The HLT instruction has the same effect as the halt pushbutton (that is, the

	15	14	13	12	11	10	9	8	7	6	5	4	3	2	1	0
	Type 3				A/B	*	H/C	Instruction			Select code					
MAC	1	0	0	0		0										
HLT	1	0	0	0		1		0	0	0						
STF	1	0	0	0		1	0	0	0	1						
CLF	1	0	0	0		1	1	0	0	1						
SFC	1	0	0	0		1	0	0	1	0						
SFS	1	0	0	0		1	0	0	1	1						
MIA	1	0	0	0	0	1		1	0	0						
MIB	1	0	0	0	1	1		1	0	0						
LIA	1	0	0	0	0	1		1	0	1						
LIB	1	0	0	0	1	1		1	0	1						
OTA	1	0	0	0	0	1		1	1	0						
OTB	1	0	0	0	1	1		1	1	0						
STC	1	0	0	0	0	1		1	1	1						
CLC	1	0	0	0	1	1		1	1	1						
STO	1	0	0	0		1	0	0	0	1	0	0	0	0	0	1
CLO	1	0	0	0		1	1	0	0	1	0	0	0	0	0	1
SOC	1	0	0	0		1		0	1	0	0	0	0	0	0	1
SOS	1	0	0	0		1		0	1	1	0	0	0	0	0	1

* Identifies macroinstructions (0), or standard input/output instructions (1)

Fig. 9-21. Input/output instructions.

halt switch lights up, all front-panel control switches are enabled, and no interrupts may occur). The HLT instruction will be displayed in the T register, and the P register will normally indicate the halt location plus 1.

STF: Set Flag

STF sets the input/output flag of the selected device, thus causing an interrupt during the next machine phase if the interrupt system is enabled and the corresponding control bit is set. The interrupt system itself is enabled by an STF instruction with a select code of six zeros (octal 00).

CLF: Clear Flag of Selected Device

CLF resets the flag, thus permitting the device to present another flag when read again. A CLF with a select code of six zeros (octal 00) disables the entire interrupt system; this does not affect the status of individual input/output flags.

SFC: Skip if Flag Clear

SFC causes the computer to skip the next instruction if the flag bit of the selected device is 0 (that is, the device is not ready).

SFS: Skip if Flag Set

The next instruction is skipped if the flag bit of the selected device is 1 (the device is ready).

MIA: Merge Input into A

The contents of the input/output buffer associated with the selected device are merged (on an INCLUSIVE OR basis) into the A register.

MIB: Merge Input into B

The contents of the input/output buffer associated with the selected device are merged (on an INCLUSIVE OR basis) into the B register.

LIA: Load Input into A

The contents of the input/output buffer associated with the selected device are loaded into the A register. The previous contents of the A register are lost.

LIB: Load Input into B

The contents of the input/output buffer associated with the selected device are loaded into the B register. The previous contents of the B register are lost.

OTA: Output from A

The contents of the A register are loaded into the input/output buffer associated with the selected device. If the buffer is less than 16 bits in length, the least significant bits of the A register normally are loaded. (Some exceptions exist, depending on the type of output device.) The A-register contents are not altered.

OTB: Output from B

The contents of the B register are loaded into the input/output buffer associated with the selected device.

STC: Set Control Bit of the Selected Device

This instruction commands or prepares the device to perform its input or output function and enables its flag bit to interrupt the program being run (provided the program is not disabling the interrupt system).

CLC: Clear Control Bit of the Selected Device

This instruction prevents the device from interrupting the routine program. A CLC instruction with a select code of 00_8 ($000\,000_2$) clears all control bits, effectively turning off all input/output devices. CLF 00 may be combined with this to additionally turn off the interrupt system.

STO: Set Overflow

STO resets the overflow register.

SOS: Skip if Overflow Set

If the overflow register is set, the next instruction of the program is skipped. Use of the H/C bit (bit 9) will hold or clear the overflow bit following execution of this instruction (whether the skip is taken or not).

SOC: Skip if Overflow Clear

If the overflow register is clear, the next instruction of the program is skipped. Use of the H/C bit will hold or clear the overflow bit following execution of this instruction.

K. MACHINE TIMING

The 70 basic computer instructions are implemented or executed in a specific timing sequence. As is generally the case in computer service literature, this timing sequence is referred to as *machine timing.* The following paragraphs summarize the various phases of machine timing.

An internal 10-MHz timing generator (crystal-controlled oscillator) automatically generates read-write memory cycles every 1.6 μS when running, as shown in Figure 9-22.

The basic HP2116 has four machine phases (fetch, indirect, execute, and interrupt), of which the first three include a memory cycle. Phases do not occur in a fixed sequence but rather are determined by conditions that occur during operation. The computer can go directly from one of the first three phases to certain others in the manner indicated in Figure 9-22, and an external device can cause the computer to go into the interrupt phase upon completion of any current phase.

Fig. 9-22. Machine timing.

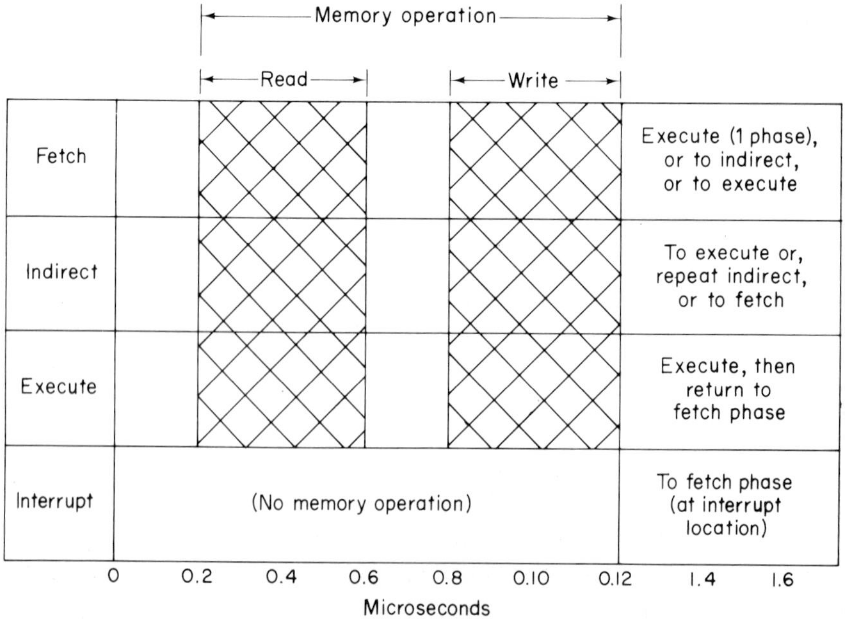

Phase	Memory operation (Read 0.2–0.6, Write 0.8–0.12)	
Fetch	Read / Write	Execute (1 phase), or to indirect, or to execute
Indirect	Read / Write	To execute or, repeat indirect, or to fetch
Execute	Read / Write	Execute, then return to fetch phase
Interrupt	(No memory operation)	To fetch phase (at interrupt location)

0 0.2 0.4 0.6 0.8 0.10 0.12 1.4 1.6

Microseconds

The fetch phase may be thought of as the "normal" or "home" condition. The processing of each instruction begins with a fetch phase and in many cases is fully executed within that phase. Each phase takes 1.6 μS with one exception: The execute phase of the ISZ instruction (increment and skip if zero) takes 2.0 μS.

1. Fetch Phase

The contents of the currently addressed memory cell are read into the T register during the read portion of the memory cycle and written back into the memory cell during the write portion of the memory cycle. The information left in the T register is taken as an instruction when read during the fetch phase. If the instruction includes an *indirect address bit*, the computer sets the indirect phase condition, and if the instruction does not have an indirect address bit but does include a memory reference (two-phase instruction), the computer sets the execute phase condition. Otherwise, the current instruction is fully executed at the end of the fetch phase, and the computer remains in the fetch state from the next memory cycle. An exception to these conditions is the JMP (jump) instruction, which is a memory reference instruction but does not require an execute phase; the computer executes the instructions at the end of the fetch phase or the indirect phase and then sets the fetch again from the next memory cycle.

2. Indirect Phase

The contents of the memory cell referenced during the fetch phase are read into the T register and the entire 16-bit word (15 bits of address plus a new direct/indirect bit) is taken as a new memory reference for the same instruction. The use of 15 bits for an address permits addressing of up to and beyond maximum memory capability. If the direct/indirect bit again specifies indirect addressing, the computer remains in the indirect state and reads another 16-bit address word out of memory as a continuation of multiple-step indirect addressing. If the direct/indirect bit specifies direct addressing, the computer sets the execute phase (or, in the case of a jump indirect, the fetch phase).

3. Execute Phase

The 16-bit data word in the memory cell referenced during a fetch phase or an indirect phase is read into the T register and is operated on by the current instruction (retained from the fetch phase) at the end of the execute phase. The computer then sets the fetch phase again to read the next instruction.

4. Interrupt Phase

An input-output device requesting service at any time during one of the phases is acknowledged at the end of that phase unless the interrupt is inhibited for any reason by the program being run. The computer then goes into the interrupt phase, which does not have a memory cycle. During this phase the P register is held so that no instruction in the main program will be skipped or executed twice. At the end of the interrupt phase, the interrupt address of the interrupting device is transferred into the M register and the fetch phase is set to read the instruction contained in the interrupt address location. The interrupt phase cannot occur again until at least this instruction is completed.

L. HOW INSTRUCTIONS ARE IMPLEMENTED

The following paragraphs describe how the basic instructions are implemented internally in the computer. Owing to space limitations, the complete details for all instructions are not given. Instead, only selected instructions are described, since they are representative of the remaining instructions.

The basic steps and timing sequence for all instructions are shown in Figures 9-23, 9-24, and 9-25. These illustrations expand on the machine-timing diagram of Figure 9-22. The simplified block diagram of Figure 9-3 is also used as a reference throughout the following descriptions. Most signals named in the three implementation illustrations (Figures 9-23, 9-24, and 9-25) can be identified in Figure 9-3. For example, the instruction "Read A into R bus" shown in Figure 9-23 can be seen in Figure 9-3 as the line from the read block to the

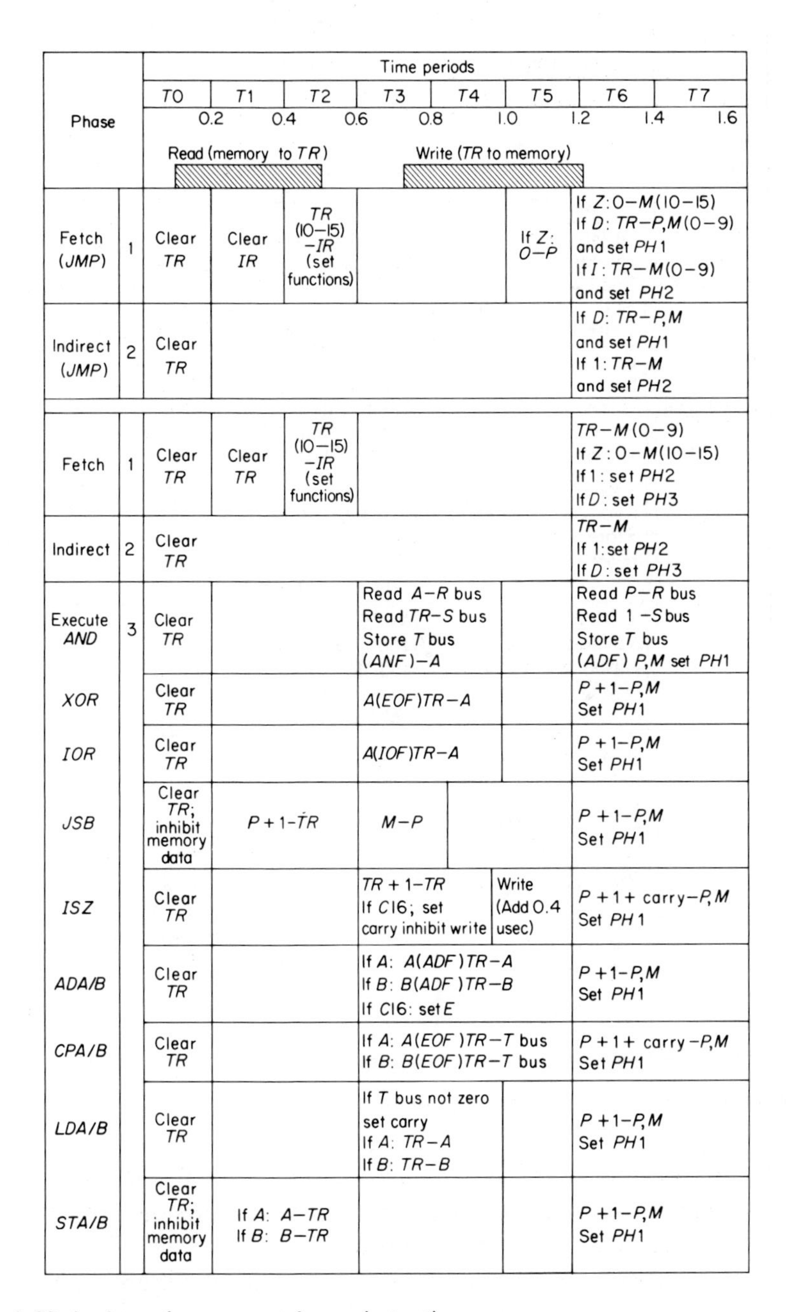

Phase		T0	T1	T2	T3	T4	T5	T6	T7
		0.2	0.4	0.6	0.8	1.0	1.2	1.4	1.6
		Read (memory to TR)			Write (TR to memory)				
Fetch (JMP)	1	Clear TR	Clear IR	TR (10–15) –IR (set functions)			If Z: 0–P	If Z: 0–M(10–15) If D: TR–P,M(0–9) and set PH1 If I: TR–M(0–9) and set PH2	
Indirect (JMP)	2	Clear TR						If D: TR–P,M and set PH1 If 1: TR–M and set PH2	
Fetch	1	Clear TR	Clear TR	TR (10–15) –IR (set functions)				TR–M(0–9) If Z: 0–M(10–15) If 1: set PH2 If D: set PH3	
Indirect	2	Clear TR						TR–M If 1: set PH2 If D: set PH3	
Execute AND	3	Clear TR			Read A–R bus Read TR–S bus Store T bus (ANF)–A			Read P–R bus Read 1 –S bus Store T bus (ADF) P,M set PH1	
XOR		Clear TR			A(EOF)TR–A			P+1–P,M Set PH1	
IOR		Clear TR			A(IOF)TR–A			P+1–P,M Set PH1	
JSB		Clear TR; inhibit memory data	P+1–TR		M–P			P+1–P,M Set PH1	
ISZ		Clear TR			TR+1–TR If C16; set carry inhibit write		Write (Add 0.4 usec)	P+1+ carry–P,M Set PH1	
ADA/B		Clear TR			If A: A(ADF)TR–A If B: B(ADF)TR–B If C16: set E			P+1–P,M Set PH1	
CPA/B		Clear TR			If A: A(EOF)TR–T bus If B: B(EOF)TR–T bus			P+1+ carry–P,M Set PH1	
LDA/B		Clear TR			If T bus not zero set carry If A: TR–A If B: TR–B			P+1–P,M Set PH1	
STA/B		Clear TR; inhibit memory data	If A: A–TR If B: B–TR					P+1–P,M Set PH1	

Fig. 9-23. Implementing memory reference instructions.

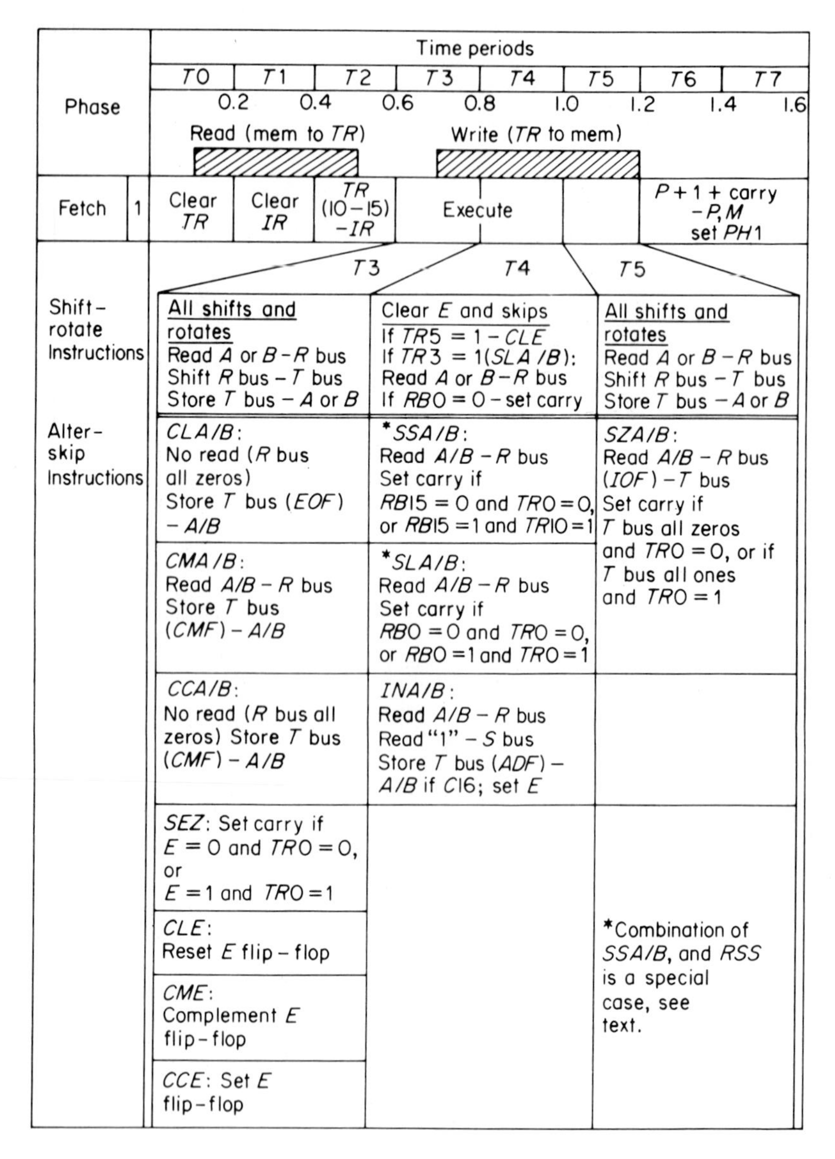

Fig. 9-24. Implementing register reference instructions.

A-register output AND gate (which outputs onto the R bus). Figure 9-3 should be referred to frequently as the discussion progresses in order to visualize the bit manipulations.

The cycle of time periods shown at the top of Figures 9-23, 9-24, and 9-25 ($T0$–$T7$) repeats continuously every 1.6 μS while computer

Phase		T0	T1	T2	T3	T4	T5	T6	T7
		Time periods							
		0.2	0.4	0.6	0.8	1.0	1.2	1.4	1.6
		Read (mem to *TR*)			Write (*TR* to mem)				
Fetch *HLT*	1	Clear *TR*	Clear *IR*	*TR* (IO–15) –*IR*				*P*+1–*P*, *M* Reset run *FF*	
STF		Clear *TR*	Clear *IR*	*TR*–*IR*	Set flag: Select code			*P*+1–*P*, *M* Set *PH*1	
CLF		Clear *TR*	Clear *IR*	*TR*–*IR*	Set flag: select code	Clear flag: select code		*P*+1–*P*, *M* Set *PH*1	
SFC		Clear *TR*	Clear *IR*	*TR*–*IR*	*SFC* Interface	*SKF* carry		*P*+1+carry – *P*, *M* Set *PH*1	
SFS		Clear *TR*	Clear *IR*	*TR*–*IR*	*SFS* interface	*SKF* carry		*P*+1+carry *P*,*M* Set *PH*1	
MIA/B		Clear *TR*	Clear *IR*	*TR*–*IR*		Read *A/B* – *R* bus buffer – *S* bus store *T* bus (IO*F*) – *A/B* *TR*9: *CLF*		*P*+1–*P*, *M* Set *PH*1	
LIA/B		Clear *TR*	Clear *IR*	*TR*–*IR*		Buffer – *S* bus store *T* bus (IO*F*) – *A/B* *TR*9: *CLF*		*P*+1–*P*, *M* Set *PH*1	
OTA/B		Clear *TR*	Clear *IR*	*TR*–*IR*		Read *A/B* – *R* *R* bus – buffer *TR*9: *CLF*		*P*+1–*P*, *M* Set *PH*1	
STC		Clear *TR*	Clear *IR*	*TR*–*IR*		Set control (*SEL* code)		*P*+1–*P*, *M* Set *PH*1	
CLC		Clear *TR*	Clear *IR*	*TR*–*IR*		Clear control (*SEL* code)		*P*+1–*P*, *M* Set *PH*1	
STO		Clear *TR*	Clear *IR*	*TR*–*IR*	*STF* overflow			*P*+1–*P*, *M* Set *PH*1	
CLO		Clear *TR*	Clea *IR*	*TR*–*IR*		*CLF* – overflow		*P*+1–*P*, *M* Set *PH*1	
SOC		Clear *TR*	Clear *IR*	*TR*–*IR*	*SFC* – *OVF*	*SKF* – carry		*P*+1+carry – *P*, *M* Set *PH*1	
SOS		Clear *TR*	Clear *IR*	*TR*–*IR*	*SFS* – *OVF*	*SKF* carry		*P*+1+carry – *P*, *M* Set *PH*1	
Interrupt	4		Read *P*–*R* bus store *T* bus (*CMF*) – *P*		Read *P*–*R* bus read "1" – *S* bus Store *T* bus (*ADF*) – *P*		Read *P*–*R* bus Store *T* – bus (*CMF*) – *P*		Reset *M* (6–15) Store *T* bus (0–5) – *M* Set *PH*1

Fig. 9-25. Implementing input/output instructions.

power is on. That is, pulses from the computer time base generator (clock) appear at all appropriate inputs at regular intervals.

The read-write memory cycle, although shown only once at the top of Figures 9-23, 9-24, and 9-25, actually occurs once in every phase (except interrupt). It is important to remember this throughout the following descriptions.

1. Implementing Memory Reference Instructions

By comparing Figures 9-23, 9-24, and 9-25 it is seen that memory reference instructions are the only type of instructions requiring more than one machine phase to execute; the indirect and execute phases are associated only with memory reference instructions.

In the case of all memory reference instructions except JMP, the action during the fetch and indirect phases (phases 1 and 2) is similar, so these phases are shown only once, implying that they are common to all memory reference instructions. The exception, JMP, is unique in that it does not use an execute phase; execution can occur in either the fetch or indirect phase. The action for JMP is shown separately in Figure 9-23 and is discussed first in the following paragraphs. A description for the AND instruction is also given. The remaining memory reference instructions are implemented in a manner similar to the AND instruction.

Implementing JMP instruction

The fetch phase for all instructions, regardless of type, begins in exactly the same way, since at this time the computer logic cannot know anything about the instruction that is about to be read out of the memory. The only fact known is that the word from memory will be read as an instruction (not data); getting an instruction from the memory is the first function of the fetch phase. During the first three time periods of the fetch phase, the following actions occur:

1. During $T0$ the T register is cleared.
2. The read portion of the memory cycle begins to read the contents of the currently addressed memory cell into the T register. This continues until the middle of $T2$.

3. During *T*1 the instruction register is cleared.
4. Bits 10–15 (the instruction group and code identification) of the T register are transferred into the six-bit instruction register.

During the latter portion of *T*2, the functions to be used in implementing the JMP instruction are set up. This includes read and store as well as any arithmetic functions (none in the case of JMP). Functions are gated with pulses at appropriate time periods to occur in the correct sequence.

At the end of *T*2, the instruction information is in bits 10–15 of the T register and in the instruction register. The memory address information is in bits 0–9 of the T register.

The next event to occur is to clear the P register at time *T*5 if the page zero condition exists (that is, if bit 10 of the instruction register is a 0). This is done by a *store-T-bus-into-P* function. Since nothing has been read onto any of the buses, the T bus is in the all-zero state, and 16 zeros are therefore stored into the P register. (Actually, for resetting the program to page zero, it is necessary only to clear bits 10–14 of the P register; however, it is convenient to clear the entire P register at this time.) Note that the six most significant bits of the page zero address are zeros. That is, the last address on page zero is

0 000 001 111 111 111.

During time periods *T*6 and *T*7, the page zero indicator (if present) clears bits 10–15 of the M register (not the entire register). The method is the same as described above: "Store T bit into M register, bits 10–15"; the T bus is still all 0s. Thus, at this time, both the P and M registers point to page zero, if so coded by bit 10 being a 0 (otherwise these registers are not changed, leaving bits 10–15 at the current page indication).

Also during *T*6 and *T*7, the direct/indirect bit (bit 15) of the T register is looked at to see if the memory address currently in the T register is the *effective address* (the final address being jumped to) or if another jump should be made from that address to whatever address is contained in that location (indirect addressing). Since the concept of indirect addressing is important and not always simple to grasp initially, it is treated separately in the following paragraphs. For direct addressing, the execution is completed by the following steps:

1. The T register contents are read onto the S bus and appear on the T bus.
2. Bits 0–9 of the T bus are stored into the P and M registers. This directs the computer to the jump location. (Remember from the preceding paragraphs that bits 10–15 of the P and M registers either have been reset to 0 for page zero or left alone for current page.)
3. The phase 1 (fetch) condition remains set so that the contents of the jump location will be read out and interpreted as an instruction during the next machine phase.

Basically, the indirect addressing indicator (bit 15 of the T register being a 1) tells the computer logic that the contents of the location being jumped are not the next instruction but rather the address for another jump. This additional jump is a continuation of the same instruction but requires an additional phase. During *T*6 and *T*7 of phase 1, the T register contents are transferred to the M register (not both P and M as for the direct condition). During *T*7 the phase 2 condition (PH2) is set and the indirect phase begins.

During *T*0, the T register is cleared. Since the jump is still in prcgress, the instruction register is not cleared during *T*1. The contents of the location now addressed by the M register are read into the T register during the read memory cycle. Then, during *T*6 and *T*7 (assuming bit 15 of the T register is now 0 for direct), all 16 bits of the T register are transferred into the P and M registers in the usual way: "Read T register onto S bus and store T bus (with no arithmetic) into the P and M registers." These registers now contain the effective address, so phase 1 is set, and the next machine phase will be a fetch phase, to read out the next instruction from the address. Note that if bit 15 of the T register were again a 1 (for indirect), a jump would be made to still another location by repeating the process.

In summary, as illustrated in Figure 9-26, an indirect jump occurs by the following register actions:

1. The word containing the jump instruction is read out of memory by a fetch phase into the T register.
2. The address portion of the readout word is transferred into the corresponding portion of the M register.
3. The zero/current page bit of the readout word tells the computer

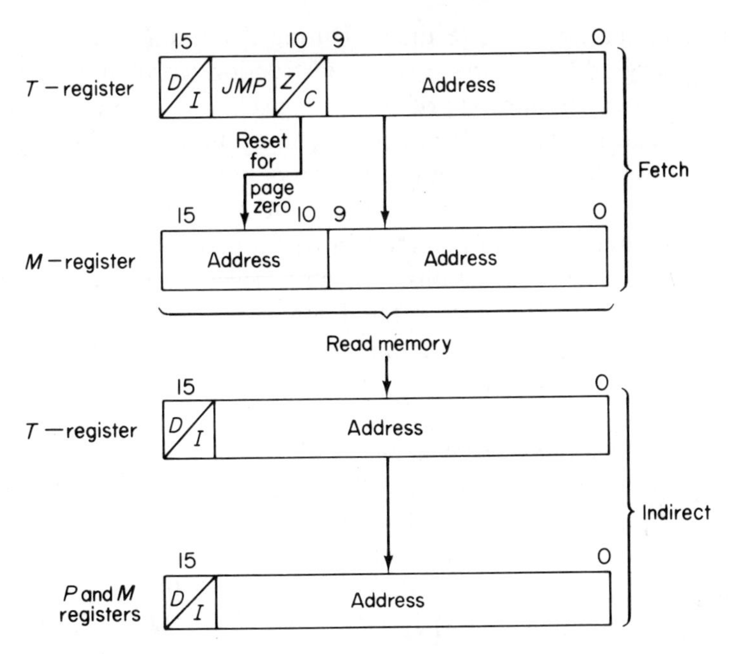

Fig. 9-26. Register manipulations for indirect jump.

logic to clear (zero) or leave (current) the remaining bits (10–15) of the M register.

4. Steps b and c now comprise the address of a location that is read out of memory into the T register at the start of the indirect phase.
5. All bits of this new readout word are transferred into the P and M registers. The computer is now "at" the location specified in these registers.

Implementing AND instruction

The fetch phase for the AND instruction is the same as for all other memory reference instructions listed below it in Figure 9-23, with the exception that different functions will be set up at *T*2. This phase begins in the same way as JMP. The T register is cleared at time *T*0, the read memory cycle reads the instruction word into the T register, the instruction register is cleared during *T*1, and T-register bits 10–15 (instruction code) are transferred into the instruction register at *T*2. At this time, all necessary functions for this instruction are set up, to be used at the appropriate times. During *T*6 and *T*7, T-register bits 0-9 (memory address portion of the instruction word) are transferred into the corresponding bits of the M register (via S and T buses). If the zero page indicator is present (bit 10 of the instruction register is a 0), a "Reset M (10–15)" command clears bits 10–15 of the M register.

Unlike the JMP instruction, an execute or an indirect phase must follow the fetch phase of an AND instruction, as is the case for other memory reference instructions. (Execute never occurs for JMP; indirect is optional.) If bit 15 of the T register is 0 (for direct), phase 3 (execute) is set. Assume that an indirect phase is required (bit 15 is 1). (If the direction condition exists, the action of the next paragraph is skipped.)

The indirect phase begins by clearing the T register during *T*0. Then a new word is read into the T register from the memory location specified by the M register. This word is an address, not data, since indirect addressing really means "Go to another location for the data." During *T*6 and *T*7 of the indirect phase, this address is transferred from the T register to the M register (all 16 bits). Note that it is possible for bit 15 to again specify indirect addressing; if so, phase 2 remains set and the procedure of this paragraph is repeated and could be repeated several times. When bit 15 is a 0 (direct), phase 3 is set.

The execute phase begins by clearing the T register. The instruction register remains unchanged, since the various functions are still needed. This time, the read portion of the memory cycle reads data from memory into the T register. During *T*3 and *T*4, these data are read onto the S bus, and the A register contents are read onto the R bus. The AND function (shown as ANF in Figure 9-23), previously set up by the instruction register, now combines the data on the two buses by ANDing. (See Figure 9-18 for the arithmetic resulting from an AND operation.) The result on the T bus is then stored into the A register.

To advance the computer to the next instruction, the P and M registers must be incremented by 1. This is done during *T*6 and *T*7 of the execute phase. It is accomplished by reading the P register onto the R bus and 1 onto the S bus and then adding the two buses (add function of ADF) and storing the result into the P and M registers.

In summary, as illustrated in Figure 9-27, an AND indirect instruction is executed by the following register actions:

1. The word containing the AND instruction is read out of memory by a fetch phase into the T register.

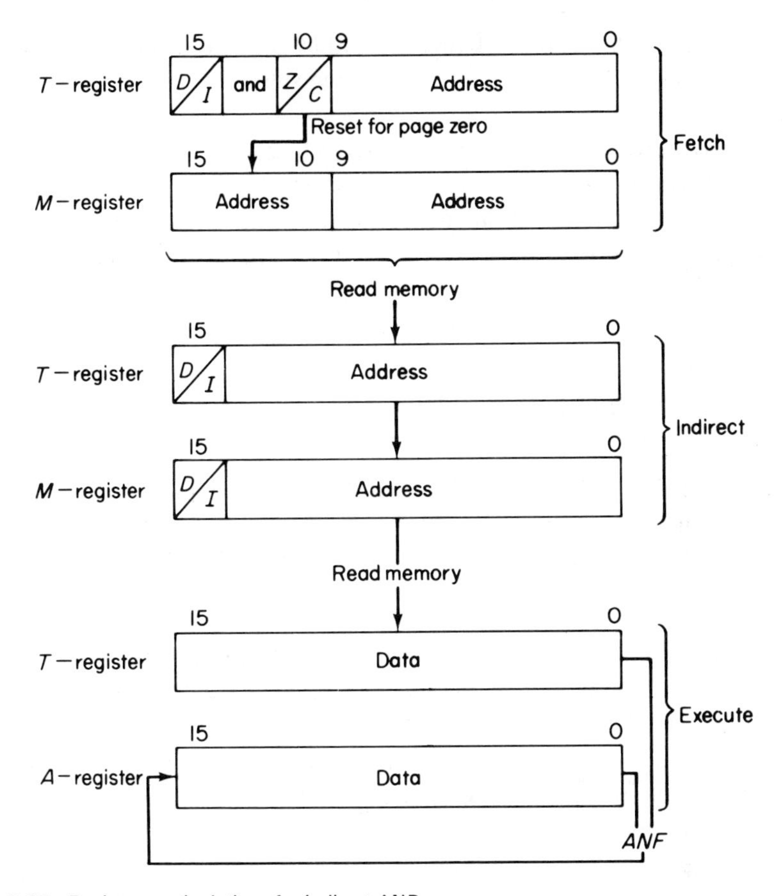

Fig. 9-27. Register manipulations for indirect AND.

2. The address portion of the readout word is transferred into the corresponding portion of the M register.
3. The zero/current page bit of the readout word tells the computer logic to clear (zero) or leave (current) the remaining bits of the M register.
4. Steps b and c now comprise the address of a location that is read out of the memory into the T register at the start of the indirect phase.
5. All bits of this new readout word are transferred into the M register, thus addressing the location of the desired data.
6. At the start of the execute phase the data thus addressed are read into the T register from the memory.

7. The contents of the T register and M register are ANDed together and deposited back into the A register.

For the remainder of the memory reference instructions, the fetch and indirect phases are the same as described for the AND instruction. Computer operations that occur during the execute phase of the remaining memory reference instructions are summarized in Figure 9-23.

2. Implementing Register Reference Instructions

All register reference instructions, as shown by Figure 9-24, are fully executed in only one phase (fetch). Actual execution is accomplished during time periods $T3$–$T5$. Actions during the other time periods are similar to those previously described for memory reference instructions.

During time periods $T0$–$T2$, the T register and instruction register are cleared, and bits 10–15 of the instruction word read out of memory are transferred to the instruction register. Unlike the memory reference, the instruction register does not set up functions but rather provides gating signals to identify the type (register reference) and group (shift-rotate or alter-skip) of instructions. The remaining bits of the T register are used to execute the individual instructions by setting up the appropriate functions. Figures 9-19 and 9-20 define which bits encode each instruction.

During time periods $T6$ and $T7$, the P register is read onto the R bus and a 1 is read onto the S bus. If the carry FF has been set by a skip condition during $T3$–$T5$, another 1 is added and the total (P register incremented by 1 or 2) is stored into the P and M registers. This advances the computer to the next instruction.

Figure 9-24 shows that the shifts and rotates can be executed either during $T3$ or $T5$ or both. These shifts and rotates are executed simply by reading the A or B register onto the R bus, applying a *shift function* to shift some or all of these bits to a different position on the T bus, and then storing the T bus back into the A or B register.

The shift function is the key to understanding register reference instructions. Figure 9-28 shows the shift sequence accomplished for each instruction. The code words used in the functions column of

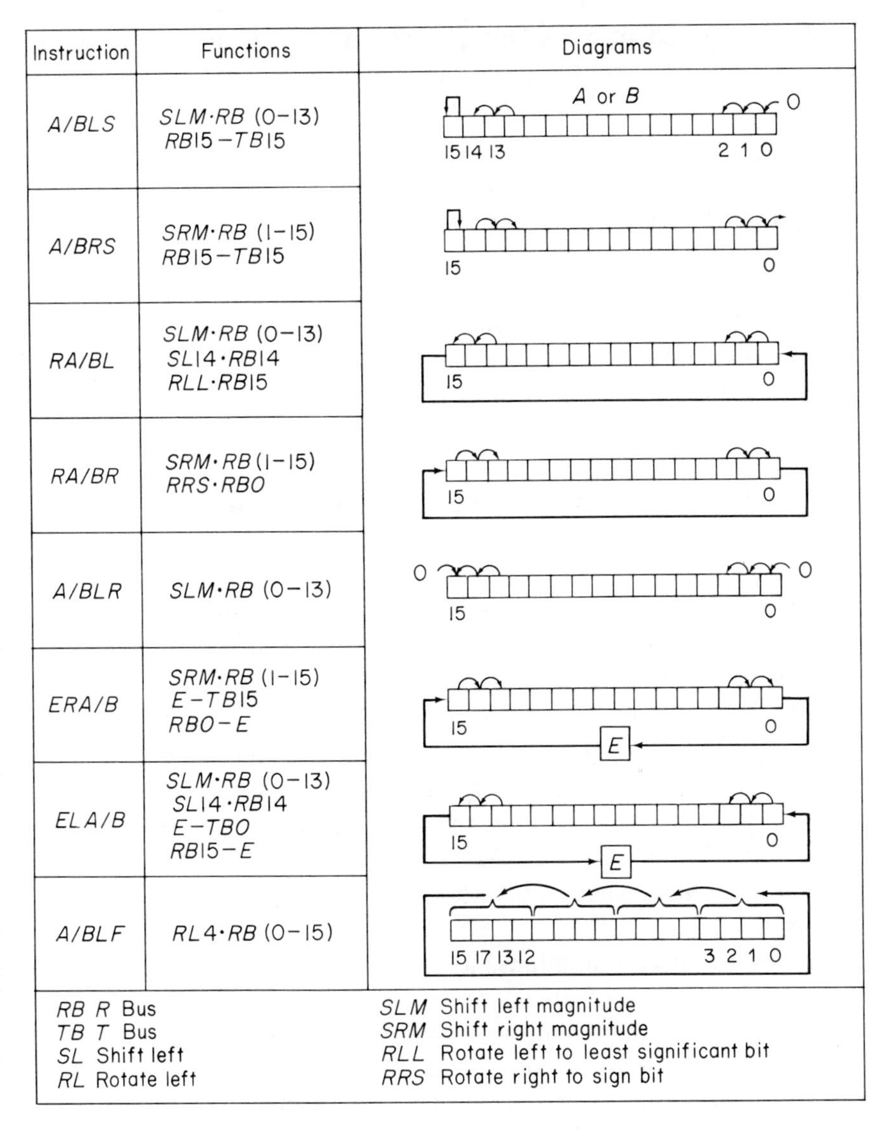

Instruction	Functions	Diagrams
A/BLS	*SLM·RB* (0–13) *RB*15–*TB*15	
A/BRS	*SRM·RB* (1–15) *RB*15–*TB*15	
RA/BL	*SLM·RB* (0–13) *SL*14·*RB*14 *RLL·RB*15	
RA/BR	*SRM·RB* (1–15) *RRS·RBO*	
A/BLR	*SLM·RB* (0–13)	
ERA/B	*SRM·RB* (1–15) *E–TB*15 *RBO–E*	
ELA/B	*SLM·RB* (0–13) *SL*14·*RB*14 *E–TBO* *RB*15–*E*	
A/BLF	*RL*4·*RB* (0–15)	

RB *R* Bus
TB *T* Bus
SL Shift left
RL Rotate left
SLM Shift left magnitude
SRM Shift right magnitude
RLL Rotate left to least significant bit
RRS Rotate right to sign bit

Fig. 9-28. Shift-rotate functions.

Figure 9-28 are defined at the bottom of the illustration. For example, four steps are required to accomplish an ELA/B instruction: A shift left magnitude is ANDed with R-bus bits 0–13, a shift left 14 is ANDed with R-bus bit 14 (shifting these bits to bits 1–15 of the T bus), the extend register contents are transferred onto the T-bus bit 0, and then bit 15 of the R bus is transferred into the extend register.

The net result of these shifts on the A or B register is shown in Figure 9-28. The detailed theory of circuit operation for an ELA/B instruction is covered in subdivision M of this chapter.

3. Implementing Input/Output Instructions

Like the register reference instructions, input/output instructions, as shown by Figure 9-25, are fully executed in only one phase (fetch). The interrupt phase of the input/output instructions is shown at the bottom of Figure 9-25.

M. DETAILED THEORY OF OPERATION

It will be seen by the discussion thus far in this chapter that overall operation of even a simple computer is actually quite complex. The detailed theory of operation for the specific circuits that accomplish the overall function is often more complex. Although the operation of individual circuit groups may appear simple when only that particular circuit is analyzed, the functions can become difficult to grasp when the individual circuit is analyzed in relation to all other circuits.

Typically, all computer circuits are **interlaced**, with each circuit having many inputs and outputs to and from other circuits. This also presents a problem when troubleshooting, as is discussed in Section IV of this book.

Owing to space limitations, it is impossible to describe the complete detailed theory of operation for the HP2116 (or any other computer) in this book. Instead, we shall limit our discussion to how one specific instruction is executed. The instruction covered is ELA/B, performed primarily by the E register. The technician is mostly interested in how theory relates to troubleshooting. With this in mind, the detailed troubleshooting procedures for the circuits affected by the ELA/B instruction are covered in Section IV (Chapter 13, subdivision C).

To understand the operation of the circuits involved in the ELA/B instructions, it is first necessary to understand the E-register circuits. The complete E register, which includes a FF, many gates, and an amplifier for the EXTEND panel light indicator, is shown in Figure

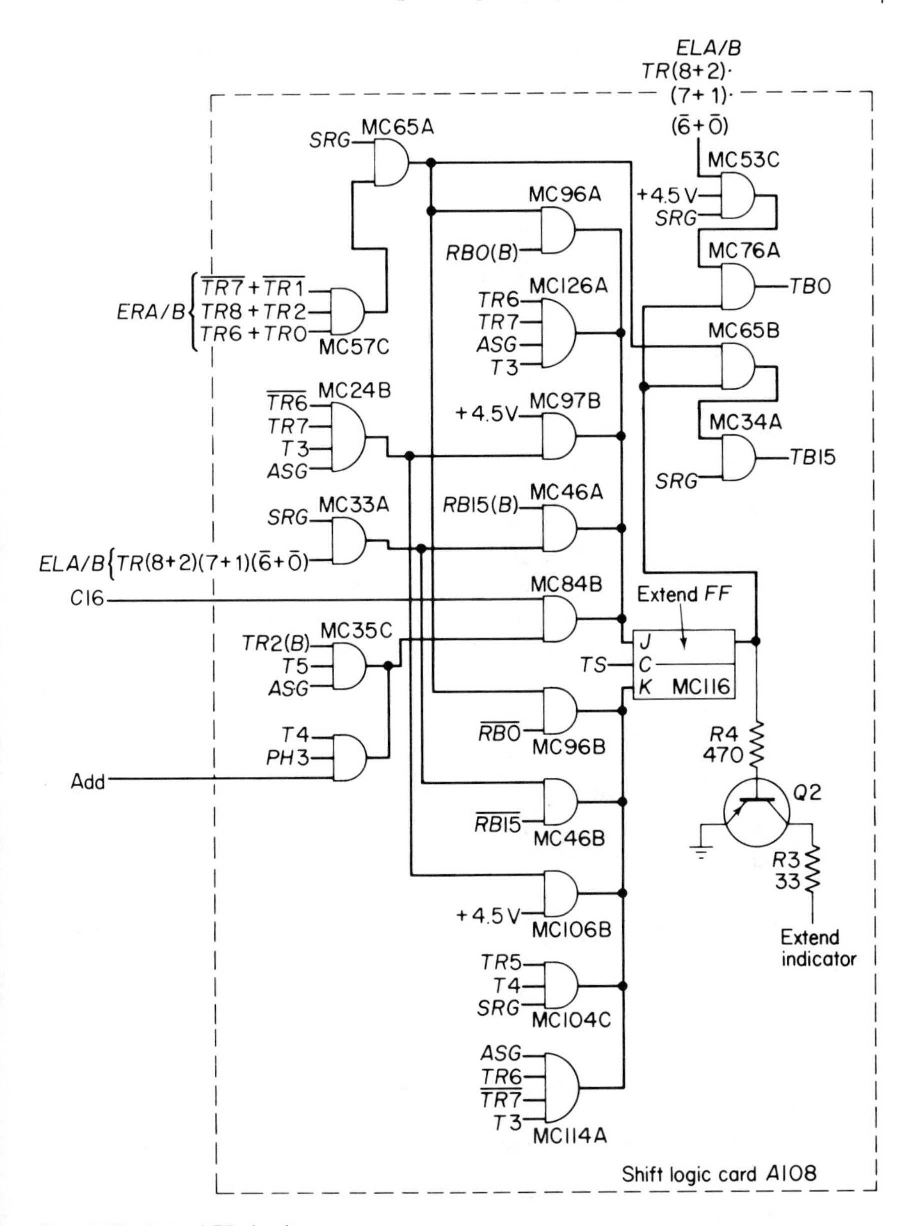

Fig. 9-29. Extend FF circuits.

9-29. All the E-register components are located on a plug-in card (designated as shift logic card A108). Although there are many gates in the E register, only five are active during an ELA/B instruction: MC33A, MC46A, MC46B, MC53C, and MC76A. Other gates are used for other instructions. For example, gate MC84B is used only during an ADA/B or INA/B instruction and has to do with the carry function of arithmetic operations (gate MC84B requires a true input from C16, which is carry bit 16).

Note that all gates are prefixed with the letters MC, which stand for *microcircuit*. This indicates that all gates are in integrated circuit form, with the IC packages mounted on the logic card. In many cases, several gates are contained in a single IC package. As is discussed in Section IV, if one gate in an IC package proves to be defective, the entire package must be replaced.

1. Extend Flip-flop

The extend FF, also known as the E register, is used for a number of purposes. The extend FF operates in conjunction with the A or B register in rotate operations brought about by the ELA/B instructions. When an ELA/B instruction is performed, the entire contents of the A or B register are shifted one position to the left, and the bit originally in the extend FF is shifted into position 0 of the register. The bit in position 15 of the A or B register is rotated into the extend FF.

The extend FF is also used to move a bit between the A and B registers. To accomplish this, the bit is rotated into the extend FF by an ELA/B instruction; then another rotate instruction shifts the bit into the other register.

The state of the extend FF is shown by the extend indicator (which lights when the FF is set).

2. ELA/B Instructions

The ELA/B instructions rotate the contents of the extend FF left one position with the contents of the A or B register. The bit in position 15 of the A or B register is moved into the extend FF, and the bit in the extend FF is moved into position 0 of the A or B register.

Gate MC33A provides an enable for gates MC46A and MC46B. The bit in position 15 of the A or B register is gated onto the R bus, and MC46A or MC46B sets or clears the extend FF when the FF receives a clock pulse.

One input to MC33A is the SRG (shift-rotate group) signal, which becomes true when a shift-rotate instruction is decoded. The other input to MC33A is TR $(8 + 2)(7 + 1)(\bar{6} + \bar{0})$. This signal is true when T-register positions 8 and 7 contain logic 1 and position 6 contains logic 0. The signal is also true when T-register positions 2 and 1 contain logic 1 and position 0 contains logic 0. Figure 9-29 shows that the T register contains the first set of bits when an ELA/B instruction is indicated by bits 8, 7, and 6 of the instruction word. The T register also contains the second set of bits when an ELA/B instruction is indicated by bits 2, 1, and 0 of the instruction word.

Gates MC53C and MC76A shift the bit originally in the extend FF onto T bus 0, from where the bit is gated into position 0 of the A or B register.

The SRG signal, which enables the principal gates used by the ELA/B instructions, becomes true at the beginning of *T*3. During *T*3, the STBA (store T bus in A register) or STBB (store T bus in B register) signal is true. The bit in the extend FF, gated onto T bus 0, is then placed in position 0 of the A or B register. Furthermore, at the start of *T*3, the bit on R bus 15 is placed in the input rank of the extend FF; at the end of *T*3, the bit is transferred to the output rank of the FF and determines the final contents of the extend FF.

BASIC OPERATION OF A WORKING COMPUTER

10

The purpose of this chapter is to relate the circuit operations described in Chapter 9 to actual visual actions as they appear on the operating control panel of the HP2116 computer. Specific information is given for the user to gain familiarity with the panel controls and to be able to perform basic operations on computers, such as the HP2116, without input/output devices (or without software aids such as diagnostic tapes). These purely manual operations are most commonly encountered by technicians (rather than operators or programmers) during computer maintenance and for loading, examining, and changing small sections of the computer memory.

It must be understood that the operating procedures described in this chapter apply specifically to the HP2116. However, since these procedures are so typical of those found in many computers of the same size and type and even in larger types, the technician will do well to study this chapter thoroughly. While it is not intended to make technicians into full-fledged programmers, a technician must be able to operate a computer in order to properly service it.

A. COMPUTER CODING

This chapter assumes familiarity with binary and octal number systems, as outlined in Chapter 3, as well as a knowledge of the basic computer instructions, as described in Chapter 9. As a reminder, a 1 is coded by a switch of the switch register being in the up position and is indicated by a register light being on. A 0 is coded by a switch in the down position and is indicated by a register light being off.

All numbers used for addresses or contents in this chapter are octal numbers unless otherwise specified. Notation of instruction codes in octal numbers is an operator's convenience for loading and reading binary information. The meaning of the octal code can be understood only when it is broken down into the binary elements. For example, in the instruction STA 3000 (store A register into memory location 003000; initial zeros of address assumed), the coded instruction word is 073000.

Refer now to the memory reference instructions shown in Figure 9-17. Note that the code for STA consists of 1 in bit positions 14, 13, and 12 and a 0 in bit position 11. Since indirect addressing is not being used at this time, bit 15 is a 0. Bit 10 must be a 1, since the program and all references will be on the same (current) memory page.

This accounts for bits 10–15, as shown in Figure 10-1. The remaining bits (0–9), which make up the memory address, are simply the corre-

Fig. 10-1. Coding a memory reference instruction word.

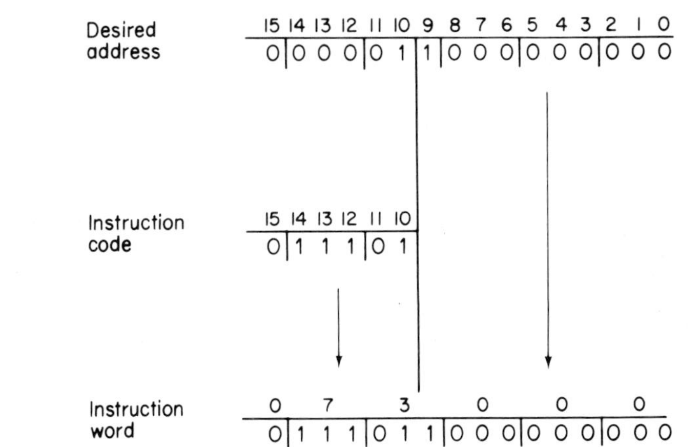

sponding bits of the desired address (003000 in this case). This breaks down in binary form as shown in the top row of Figure 10-1. Note that all bits higher than bit 9 of the desired address are disregarded by the programmer when composing the instruction word, because these bits fall outside of the page-size limits. The M register, which contains the page-designating bits, will hold the bits constant at execute time, as commanded by bit 10 of the instruction code.

It is evident that the octal digit 3 in the resultant instruction word 073000 is the result of three individual factors: Bit 11 (a 0) specifies the A register, bit 10 (a 1) specified current page, and bit 9 (a 1) is an address bit. This requirement of using bits having separate, individual means to compose an octal digit is frequently encountered in computers of this type. For example, suppose that it is desired to rotate the B register left three places and clear the extend bit, all in one instruction. From the shift-rotate group of instructions (Chapter 9, Figure 9-19) it is determined that a suitable method for a three-place rotation is to rotate the B register left four places (BLF) and then right one place (RBR). The resultant octal code for the instruction that will accomplish these actions (including the clearing of the extend bit) is 005763. The way this number is composed can be shown by breaking it down into the binary components, as shown in Figure 10-2.

The ability to code instructions in octal form is essential to the procedures given in this chapter and to the operation of almost all computers. It is therefore strongly recommended that the technician take time at this point to study the composition of the previous instruction word (Figure 10-2) in relation to the information of Chapter 9 (sub-

Fig. 10-2. Composition of octal words on computer registers.

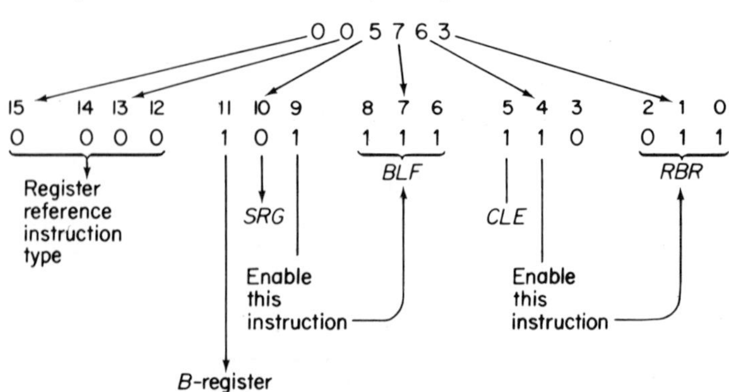

division J and Figure 9-19). The following is a bit-by-bit analysis of the instruction, showing how it was composed from the information given.

In the original problem, it is desired to produce one instruction word (in octal and/or binary notation) that will rotate the B register left three places and clear the extend bit. These actions involve shifting and rotating bits within the computer but do not have any effect on the memory reference. Likewise, the instruction does not require altering or skipping instructions or have any effect on input/output registers. Thus only the shift-rotate group of instructions need to be considered.

A study of the shift-rotate instructions shows that there are no single instructions that will produce a three-place rotation or shift. However, there are many four-place and one-place shifts (or rotations). A combination of the BLF (four-place left) and the RBR (one place right) will produce the net effect of having a three-place left shift. Thus both BLF and RBR must be accomplished during the shift-rotate instruction. Likewise, the extend bit (E register) must be cleared during the same instruction.

Now, referring to Figure 9-19, let us examine each bit in the register.

1. Bits 12–15 are set to 0 for all shift-rotate instructions.
2. Bit 11 is set to a 1 since the B register is involved.
3. Bit 10 is set to 0 for all shift-rotate instructions.
4. Bit 9 is set to a 1 since the first instruction (BLF) appears in column 1 of the Figure 9-19 selection table. This is required by step 2 of the Figure 9-19 combining guide.
5. Bit 4 is also set to a 1 since the second instruction (RBR) appears in column 4 of the Figure 9-19 selection table.
   Note that columns 1 and 4 of the selection table are identical. Column 4 can be ignored if only one shift-rotate instruction is required. (For example, column 4 can be ignored if only BLF is required.)
6. Bits 8, 7, and 6 are set to 111, respectively, since this is the required code for the BLF instruction.
7. Bits 2, 1, and 0 are set to 011, respectively, since this is the required code for the RBR instruction.
   Note that bits 8, 7, and 6 are identical (in function) to bits 2, 1, and 0. The 2, 1, and 0 bits can be ignored (all set to 0) if only one shift-rotate instruction is required.

8. Bit 5 is set to 1 since the CLE (clear E register) is to be used, This is shown in step 3 of the combining guide.
9. Bit 3 is set to 0 since SLB (a skip instruction) is not to be used. This is shown in step 4 of the combining guide.

Thus the binary bits and corresponding octal codes are

0	000	101	111	110	011
0	0	5	7	6	3.

B. COMPUTER TURN-ON

Assuming that installation of the computer has been completed, power is turned on simply by pressing the power switch. See Figure 9-2 for location of the computer operating controls. The power pushbutton lights when computer power is on, and initially the halt pushbutton and the fetch indicator should also light. The various register lights will come on in a random pattern. Should one or more of these indications fail when turning on the computer, refer to the service literature. As is discussed in Section IV, most troubleshooting charts (found in computer service literature) are based upon operating the computer in a given sequence and noting the presence (or absence) of indications (usually lights on or off) at the computer control panel.

It is good practice when turning on any computer, or when beginning any new operation, to press the preset pushbutton and to check that the loader switch is in the protected position (or, on computers other than the HP2116, that corresponding switches are in the appropriate positions). The following procedures are designed to be performed on the computer while reading the text. Considerable loading effort can be saved if the entire set of procedures is performed in the sequence given, without any interruptions that might disturb procedures in progress. Since many operating procedures *alter memory*, the technician should also *be certain* that he is not destroying valuable information that may have been stored previously in the computer. Needless to say, computer operators and programmers take a very dim view of technicians who do anything to destroy data in the memory when attempting to check out the computer.

C. PRELIMINARY OPERATIONS

The first and most basic operation is to put some information into the computer's memory. The following paragraphs outline two methods of doing this. One method is to manually store the setting of the switch register directly into a specific memory cell by using the front-panel operating controls. The other method is to let the computer itself do the storing operation. The purpose in showing these two methods is to demonstrate that computer "instructions" are equivalent to operating controls.

Figure 10-3 illustrates the two memory-storing methods. Note that in the first case the information is transferred from the switch register

Fig. 10-3. Two methods of storing information in memory.

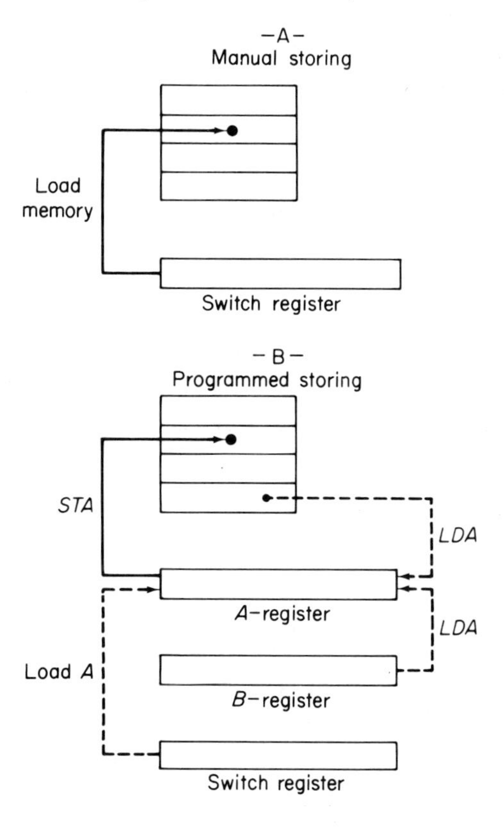

to a location in memory. In the second case (programmed loading), the transfer is from the A register. For simplicity, information will be put into the A register manually from the switch register (broken LDA line). However, as is discussed in later paragraphs, this information could come from anywhere in the memory or from the B register (broken LDA lines). Note also that, for simplicity, Figure 10-3 omits detailed routing via the bus system and the T register, as described in Chapter 9.

1. Manual Storing

First it is necessary to decide where in the memory the information is to be stored. For illustrative purposes, an address in the middle of the second memory page has been selected, location 003000. To direct the computer to this address, set the number into the switch register, as shown in step 1 of Figure 10-4. Then press the load address pushbutton (step 2). This immediately transfers the setting of the switch registers into the P and M registers, as can be read from the P- and M-register

Fig. 10-4. Storing information manually.

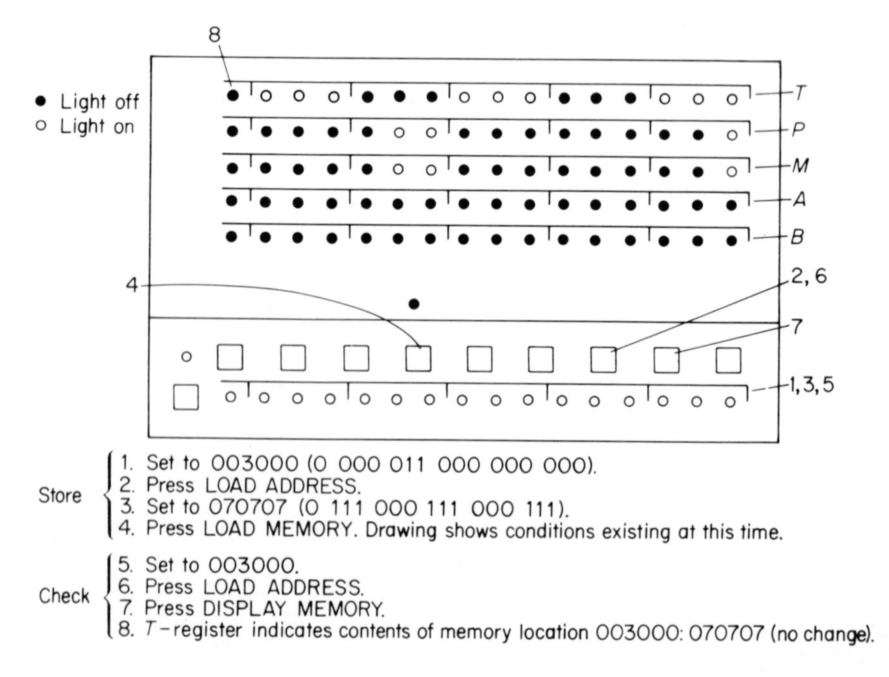
8
● Light off
○ Light on
T
P
M
A
B
4
2, 6
7
1, 3, 5
Store
1. Set to 003000 (0 000 011 000 000 000).
2. Press LOAD ADDRESS.
3. Set to 070707 (0 111 000 111 000 111).
4. Press LOAD MEMORY. Drawing shows conditions existing at this time.
Check
5. Set to 003000.
6. Press LOAD ADDRESS.
7. Press DISPLAY MEMORY.
8. T-register indicates contents of memory location 003000: 070707 (no change).

lights. The computer is now "at" location 003000 (the addressed location).

Now the operator can store any desired information into the addressed location. An easy-to-recognize pattern of 0 and 1 in alternating groups of three is suggested in Figure 10-4 (in octal, 070707). (Such a pattern is often referred to as a *checkerboard*; refer to the Glossary.) Complete steps 3 and 4 of Figure 10-4. Note that the P and M registers have incremented to the next location (which will not be used at this point). The T register indicates the information (070707) that went into the memory.

To verify that location 003000 does indeed contain the information 070707, complete steps 5–8. Again, note that the P and M registers, at the conclusion of this procedure, are one step "ahead" of the information displayed in the T register. That is, the P- and M-register lights indicate 0 000 011 000 000 001 (octal 003001), because the P and M registers must direct the computer to the next location, whereas the T register always indicates information resulting from *previous* action.

2. Programmed Storing

For the computer to perform its own storing operation, it is first necessary to put into the memory the instruction (STA, store contents of A register) that will accomplish this. Then the computer can be directed to the place in the memory where this instruction is located; pressing the run pushbutton will then let the computer go ahead and execute the instruction. After doing so, the computer will look for its next instruction in the following location and will attempt to continue running. Since it is unknown what other information may be in the memory, it is necessary to stop the computer as soon as the desired action is completed, simply by putting a halt (HLT) instruction in the immediately succeeding location. The required "program" therefore consists of two instructions, STA and HLT.

The manual-storage procedure put an easy-to-recognize pattern (070707) into location 003000. The programmed-storing procedure will let the computer put a different pattern (all 1, octal 177777) into the same location, replacing the previous pattern. This new pattern is loaded into the A register before the program is run.

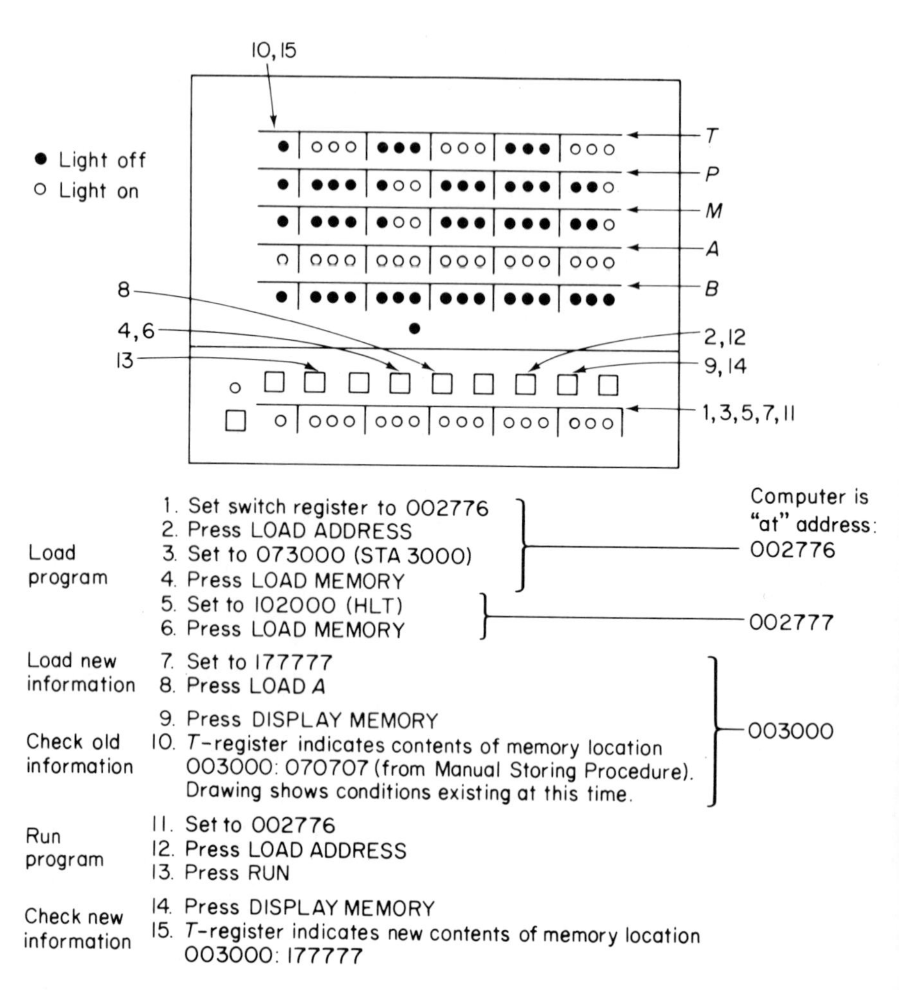

Fig. 10-5. Storing information by program.

Steps 1–6 of Figure 10-5 store the two-word program into memory, using the two locations (002776 and 002777) immediately preceding the location to be altered (003000). Steps 7 and 8 load the new pattern (177777) into the A register. Steps 9 and 10 verify that the old pattern (070707) is still in location 003000. Steps 11–13 cause the program to be run. Typically, such a program will require 4 to 5 μS. Thus the computer will be back in the halt condition (halt light on) faster than can be visually detected. Steps 14 and 15 verify that the new pattern (177777) is now in location 003000.

D. THE STORED PROGRAM

The preceding descriptions have demonstrated that internal preset-able commands can control the operation of the computer in the same manner as the front-panel control. If the computer were constructed like a mechanical calculator, there might be panel controls to "add" or "subtract," but this would be defeating the design principles of a computer. The intent is to provide flexibility through the use of internal commands that can be arranged to occur in a specific sequence and to limit panel controls to the mininum required to initiate operation. This, in essence, is the concept of the stored-program computer. The following paragraphs discuss the elements of the stored program.

A program consists of a sequence of computer words, stored in the memory, that control operation of the computer. The general term *computer words* is used rather than the restrictive term *instructions* since the stored information generally includes three types of words: the **instruction word**, the **address word**, and the **data word.**

Although these terms are to some extent self-explanatory, the distinction and usage requires illustration. For purposes of illustration, the simple program example used in the preceding descriptions will be expanded and examined in more detail. Before proceeding, however, the method of writing programs in a concise, meaningful form is presented. Notation of this kind becomes an absolute necessity when large programs are involved.

1. Program Table

The table of Figure 10-6 puts into tabular form the two-word program previously used as an example. The information in Figure 10-6

Fig. 10-6. Program table.

Address	Contents						Remarks
	Instructions (or data)	Memory reference	*D/I*	*A/B*	*Z/C*	Octal code	
002776	*STA*	3000			*C*	073000	Get pattern from *A*, put in 3000.
002777	*HLT*					102000	Halt.
003000							Reserved for answer.

corresponds to steps 1–6 of Figure 10-5. The format of Figure 10-6 is used for explanatory purposes here. However, the format resembles in general arrangement the assembler coding forms (or simply *assembler*; see the Glossary) used for many computers.

Address

The address column of the program table states where in the memory the program words (contents) are to be stored. The first listed address states where the program is to begin; this is termed the *starting address*. The starting address of Figure 10-6 is 002776; the program stops at the location immediately following (002777). Although the program never advances to location 003000 (the location immediately following 002777), this address must be listed in the program table as a reminder that this memory location will be used in the program (reserved for the answer).

Contents

The stored program can consist of three types of words: instructions, data, or even the address of another location. Therefore the contents of a location specified by an address may take various forms in the contents column of Figure 10-6. Most memory locations of a program will be instructions; the instruction mnemonic is listed in the instruction (or data) column. If the content is not an instruction (usually a pure number representing data or an address), it will also appear under this heading, as shown in Figure 10-7.

Fig. 10-7. Program to show instruction, data, and address words.

Address	Contents						Remarks
	Instructions (or data)	Memory reference	*D/I*	*A/B*	*Z/C*	Octal code	
002774	*LDA*	3001			*C*	063001	Put augent in *A*.
002775	*ADA*	3777	1		*C*	143777	Add the addend specified by 3777.
002776	*STA*	3000			*C*	073000	Put answer in 3000.
002777	*HLT*					102000	Halt.
003000						---	Reserved for answer.
003001	5					000005	Data.
003777	3001					003001	Address of addend is 3001.

In the case of memory reference instructions, the address of the location affected by the instruction is listed under the memory reference heading. For example, the first instruction listed in Figure 10-6 is a command to store the A-register contents into location 003000. Thus location 003000 is the affected location (that is, the memory reference).

The D/I, A/B, and Z/C headings are used only in the case of memory reference instructions. As a reminder to code a 1 bit for I (indirect addressing), B (B register), and C (current page), only these three indicators are given in the tables. D (direct addressing), A (A register), and Z (page zero), all coded by 0 bits, are otherwise assumed. For example, in Figure 10-6, the D/I bit should be a 0 (for a D), the A/B bit should be a 0 (for A), and the Z/C bit should be a 1 (for C).

The octal code column is used for the coded version of the desired contents. Thus the octal code column comprises the machine-language program, since this is the information loaded into the computer. Insofar as the computer is concerned, these numbers are the program. Note that no specific contents need be loaded for address 003000, since the STA 3000 instruction will destroy any information previously contained here.

Remarks

A short explanation accompanying each assigned address of the program is helpful in communicating the intent of program details to other persons and also can serve as a reminder to the original programmer when reexamining the program at a later time. The remarks column should always be studied by the technician, since the comments are often helpful in troubleshooting. Hopefully, words used for the remarks column are carefully chosen to be as concise and meaningful as possible. Understanding a given program can be difficult enough without adding confusion through vague documentation.

As an example, it would not be incorrect to say for the first instruction in Figure 10-6, "Store contents of A in location 3000." However, this does not say any more than the instruction word itself says (STA 3000). The remark suggested in Figure 10-6 states what is expected to be in the A register (a *pattern*) and raises the question of what the pattern is and how it happened to get into the A register. This leads the technician to look for further documentation (such as the operation and service manual), which should tell him how to preset the A register.

Of course, additional words to indicate the need for presetting the A register could be added, thus improving the message still further. On the other hand, the single remark "halt" in the next line requires no additional comment.

2. Program Execution

The table of Figure 10-7 lists the program used as an example in this discussion. The main purpose of the program is to show where and when the three types of program words (instruction, data, and address) occur. In the process of doing so, detailed actions for simple addition and indirect addressing are also illustrated. The program adds 5 to 5 and puts the result (10 decimal or 12 octal) into location 003000. Note that the middle three lines of the program are the same as the example given in Figure 10-6. The first two lines expand the program to accomplish the addition, and the last two lines are data and address words used by the program.

Loading the program

The program is loaded into the computer manually, using the sample procedure given in steps 1–4 of Figure 10-4. Steps 1 and 2 need be done only once for most of the program, since each load memory operation automatically increments the address in the P and M registers. Specifically the procedure is

1. Set the switch register to the stating address (002774) and press the load address pushbutton.
2. Set the switch register to the first word of the program (063001) and press the load memory pushbutton.
3. Set the switch register to the next word of the program, press the load memory pushbutton, and repeat this step until the first six words have been loaded. For the fifth word (which required no contents but is reserved for the answer), it is convenient to simply press the load memory pushbutton with the HLT code still in the switch register. A halt instruction in this location does no harm.

4. For the seventh word, which is not in sequence with the other six, it is necessary to set the address (003777) into the switch register and press the load address pushbutton. Then set the switch register to the contents (003001), which is back in sequence again, and press the load memory pushbutton.

Running the program

Again set the switch register to the starting address (002774) and press the load address pushbutton. Now press the run pushbutton. Immediately the computer switches to the halt condition, having excuted the problem and stored the answer in location 003000 in 12.8 μS. To verify that the computer has arrived at the right answer (000012), press the display memory pushbutton. The answer is in the T register.

This demonstrates how fast the computer operates but does not show what operations it went through to arrive at its answer. Therefore the following paragraphs rerun the program step by step (using the single-cycle feature of the computer) in order to show these operations. This brings up an important troubleshooting technique for the technician. When a computer fails to perform a given program and the computer has a single-cycle feature (or some similar mode of operation where each step of the program can be executed manually one at a time), use the single cycle. Start with the first step or address and execute each step in turn until the computer fails to perform properly. Often, this will pinpoint the problem.

As an oversimplified example, assume that one location in the memory is defective (say the wiring to one ferrite core is broken). Also assume that this location in the memory is referenced as the seventh step in a 100-step program. No matter how well the computer is programmed or how perfect all other components in the computer are operating, the program will never get beyond step 7.

Single-cycle operation

The table of Figure 10-8 shows the contents of each register following each operation of the single-cycle pushbutton. The program is executed in eight steps (that is, eight machine phases). The following eight paragraphs describe each of these steps. The program is initially set up by setting the switch register to the starting address (002774) and pressing the load address pushbutton. The conditions then existing are

Step	Instruction	*T* register	*P* register	*M* register	*A* register	*B* register	Phase
		Any	002774	002774	Any	(Not used)	Fetch
1	*LDA*	063001	002774	003001	Any		Execute
2		000005	002775	002775	000005		Fetch
3	*ADA, I*	143777	002775	037777	000005		Indirect
4		003001	002775	003001	000005		Execute
5		000005	002776	002776	000012		Fetch
6	*STA*	073000	002776	003000	000012		Execute
7		000012	002777	002777	000012		Fetch
8	*HLT*	102000	003000	003000	000012		Fetch

Fig. 10-8. Single-cycle execution of a program.

shown in the top line of Figure 10-8: The P and M registers hold the starting address, and the remaining registers can be in any state. The fetch phase indicator light on the panel is on, indicating that the first machine phase will be a fetch phase; this is an effect of the load address switch.

Step 1. Press the single-cycle pushbutton

The conditions of the registers after the computer has completed this first phase are shown in the step 1 line of Figure 10-8. As an additional reference, refer back to Figure 9-23. The fetch phase actions for all memory reference instructions except JMP apply to this discussion. Note also the read-write memory cycle, which is what reads the contents of the addressed location (the contents of 002774 is 063001) into the T register. This is accomplished early in the fetch phase. The computer interprets any word read out of memory during a fetch phase as an *instruction* word. It is the programmer's responsibility to ensure that the computer does find an instruction in every location to which the P register goes. This is ensured by properly filling out the program table. For example, in the program table of Figure 10-7 the program (P register) starts at 002774 and stops at 002777. Every one of these locations must have an instruction word as its contents. Later in the fetch phase (*T*6 and *T*7), the memory reference bits (0–9) of the T register are transferred into bits 0–9 of the M register. The remaining bits of the M register are left unchanged (since there is no reference to page zero), thus completing the memory reference address in the M register. In comparing the contents of the T and M registers in step 1 of Figure 10-8, be careful not to assume that the complete octal digits 3001 are transferred; the digit 3 (like the situation shown in Figure 10-1) is a composite of three binary bits with different code meanings. Also occurring at the end of the fetch phase is the execute (phase 3) condition. The P and A registers are not yet affected.

Step 2. Press the single-cycle pushbutton again to complete execution of the LDA 3001 instruction

Step 2 of Figure 10-8 shows register conditions existing after completion of the execute phase. This is the phase in which the computer gets the data requested by the memory reference and does with them whatever is commanded by the instruction code. The read portion of the memory cycle reads the contents of the location addressed by the M register (now at 003001) into the T register. This information, read out of memory by the execute phase, is a *data* word. It is the programmer's responsibility to ensure that a data word (or an indirect address) is contained in all locations to which there is a memory reference (unless the location is to be used by the program for storage, such as reserved for an answer and the like). As seen in Figure 10-7, there are three memory references; thus the table accounts for three addresses in addition to the four addresses assigned to the program instructions. One of these three is a storage location, one is data, and one is an indirect address. In this step, the information read out is the data 5. As shown in Figure 9-23 (LDA/B), the data are transferred from the T register to the A register during the execute phase. Thus the number 5 appears in both registers (A and T). At the end of this phase, the P and M registers are set to the address of the next instruction (002775), and the fetch condition is set (fetch light on) for reading of the next instruction.

Step 3. Press the single-cycle pushbutton again

This fetches the next instruction (143777) out of location 002775. The code 143777 means "Add to whatever is in the A register the contents of a memory location that can be found by going first to location 3777 for more information." This is what is implied by the symbolic form ADA 3777, indirect. The indirect bit (bit 15 of the word now in the T register) caused the setting of the indirect phase (indirect light on), and the memory reference bits (0–9) have been transferred into the M register. The P and A registers remain as they were. The indirect phase is ready to begin.

Step 4. Press the single-cycle pushbutton again

The computer always interprets information read out of the memory during an indirect phase as an *address* word. The word (003001) is transferred to the M register as the new memory reference for the current ADA instruction. Both T and M registers therefore now contain 003001. Since bit 15 of this word is a 0 (direct address), the execute condition is set (execute light on). If this bit 15 had been a 1 (indirect), the indirect condition would remain set, and a further memory reference would be obtained in the next step. However, with this example, the computer now knows that the added data are located in 003001. It happens in this example that this is the same location from which the augend was taken. However, the address word could just as well refer to any location in memory.

Step 5. Press the single-cycle pushbutton again

In the execute phase of the ADA instruction, the data in location 003001 are read out (the number 5) and are to be added to the existing contents of the A register (which up until now also contained the number 5). The T register therefore contains 5, and the A register contains 12. As usual, the last operation for any instruction is to advance the P and M registers to the location of the next instruction (002776) and to set the fetch phase condition.

Step 6. Press the single-cycle pushbutton again

The fetch phase of the STA 3000 instruction reads the instruction word (073000) out of location 002776, transfers the memory reference bits to the M register, and sets the execute phase.

Step 7. Press the single-cycle pushbutton again

The execute phase puts the A-register contents (000012) into the memory via the T register. Therefore both registers indicate this value. As usual, the P and M registers are advanced to the address of the next instruction (002777), and the fetch phase condition is met.

Step 8. Press the single-cycle pushbutton again (for the last time during this program).

The halt instruction is read out of the memory, and the computer is in the same state as after running the program automatically. As before, the display memory pushbutton can now be pressed to verify that location 003000 again has received the correct answer, 000012 (or 10 in decimal numbers).

COMPUTER TROUBLE-SHOOTING

IV

The chapters of this section describe those basic troubleshooting techniques that apply to all digital circuits in general and to digital computer circuits in particular. Although the principles of troubleshooting and service that are used with all electronic devices also apply to digital computers, there are many practical techniques that apply only to digital equipment.

As one example, the key technique described here is based upon measurement of pulses at inputs and outputs of computer circuits. From a troubleshooting standpoint, a complete computer logic diagram can appear as a hopeless maze, since most computer circuits are **interlaced** (that is, multiple functions for the same signal at different times or one signal being dependent on many other signals or signal conditions). However, if pulses can be checked at the input and/or output of each circuit or group of circuits, the condition of that circuit can be checked quickly.

This troubleshooting technique requires the use of an oscilloscope and possibly a pulse generator. Such a combination of test equipment will quickly determine the presence (or absence) of pulses at circuit inputs and outputs, as well as the pulse duration, amplitude, and delay. For example, an AND gate may show an incorrect output, even though there are two input pulses of correct amplitude and duration, if one pulse is delayed.

These measuring and monitoring techniques, together with many other test and fault location methods for computers, are discussed in the following chapters. It is assumed that the reader is already familiar with basic solid-state troubleshooting methods and particularly the specialized repair methods for integrated circuits. Such information is contained in *the author's Handbook of Practical Solid-State Troubleshooting*.*

*John D. Lenk, *Handbook of Practical Solid-State Troubleshooting* (Englewood Cliffs, N. J.: Prentice-Hall, Inc., 1971).

COMPUTER TEST EQUIPMENT

11

The test equipment and tools required for service of computers are essentially the same as for other solid-state digital units. Much of the service work can be done with an oscilloscope, pulse generator, VOM, and common hand tools. However, the test equipment capabilities are usually much greater for computer work. Also, there are certain items of test equipment made specifically for digital use. These special test instruments, together with the special capability requirements of common test equipment, are discussed in the following paragraphs.

A. OSCILLOSCOPES FOR COMPUTERS

An oscilloscope for computer work should have a bandwidth of at least 50 MHz, preferably 100 MHz. The pulse widths (or pulse durations) found in most computers are on the order of a few microseconds, often only a few nanoseconds wide.

A **triggered horizontal sweep** is an essential feature. Preferably, the delay introduced by the trigger should be very short. Often, the pulse to be monitored occurs shortly after an available trigger. In other cases, the horizontal sweep must be triggered by the pulse to be monitored. In some oscilloscopes, a delay is introduced between the input and the vertical deflection circuits. This permits the horizontal sweep to be triggered before the vertical signal is applied, thus assuring that the complete pulse will be displayed.

Dual-trace horizontal sweeps are also essential. Most computer troubleshooting is based upon the monitoring of two time-related pulses (say an input pulse and an output pulse or a clock pulse and a readout pulse). With dual trace, the two pulses can be observed simultaneously, one above the other, or superimposed if convenient. In other test configurations, a clock pulse is used to trigger both horizontal sweeps. This allows for a three-way time relation measurement (clock pulse and two circuit pulses, such as one input and one output). A few oscilloscopes have multiple-trace capabilities. However, this is not standard. Usually, such an oscilloscope is provided with plug-in options that increase the number of horizontal sweeps.

The **sensitivity** of both the vertical and horizontal channels should be such that full-scale deflection can be obtained (without overdriving or distortion) with less than a 1-V signal applied. Typically, the signal pulses used in computer work are in the order of 5 V, but often they are less than 1 V.

In some cases, storage oscilloscopes (for display of transient pulses) and sampling oscilloscopes (for display and measurement of very short pulses) may be required. However, most computer service work can be done with an oscilloscope having the bandwidth and sweep capabilities just described.

B. VOLTMETERS FOR COMPUTERS

The voltmeters for computer work should have essentially the same characteristics as for other solid-state troubleshooting. For example, a very high input impedance is not critical (20,000 Ω/V is usually sufficient).

Typically, computer circuit operating voltages are 12 V, while the logic voltages (pulse levels) are 5 V or less. Therefore the voltmeter should have good resolution on the low-voltage scales. For example, a typical computer logic level might be where 0 = 0 V and 1 = +3 V. This means that an input of +3 V or greater to an OR gate will produce a 1 (or true) condition, while an input of something less than +3 V, say +2 V, will produce a 0 (false) condition.

As is typical for computer logic-level specifications, the region between +2 and +3 V is not spelled out. If the voltmeter is not capable of reading out clearly between 2 and 3 V on some scale, an incorrect conclusion could easily be reached. If the OR gate in question is tested by applying a supposed +3 V, which was actually 2.7 V, the OR gate might or might not operate to indicate the desired 1 or true output.

Generally, d-c voltage accuracy should be ±2 percent or better, with ±3- to ±5-percent accuracy for the a-c scales. The a-c scales will probably be used only in checking power supply functions in computers, since all signals are in the form of pulses (requiring an oscilloscope for display and measurement).

The ohmmeter portion of the instrument should have the usual high-resistance ranges. Many of the troubles in the most sophisticated and complex computers boil down to such common problems as cold solder joints, breaks in printed circuit wiring that result in high resistance, as well as shorts or partial shorts between wiring (producing an undesired high-resistance condition). The internal battery voltage of the ohmmeter should not exceed any of the voltages used in the circuits being checked.

C. PULSE GENERATORS FOR COMPUTERS

Ideally, a pulse generator should be capable of duplicating any pulse present in the circuits being tested. Thus the pulse generator output should be continuously variable (or at least adjustable by steps) in amplitude, pulse duration (or width), and frequency (or repetition rate) over the same range as the circuit pulses. This is not always possible in every case. However, with modern laboratory pulse generators, it is generally practical for most computers.

Typically, the pulses are ±5 V or less in amplitude, but could be 10 V in rare cases. The pulses are rarely longer than 1 second or shorter than 10 nS, although there are exceptions here, too. Repetition rates are generally less than 100 MHz but could run up to 100 MHz.

Some pulse generators have special features, such as two output pulses with variable delay between the pulses or an output pulse that can be triggered from an external source. However, most routine computer troubleshooting can be performed with standard pulse generators.

D. LOGIC PROBE

Hewlett-Packard has developed a logic probe for digital trouble-shooting. This probe, shown in Figure 11-1, will detect and indicate logic levels or states (0 or 1) in digital circuits. The probe will also detect the presence (or absence) and polarity of any single pulse 30 nS or

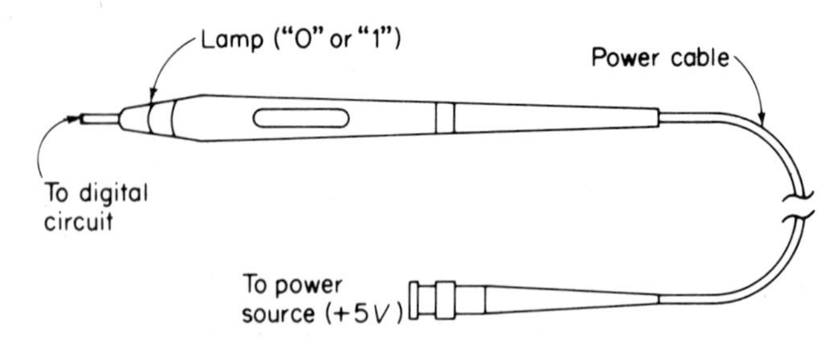

Fig. 11-1. Hewlett-Packard logic probe.

greater in duration. The probe receives power (+5 V) from an external source (or the equipment under test) through the cable. The input impedance is 10 K nominal, which makes the probe compatible with most transistor-transistor-logic (TTL) and diode-transistor-logic (DTL) digital integrated circuits common use. There are no operating or adjust-ment controls. The only indicator is a lamp (which appears as a band of light near the probe tip). The probe has a preset threshold of 1.4 V.

When the probe is touched to a high level or is open-circuited, a band of light appears around the probe tip. When the probe is touched to a low level, the light goes out. Single pulses of about 30 nS or wider are stretched to give a light indication of 0.1 second. The light flashes on or blinks off, depending on the pulse polarity. When the probe is connected to a pulse train, partial illumination (partial brilliance) is displayed by the probe lamp. Pulse trains up to about 1 MHz produce partial (not full) brilliance. Pulse trains from 1 to 20 MHz produce either partial brilliance or momentary extinction, depending the duty cycle of the pulse. The probe response to different inputs is shown in Figure 11-2.

When the logic probe is used to detect logic levels, the indicator lamp will be on when the input is high and off when the input is low, giving an indication of a logical 1 or 0, respectively. With power applied and no connection to a circuit, the probe lamp will normally be on.

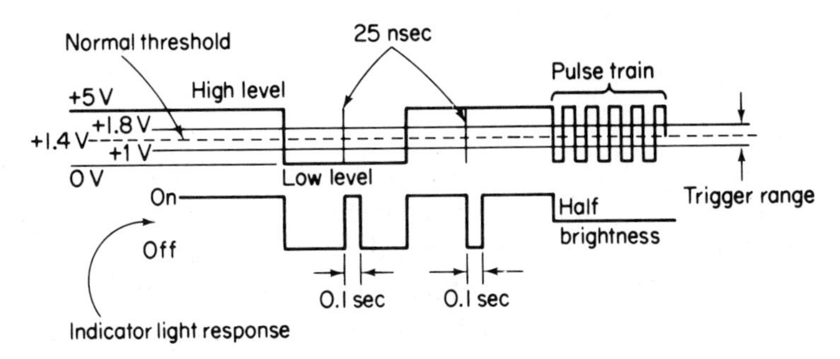

Fig. 11-2. Logic-probe response.

As shown in Figure 11-2, the logic probe is ideal for detecting pulses of short duration and low repetition rates that would normally be very difficult to observe on an oscilloscope. Positive pulses 30 nS or greater in width are stretched and cause the indicator to flash on for 0.1 second. Negative pulses similarly cause the indicator lamp to momentarily extinguish. High-frequency pulse trains, too fast for the eye to follow, are indicated by partial illumination. It can be seen that the minimum *on time* of the indicator lamp for positive pulses (or *off time* for negative pulses) is 0.1 second. The maximum time is dependent on input pulse width.

Figure 11-3 is the block diagram for the logic probe. Note that both the input circuit and the power supply are protected from overvoltage. Normally, the voltages involved in logic circuits are low (typically 5 V). However, the probe tip could be touched to a power supply circuit, a power bus for Nixie indicator lamps, or some similar circuit operating at high voltages. Input overload protection is provided from +50 to +200 V for continuous d-c overloads and 120-V for a-c overloads.

The threshold discriminator and input amplifier circuit sets the threshold at about 1.4 V. The input amplifier is followed by two pulse

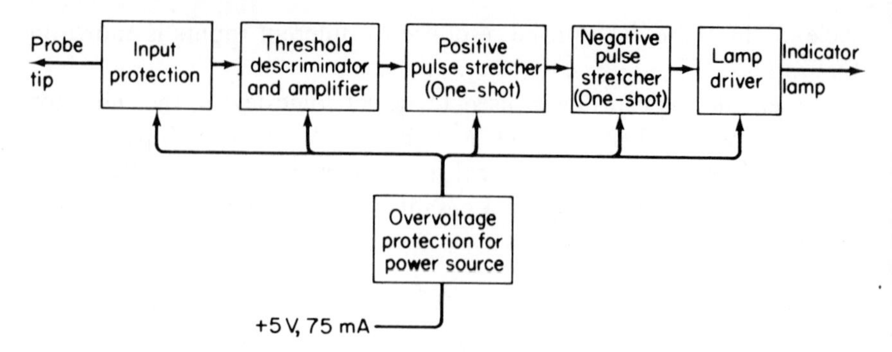

Fig. 11-3. Logic-probe block diagram.

stretchers, one of which triggers automatically on each incoming pulse, depending on the pulse polarity. Each stretcher consists of a monostable multivibrator, or *one-shot* (OS), formed by cross-connecting two gates. When one OS is stretching, the other is acting as an inverting amplifier. The output of the second stretcher drives the indicator lamp through a transistor switch.

The logic probe can be used with several logic circuit analysis techniques. The two most helpful techniques are **pulse-train analysis** and **real-time analysis**. Both techniques are discussed more fully in later chapters.

The basic pulse-train analysis (using the logic probe) is to run the circuit under test at its normal clock rate while checking for "key" logic pulses such a reset, start, transfer, or clock. Questions such as "Is a particular decade counting?" are easily resolved by noting if the probe indicator lamp is partially lit (which only occurs when fast repetition pulse trains are monitored).

With real-time analysis, the normal fast clock signal is replaced by a very slow clock signal from a pulse generator or by manual pulse triggering. The logic changes in the circuit under test will occur at a rate sufficiently slow that individual level changes and proper pulse occurrences can be observed on a real-time basis.

The logic probe can be tested at any time by touching the tip to a variable d-c source. When the source is above the threshold level, the indicator lamp should be on. When the source is dropped below the threshold level, the indicator lamp should go out.

E. LOGIC CLIP

Hewlett-Packard has developed a logic clip for digital trouble-shooting where the digital elements are contained in IC form. Although the logic clip will perform all its functions without additional equipment, it is particularly effective when used with the logic probe.

The logic clip, shown in Figure 11-4, clips onto dual in-line ICs and instantly displays the logic states of all 14 or 16 pins. Each of the

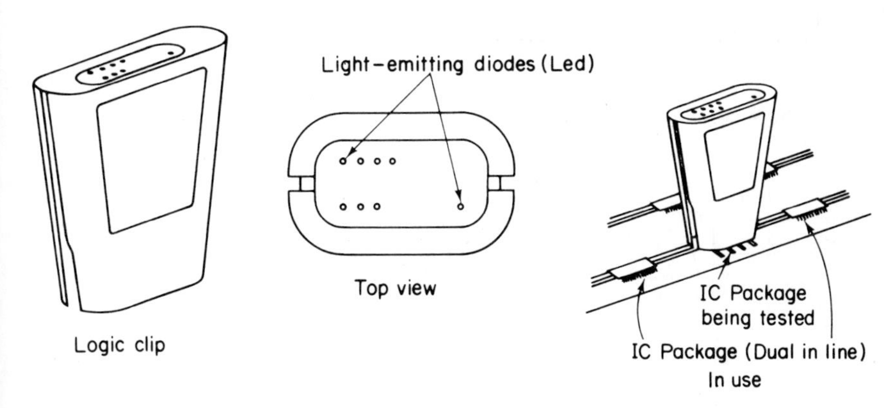

Fig. 11-4. Hewlett-Packard logic clip.

clip's 16 light-emitting diodes (LED) independently follows level changes at an associated input. A lighted diode corresponds to a high, or 1, logic state.

The logic clip's real value is in its ease of use. The clip has no controls to be set, needs no power connections, and requires practically no explanation as to how it is used. Since the clip has its own gating logic (for locating the ground and $+5V_{cc}$ points), it works equally well upside down or right side up. Buffered inputs ensure that the circuit under test will not be loaded down. Simply clipping the unit onto a TTL or DTL dual in-line package of any type makes all logic states visible at a glance.

The logic clip is much easier to use than either an oscilloscope or voltmeter when the troubleshooter is interested in whether a lead is in the high or low state (1 or 0) rather than in the lead's actual voltage. The clip, in effect, is 16 binary voltmeters, and the user does not have to shift his eyes away from his circuit to make the readings.

The fact that lighted diodes correspond to high logic states greatly simplifies the troubleshooting procedure. The user is free to concentrate his attention on circuits rather than on measurement techniques.

When the clip can be used on a real-time basis (when the clock is slowed to about 1 Hz or manually triggered) timing relationships become especially apparent. The malfunction of gates, FF, counters, adders, subtractors, and so forth then becomes readily visible as all the inputs and outputs of an IC are seen in perspective.

When pulses are involved, the logic clip is best used with the logic

Fig. 11-5. Logic-clip block diagram.

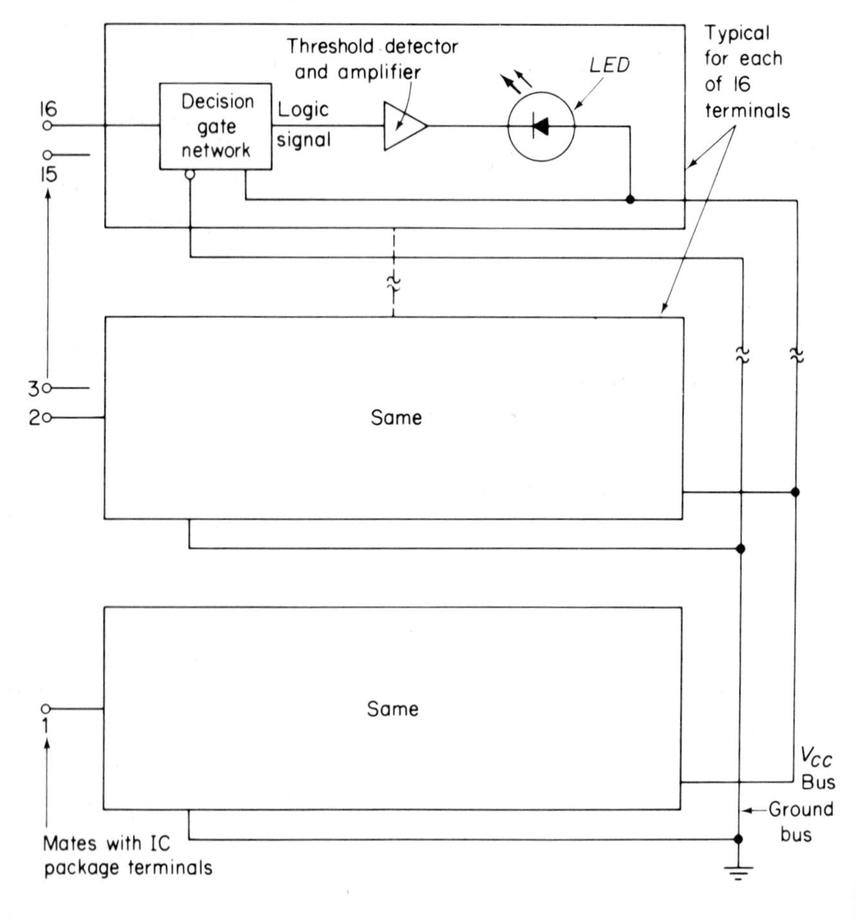

probe. Timing pulses can be observed on the probe, while the associated logic-state changes can be observed on the clip.

Figure 11-5 is the block diagram of the logic clip. As shown, each pin of the logic clip is internally connected to a decision gate network, a threshold detector, and a driver amplifier, connected to an LED. Figure 11-6 shows the decision sequence of the decision gate network. In brief, the decision gate networks do the following:

1. Find IC V_{cc} pin (power voltage) and connect it to the clip power voltage bus. (This also activates an LED.)
2. Find all logic high pins and activate corresponding LEDs.
3. Find all open circuits and activate corresponding LEDs.
4. Find the IC ground pin, connecting it to the clip ground bus, and blank the corresponding LED.

The threshold detector measures the input voltage. If the voltage is not over the threshold voltage, the LED is not activated. An amplifier at the output of the threshold detector drives the LED. The LED will indicate high (glow) if the IC pin is above +2 V and low (no glow) if the pin is below + 0.8 V. (If the IC pin is open, LED will show high.)

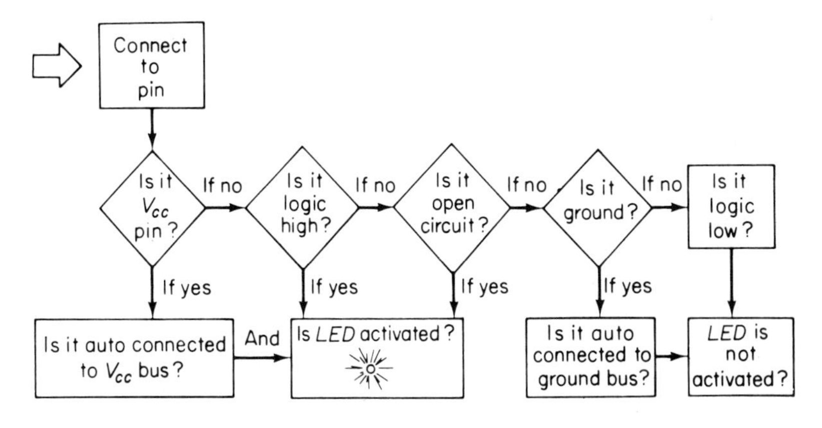

Fig. 11-6. Logic-clip decision sequence.

F. CAPACITOR PULSE GENERATOR

It is often convenient to trigger computer logic circuits manually during troubleshooting. That is, the pulse trains normally present on a particular circuit line or a particular input are removed and replaced by pulses manually injected one at a time. The obvious method to do this is by momentarily connecting the line or input to a bus (of appropriate voltage and polarity). This is not recommended for two reasons: First, some circuits can be damaged by prolonged application of the voltage. In other circuits, no damage will occur, but the results will be inconclusive. For example, many faulty circuits will operate normally when a bus voltage is applied (even momentarily) but will not respond to a pulse.

A better method is to use a capacitor as a *pulse generator*. The technique is shown in Figure 11-7. Simply charge the capacitor by connecting it between ground and a logic bus (typically +5 V). Then connect the charged capacitor between ground and the input to be tested. The capacitor will discharge, creating an input "pulse." Make sure to charge the capacitor to the correct voltage level and polarity. Generally, the capacitor value is not critical. Try a 0.1-μF capacitor as a starting value. Often, it is convenient to connect one lead of the capacitor to a ground clip, with the other lead connected to a test prod. The capacitor can be clipped to ground, and the prod tip can then be moved from bus to input as needed.

Fig. 11-7. Capacitor pulse generator for real-time testing of digital circuits.

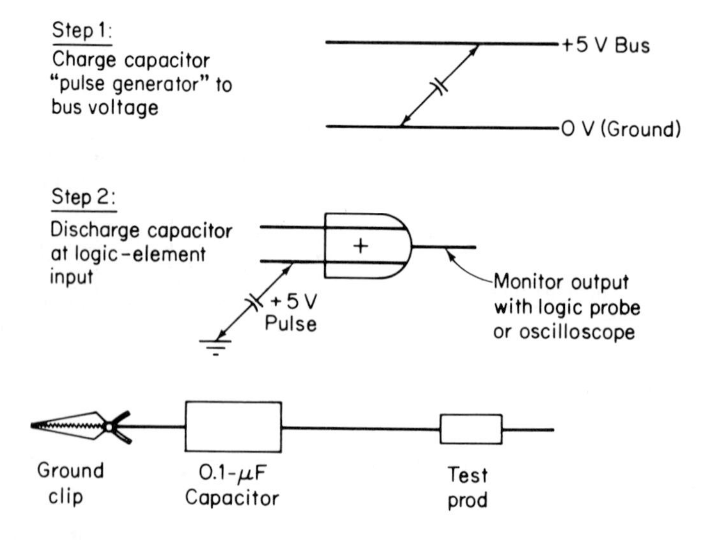

TESTING COMPUTER CIRCUITS

12

No matter what computer is involved or what digital troubleshooting technique is used, you must be able to work with pulses. That is, you must be able to monitor pulses on an oscilloscope and measure their amplitude, duration, or width and frequency or repetition rate. You must also be able to measure delay between pulses and to check operation of basic computer circuits, or "building blocks," such as OR gates, AND gates, FF, and delays.

These basic digital measuring techniques, together with descriptions of the test equipment involved, are discussed in the following paragraphs.

A. BASIC PULSE MEASUREMENT TECHNIQUES

The following measurement techniques apply to all types of pulses, including square waves, used in digital circuits.

1. Pulse Definitions

The following terms are commonly used in describing pulses found in computer circuits. The terms are illustrated in Figure 12-1. The input pulse represents an ideal input wave form for comparison purposes. The other wave forms in Figure 12-1 represent the shape of pulses that

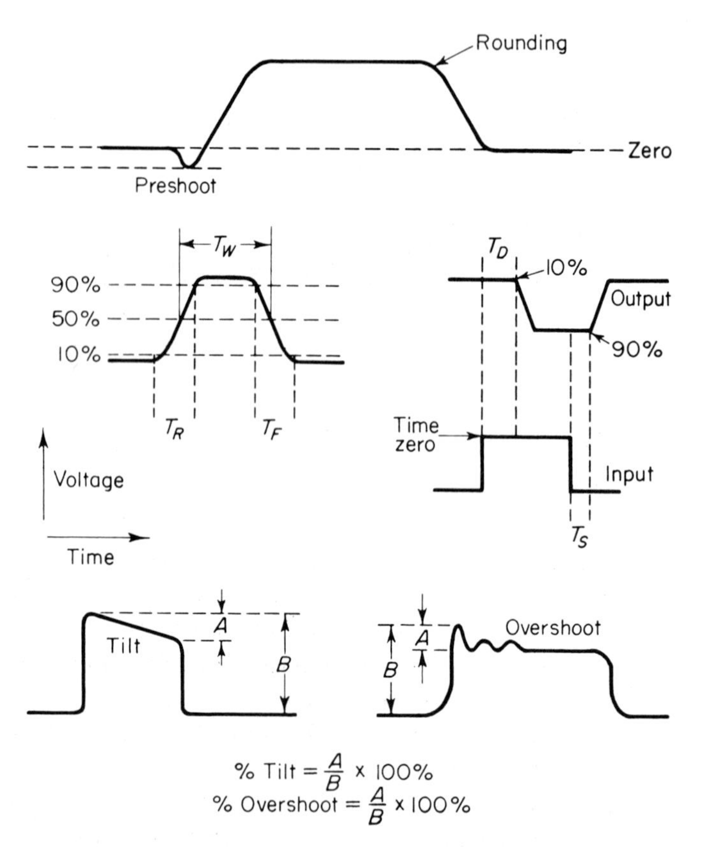

Fig. 12-1. Basic pulse and square-wave definitions.

may appear in computer circuits, particularly after they have passed through many gates, delays, etc. For example, compare the theoretical timing pulses of a typical computer (Figure 6-70) with the actual pulses as they appear on an oscilloscope (Figure 6-71). The terms are defined as follows:

Rise time, t_r

The time interval during which the amplitude of the output voltage changes from 10 to 90 percent of the rising portion of the pulse.

Fall time, t_f

The time interval during which the amplitude of the output voltage changes from 90 to 10 percent of the falling portion of the wave form.

Time delay, t_d

The time interval between the beginning of the input pulse (time 0) and the time when the rising portion of the output pulse attains an arbitrary amplitude of 10 percent above the baseline.

Storage time, t_s

The time interval between the end of the input pulse (trailing edge) and the time when the falling portion of the output pulse drops to an arbitrary amplitude of 90 percent from the baseline.

Pulse width (or pulse duration), t_w

The time duration of the pulse measured between two 50-percent amplitude levels of the rising and falling portions of the wave form.

Tilt

A measure of the tilt of the full-amplitude flat-top portion of a pulse. The tilt measurement is usually expressed as a percentage of the amplitude of the rising portion of the pulse.

Overshoot and preshoot

A measure of the overshoot or preshoot occurring above or below the 100-percent amplitude level. These measurements are also expressed as a percentage of the pulse rise.

These definitions are for guide purposes only. When pulses are very irregular (such as excessive tilt and overshoot), the definitions may become ambiguous.

2. Rule-of-Thumb for Rise-time Measurements

Since rise-time measurements are of special importance in any pulse circuit testing, the relationship between the oscilloscope rise time and the rise times of the computer circuit components under test must be taken into account. Obviously, the accuracy of rise-time measurements can be no greater than the rise time of the oscilloscope. Also, if the device is tested by means of an external pulse from a pulse generator, the rise time of the pulse generator must also be taken into account.

For example, if an oscilloscope with a 20-nS rise time is used to measure the rise time of a 15-nS component, the measurement will be hopelessly inaccurate. If a 20-nS pulse generator and a 15-nS oscilloscope are used to measure the rise time of a component, the fastest rise time for accurate measurement is something greater than 20 nS. Two basic rules-of-thumb can be applied to rise-time measurements.

The first method is known as the *root of the sum of the squares.* It involves finding the squares of all the rise times associated with the test, adding these squares together, and then finding the square root of the sum. For example, using the 20-nS pulse generator and the 15-nS oscilloscope, the calculation is

$$20 \times 20 = 400; \qquad 15 \times 15 = 225;$$
$$400 + 225 = 625; \qquad \sqrt{625} = 25 \text{ nS}.$$

This means that the fastest possible rise time capable of measurement is 25 nS.

One major drawback to this rule is that the coaxial or shielded cables required to interconnect the test equipment are subject to *skin effect.* As frequency increases, the signals tend to travel on the outside or skin of the conductor. This decreases conductor area and increases resistance. In turn, this increases cable loss. The losses of cables do not add properly to apply the root-sum-squares method, except as an approximation.

The second rule or method states that if the equipment or signal being measured has a rise time ten times slower than the test equipment, the error is 1 percent. This amount is small and can be considered as negligible. If the equipment being measured has a rise time three times slower than the test equipment, the error is slightly less than 6 percent. By keeping these relationships in mind, the results can be interpreted intelligently.

3. Measuring Pulse Amplitude

Pulse amplitudes are measured on an oscilloscope, preferably a laboratory-type oscilloscope where the vertical scale is calibrated directly in a specific deflection factor (such as volts per centimeter, or V/cm). Such oscilloscopes usually have a step attenuator (for the vertical amplifier) where each step is related to a specific deflection factor. Typically, the pulses used in computers are 5 V or less. Often, the pulse amplitude is critical to operation of the equipment. For example, an AND gate may require two pulses of +3 V to produce an output. If the two pulses are slightly less than 3 V, the AND gate may act as if there is no input, or both inputs may be false. Thus when troubleshooting a computer, always check the actual pulse amplitude against that shown in the service literature. Generally, computer circuits are designed with considerable margin in pulse amplitude, but equipment aging or some malfunction can reduce the safety margin.

The basic test connections and corresponding oscilloscope display for pulse amplitude measurement are shown in Figure 12-2. As an example, assume that a vertical deflection of 4.7 cm is measured using a vertical deflection factor (step attenuator setting) of 1 V/cm. Then the peak-to-peak pulse amplitude is $4.7 \times 1 = 4.7$ V.

Fig. 12-2. Measuring pulse amplitude.

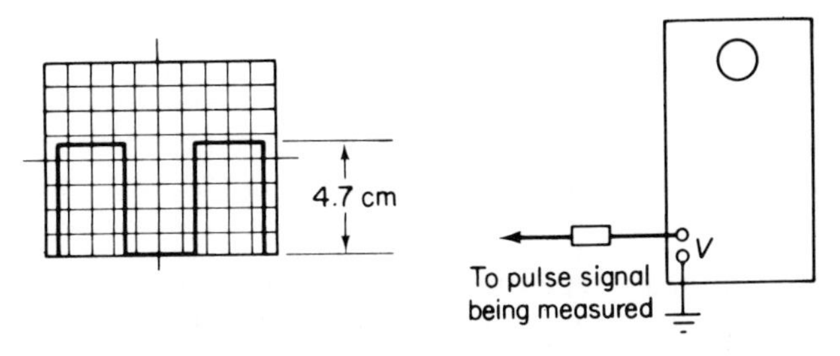

4. Measuring Pulse Width or Duration

Pulse width or pulse duration is measured on an oscilloscope, preferably a laboratory type, where the horizontal scale is calibrated directly in relation to time. The horizontal sweep circuit of a laboratory oscilloscope is usually provided with a selector control that is direct-reading in relation to time. That is, each horizontal division on the screen has a definite relation to time at a given position of the horizontal sweep rate switch (such as microsecond per centimeter, or μS/cm). Laboratory oscilloscopes are also provided with sweep magnification controls. Such magnification is generally required since the pulses used in computer circuits are on the order of nanoseconds or microseconds (but can be as long as a few milliseconds).

The basic test connections and corresponding oscilloscope display for pulse-width measurements are shown in Figure 12-3.

As an example, assume that the horizontal sweep rate is 0.1 μS/cm, the sweep magnification is 100, and a horizontal distance of 5 cm is measured (between the 50-percent points). Then the pulse width is $5 \times 0.1/100 = 0.005$ μS (or 5 nS).

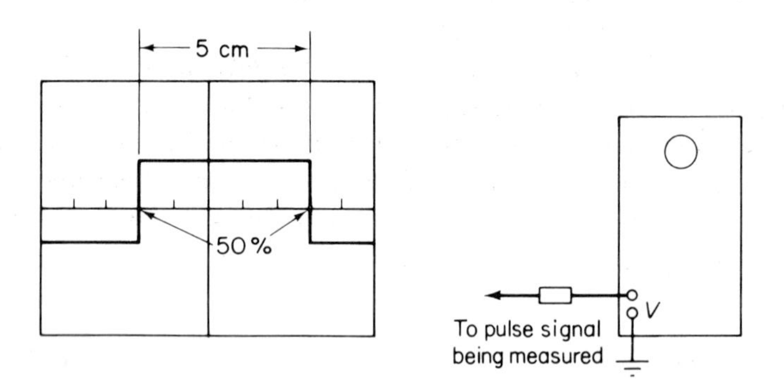

Fig. 12-3. Measuring pulse width.

5. Measuring Pulse Frequency or Repetition Rate

Pulse frequency or repetition rate is measured on an oscilloscope, preferably a laboratory type, where the horizontal scale is calibrated in relation to time. Pulse frequency is found by measuring the time duration of one complete pulse cycle (not pulse width) and then dividing the time into 1 (since frequency is the reciprocal of time).

The basic test connections and corresponding oscilloscope display for pulse-frequency measurement is shown in Figure 12-4.

As an example, assume that the horizontal sweep rate is 0.1 μS/cm, the sweep magnification is 100, and a horizontal distance of 20 cm is measured between the beginning and end of a complete cycle. Then the frequency is $20 \times 0.1/100 = 0.020\ \mu$S (or 20 nS); $\frac{1}{20\text{nS}} = 50$ MHz.

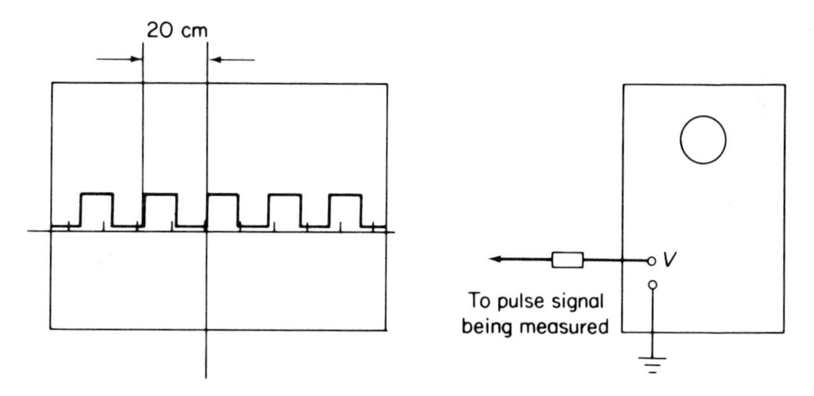

Fig. 12-4. Measuring pulse frequency or repetition rate.

6. Measuring Pulse Delay

The time interval or delay between two pulses (say, an input pulse and an output pulse) introduced by a gate, FF, or complete logic circuit can be measured most conveniently on an oscilloscope with a dual-trace or multiple-trace feature. It is possible to measure delay on a single-trace oscilloscope, but it is quite difficult.

The basic test connections and corresponding oscilloscope display for pulse-delay measurements are shown in Figure 12-5.

As an example, assume that the horizontal sweep rate is 100 nS/cm, there are seven screen divisions between input and output pulses, and each horizontal screen division is 1 cm. Then the delay is $7 \times 100 = 700$ nS.

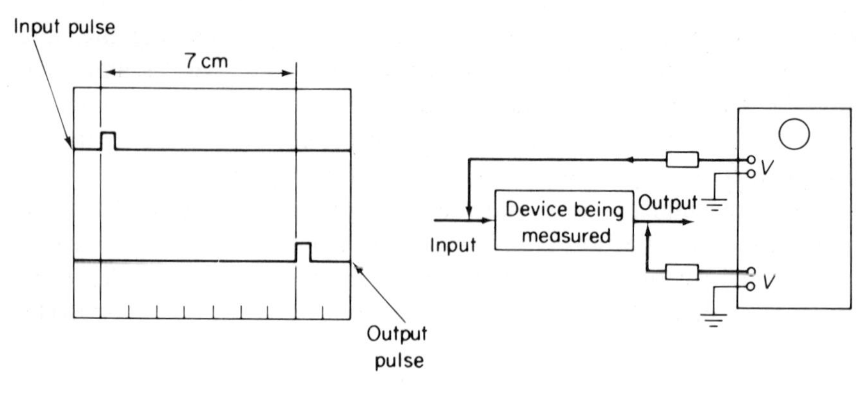

Fig. 12-5. Measuring pulse delay.

B. TESTING COMPUTER LOGIC CIRCUITS

The following paragraphs describe procedures for test or checkout of basic computer circuits (gates, delays, FF, etc.). Such circuits can be tested on a real-time basis or with pulse trains. Both test methods are described.

An oscilloscope is the best tool for pulse-train testing. In its simplest form, pulse-train testing consists of measuring the pulses at the input and output of a circuit. These pulses can be those normally present in the circuit or pulses introduced from an external generator. If the input pulses are normal but the output pulses are absent or abnormal, the fault is most likely in the circuit being tested. An exception to this is where the following circuit is defective (say a short circuit) and makes the output of the circuit under test appear to be absent or abnormal. Either way, the trouble is localized to a specific point in the overall circuit.

If the input pulses to the circuit under test are absent or abnormal, the trouble is most likely in circuits ahead of the point being tested. Thus, when input pulses are found to be abnormal at a certain circuit point, this serves as a good starting point for troubleshooting.

The Hewlett-Packard logic probe (Chapter 11) can also be used for pulse-train analysis. However, the logic probe will indicate only that a pulse train exists at a given point. The logic probe cannot tell the pulse width, frequency, or amplitude or that the pulse is in step with other pulses. Only an oscilloscope will show this information.

The logic probe and logic clip are ideal tools for real-time analysis. Such testing can take several forms. The clock frequency can be slowed to some very low rate (typically 1 Hz), so that input and output pulses can be monitored individually (on the probe, clip, or oscilloscope). The clock rate is slowed by substituting an external pulse generator for the normal (internal) clock signal. If this is not convenient, it is possible to inject pulses from the generator directly at the inputs of a given circuit, or pulses can be introduced with a charged capacitor.

Keep in mind that computer troubleshooting usually starts with tests of several circuits simultaneously. There may be several hundred (or thousand) circuits in a computer. It could take months to check each circuit on an individual basis. However, there are tests that check whole groups of circuits simultaneously. The self-check or operational-check procedures found in computer service literature are based upon this technique. Self-check techniques are described in Chapter 13.

A classic example of testing several computer circuits simultaneously is where four FFs are connected as a decade counter. If there is an output pulse train at the fourth FF and this pulse train shows one pulse for every ten input pulses at the first FF, the entire counter circuit can be considered as good.

Also keep in mind that many computer circuits are often combined in one IC package. Even if it is possible to test the individual circuits, they cannot be replaced. The complete IC function must be checked as a package by monitoring inputs and outputs at the IC terminals.

Before going into detailed test procedures, the **marginal test technique** should be considered. The power supplies for most computers are adjustable, usually over a ±10-percent range. When computer failure is intermittent or the failure is not consistent, it is sometimes helpful to test the circuits with the power supply output voltage set to extremes (both high and low). This will show marginal failures in some cases. The technique is not recommended by all manufacturers since the results are not certain. However, it is usually safe to apply the technique to any computer on a temporary basis. Of course, the computer service literature should be consulted to make sure.

The following procedures are based upon the assumption that the corresponding computer circuits can be tested on an individual basis.

1. Testing AND Gate Circuits

Figure 12-6 shows the basic connections for testing an AND circuit. Ideally, both inputs and the output should be monitored simultaneously, since an AND gate circuit produces an output only when two inputs

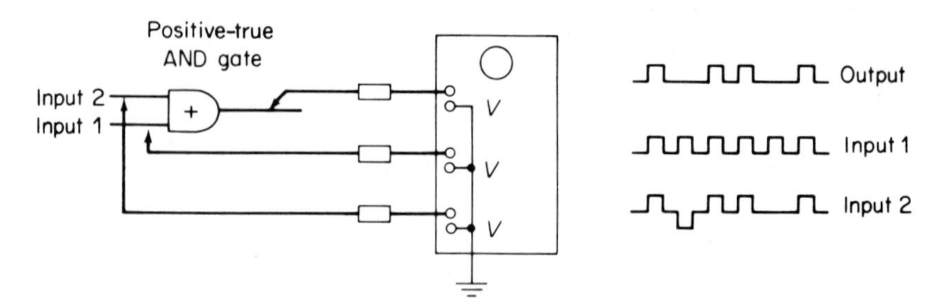

Fig. 12-6. Testing AND gate circuits.

are present. If pulse trains are monitored on an oscilloscope, check that an output pulse is produced each time that there are two input pulses of appropriate amplitude and polarity. If this is not the case, check carefully that both input pulses arrive at the same time (not delayed from each other).

If the oscilloscope has a dual-trace feature, first check for a series of simultaneous pulses at both inputs. Then move one oscilloscope probe to the output and check for an output pulse. Note that in Figure 12-6 the input pulse trains are not identical, which is often the case. Input 2 has less pulses for a given time interval than input 1. Also, input 2 has one negative pulse simultaneously with one positive pulse at input 1. This should not produce an output pulse. Often, one input will be a long pulse (long in relation to the pulses at the other input). In other cases, one input will be a fixed d-c voltage applied by operation of a switch.

If the AND circuit is tested with pulse trains and a logic probe, simply check for a pulse train at both inputs and at the output. If the circuit is checked on a real-time basis, inject simultaneous pulses at both inputs (with a charged capacitor or whatever is convenient) and monitor the output (with a logic probe or oscilloscope).

The complete truth table of the circuit can be checked using the basic connections of Figure 12-6. For example, an output pulse train (or single pulse in the case of real-time testing) should not appear if only one input of appropriate polarity is present.

2. Testing OR Gate Circuits

Figure 12-7 shows the basic connections for testing an OR circuit. Ideally, all inputs and the output should be monitored simultaneously.

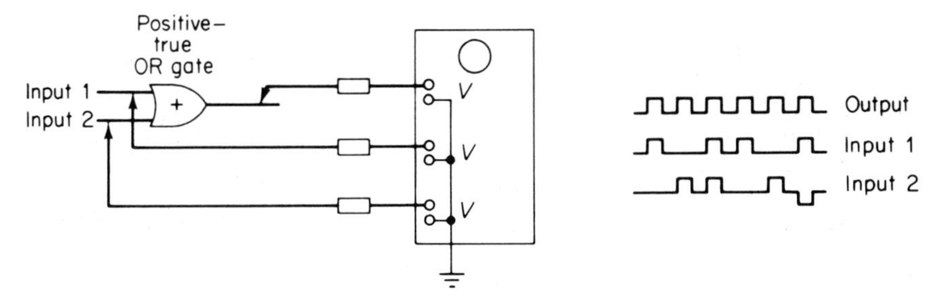

Fig. 12-7. Testing OR gate circuits.

An OR gate produces an output when any inputs are present. If pulse trains are monitored on an oscilloscope, check that an output pulse is produced for each input pulse of appropriate amplitude and polarity.

If the oscilloscope has a dual-trace feature, monitor the output with one trace; then monitor each of the inputs, in turn, with the other trace. Note that in Figure 12-7 the input pulse trains are not identical. That is, the input pulses do not necessarily coincide. However, there is an output pulse when either input has a pulse and when both inputs have a pulse. This last condition marks the difference between an OR gate and an EXCLUSIVE OR gate.

If the OR circuit is tested with pulse trains and a logic probe, check that there is a pulse train at the output whenever there is a pulse at any input. If the circuit is checked on a real-time basis, monitor the output and inject a pulse at each input, in turn. The complete truth table of the circuit can be checked using the basic connections of Figure 12-7.

3. Testing EXCLUSIVE OR Gate Circuits

Figure 12-8 shows the basic connections for testing an EXCLUSIVE OR circuit. Ideally, all inputs and the output should be monitored simultaneously. An EXCLUSIVE OR gate produces an output when any one input is present but not when both inputs are present. If pulse trains are monitored on an oscilloscope, check that an output pulse is produced for each input pulse that does not coincide with another input pulse.

If the EXCLUSIVE OR circuit must be checked with a logic probe, it is necessary to do so on a real-time basis. (The logic probe can indi-

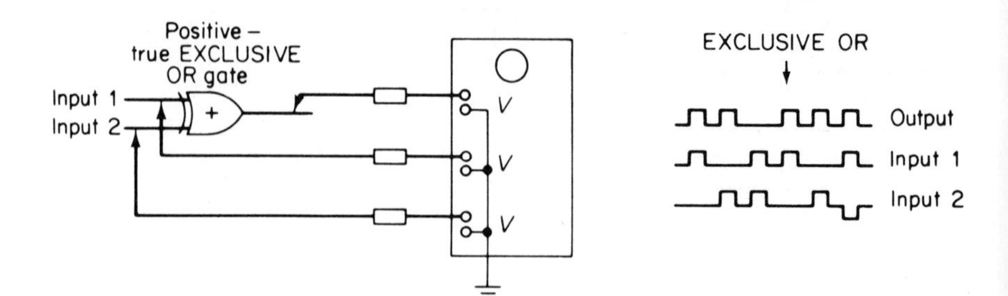

Fig. 12-8. Testing EXCLUSIVE OR gate circuits.

cate the presence of pulse trains but not the coincidence of pulses in pulse trains.) Monitor the output and inject a pulse at each input, in turn. An output pulse should be produced for each input pulse. Then apply simultaneous pulses to both inputs. There should be no output. The complete truth table of the circuit can be checked using the basic connections of Figure 12-8.

4. Testing NAND, NOR, and EXCLUSIVE NOR Circuits

Figures 12-9, 12-10, and 12-11 show the basic connections for testing NAND, NOR, and EXCLUSIVE NOR circuits, respectively. Note that the connections are the same as for corresponding AND and OR circuits, as are the test procedures. However, the output pulse will be inverted. That is, a NAND circuit produces an output under the same logic conditions as an AND circuit, but the output is inverted. For example, if the logic is positive-true and a positive pulse is present at

Fig. 12-9. Testing NAND gate circuits.

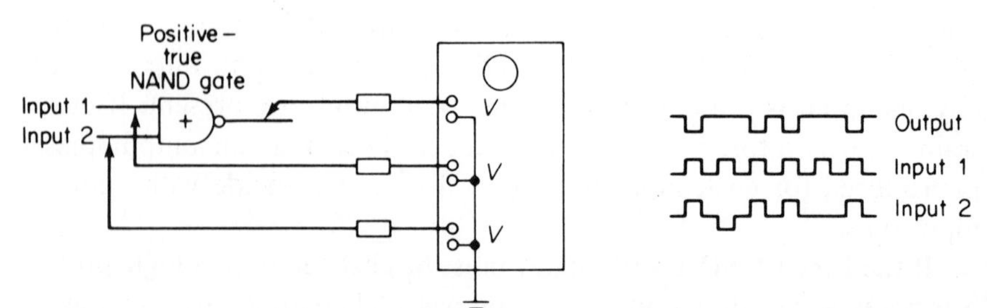

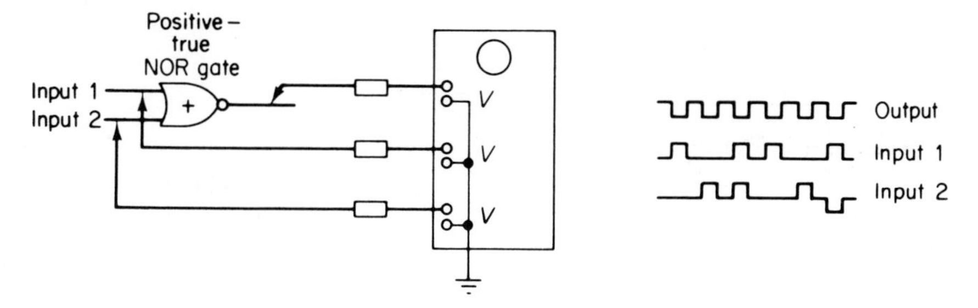

Fig. 12-10. Testing NOR gate circuits.

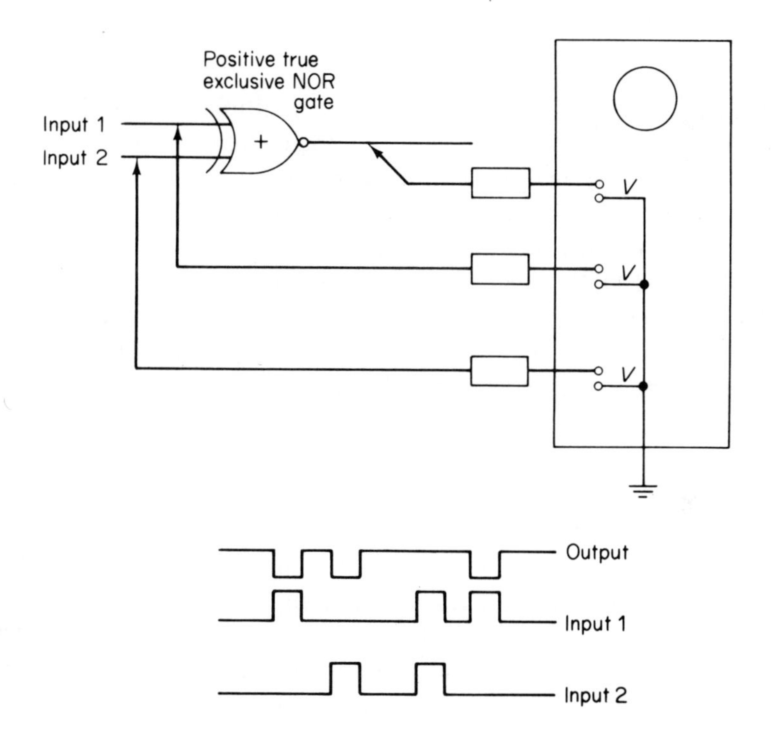

Fig. 12-11. Testing EXCLUSIVE NOR gate circuits.

both inputs of a NAND gate simultaneously, there is an output pulse, and the pulse is negative (or false).

5. Testing ENCODE Gate Circuits

Figure 12-12 shows the basic connections for testing an ENCODE circuit. Ideally, all outputs and the input should be monitored simul-

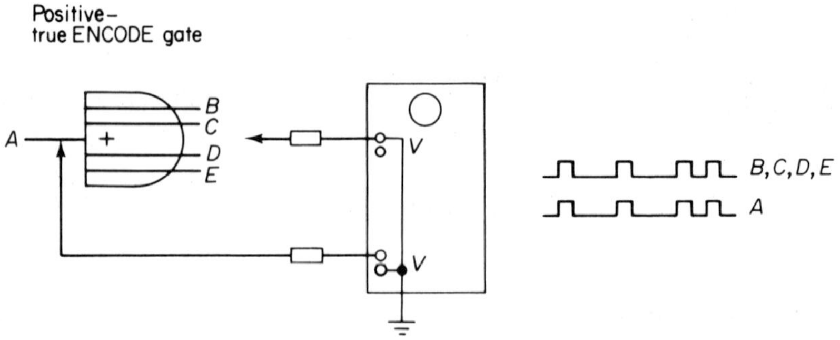

Fig. 12-12. Testing ENCODE gate circuits.

taneously. An ENCODE gate produces multiple outputs (simultaneously) that correspond in polarity or logic state to the input.

If the pulse trains are monitored on an oscilloscope with a dual-trace feature, monitor the input with one trace; then monitor each of the outputs, in turn, with the other trace.

If the ENCODE circuit is tested with pulse trains and a logic probe, check that there is a pulse train at each input whenever there is a pulse train at the input. If the circuit is checked on a real-time basis, inject a pulse at the input and monitor each output.

6. Testing Amplifiers, Inverters, and Phase Splitters

Figure 12-13 shows the basic connections for testing amplifiers, inverters, and phase splitters used in computers. Note that the same connections are used for all three circuits. That is, each circuit is tested by monitoring the input and output with an oscilloscope or logic probe. However, the relationship of output to input is different for each of the three circuits.

With the amplifier, the output pulse amplitude should be greater than the input pulse amplitude. With the inverter, the output pulse may or may not be greater in amplitude than the input pulse, but the polarity is reversed. In the case of the phase splitter, there are two output pulses of opposite polarity for each input pulse.

Polarity is easy to determine if the pulses are monitored on an oscilloscope. The ability of the logic probe to show polarity is dependent on the logic system used. The logic probe responds to systems where

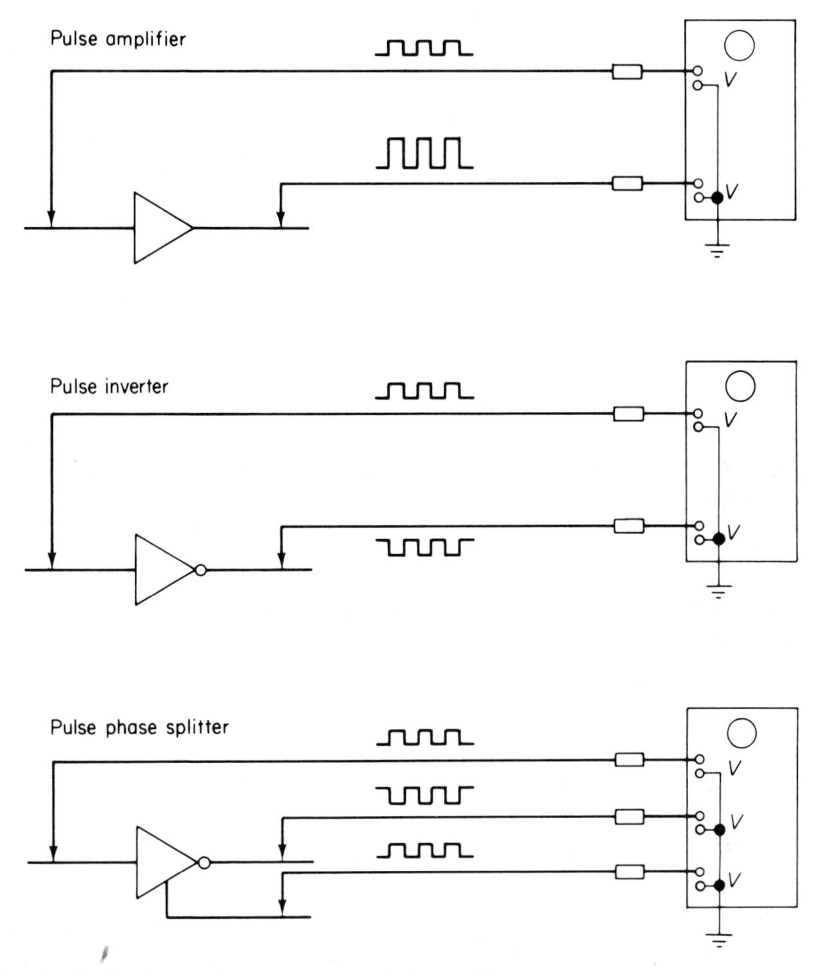

Fig. 12-13. Testing amplifiers, inverters, and phase splitters.

the logic levels are between 0 and +5 V. That is, a true or high level is +5 V, while a false or low level is 0 V. The logic probe blinks on for each pulse if the pulse goes from some level below about 1.4 V to a level above 1.4 V and blinks off when the pulse drops from a high level to some voltage below about 1.4 V. If the probe is used to check an inverter where the input goes from 0 to +5 V and the output goes from +5 V to 0, the input pulse train will produce a series of *on blinks*, while the output pulse train produces *off blinks*. The difference between on and off may be difficult to distinguish if the pulse trains are fast. It may be necessary to make such tests on a real-time basis. Also, if the inverter produces an output that goes from 0 to −5 V, the logic probe will not respond properly.

7. Testing Flip-Flops

Figurc 12-14 shows thc basic connections for testing a FF. There are many types of FFs used in computers (R-S, J-K, toggle, latching, delay, etc.). Each FF responds differently to given set of pulse conditions. Thus each type of FF must be tested in a slightly different way. However, all FFs have two states (even though there may be only one output and it may not be possible to monitor both states directly). Some FFs require only one input to change states. Other FFs require two simultaneous pulses to change states (such as a clock pulse and a reset or set pulse).

The main concern in testing any FF is that the states change when the appropriate input pulse (or pulses) are applied. Thus at least one input and one state (output) should be monitored simultaneously. For example, an R-S FF (without a clock) can be tested by monitoring the pulse train at the set input and set output. If there is a pulse train at the set input and a set output pulse train, it is reasonable to assume that the FF is operating. If the set output remains in one state or there are no reset pulses, the next step is to monitor the reset input and output. If both the set and reset trains are present but the FF does not change states, the FF is defective.

There are exceptions, of course. For example, if the reset and set pulses arrive simultaneously, due to an unwanted delay in other circuits, the FF may remain in one state.

This brings up another point in computer troubleshooting. Often, it is convenient to test the response of FFs (and related circuits) to improper inputs. It is possible that such tests will produce failure symptoms similar to those found in malfunctioning computers. For example, a FF may change states a second time if a clock pulse is too long or delayed in relation to the set and reset pulses. This results in apparent failure of all computer circuits following the FF.

Thus, when testing the operation of any FF (or related circuit), check for possible abnormal inputs (incorrect amplitude, width, frequency, or timing).

If a FF requires a clock pulse, first check that both the clock pulse

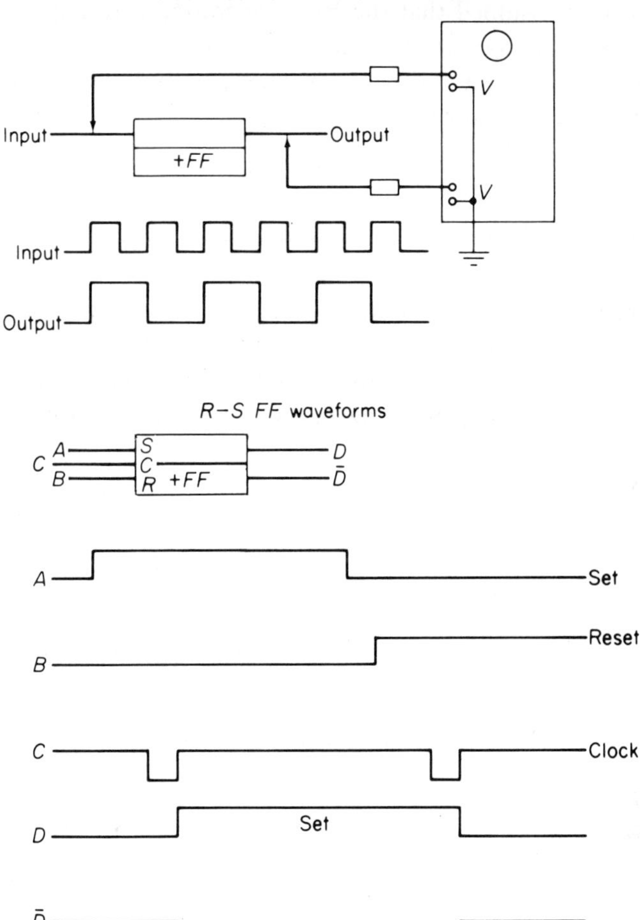

Fig. 12-14. Testing FF circuits.

and a set or reset pulse arrive simultaneously. Then check that the FF changes states each time there is such a pulse coincidence. For example, assume that pulse trains are measured on a dual-trace oscilloscope and that a set pulse occurs on every other clock pulse. Next, monitor the clock pulse and the set output and note that the set output occurs for every two clock pulses. Or, monitor the set input and output, noting that the FF changes states on a pulse-for-pulse basis.

To test a FF with pulse trains and a logic probe, simply check that a pulse train exists at each output, with a pulse train at the inputs.

It can then be assumed that the FF is operating properly. To remove all doubt, use the logic probe to test the FF on a real-time basis. Inject a pulse at the set input and monitor the set output. Then inject a reset input and note a change in states.

8. Testing Multivibrators

Figure 12-15 shows the basic connections for testing a multivibrator. There are three basic types of multivibrator: free-running, one-shot (or monostable), and Schmitt trigger (or bistable). In the case of the free-running multivibrator, only the output need be monitored since the

Fig. 12-15. Testing multivibrators.

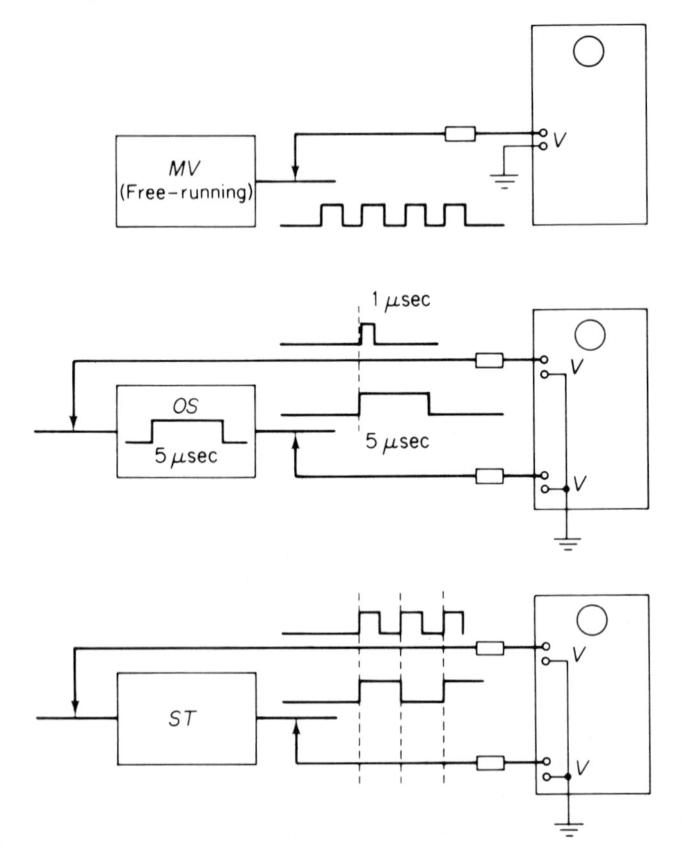

circuit is self-generating. Both the one-shot (OS) and Schmitt trigger (ST) require that the input and output be monitored.

If a logic probe is used to monitor pulse trains from a multivibrator, the presence of a pulse train at the output indicates that the multivibrator is probably working. The OS and ST multivibrators can also be tested on a real-time basis by injecting pulses at the input.

Keep in mind that the ST required two input pulses for a complete cycle. That is, two input pulses are required to change output states and then return the states back to the original condition. More simply, two input pulses are required for one complete output pulse. The OS multivibrator produces one complete output pulse for each input pulse, even though the output pulse may be different in duration than the input pulse.

If multivibrator pulse trains are monitored on an oscilloscope, the frequency, pulse duration, and pulse amplitude can be measured. While these factors may not be critical for all computer circuits, quite often one or more of the factors are important. For example, the logic symbol for a OS multivibrator (when properly drawn) includes the output pulse duration or width.

9. Testing Delays

Figure 12-16 shows the basic connections for testing delay lines or delay elements used in computer circuits. The test procedure is the same

Fig. 12-16. Testing delays.

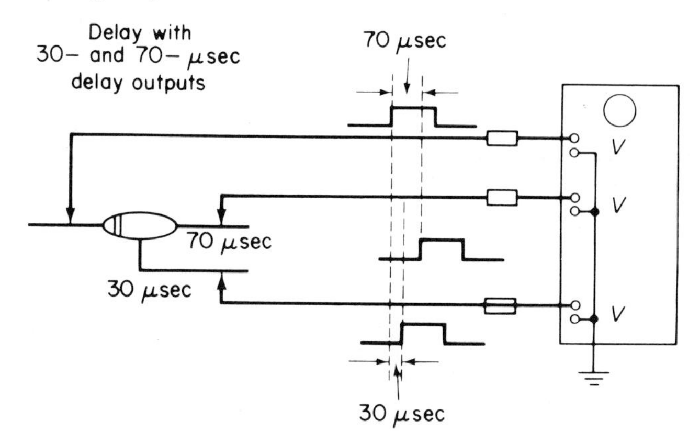

as for the measurement of delay between pulses, as described in Chapter 12, subdivision A, 6.

Keep in mind that the delay shown on the logic symbol *usually* refers to the delay between leading edges of the input and output pulses. This can be assumed if the symbol is not further identified. Some manufacturers (such as Hewlett-Packard) identify their delay symbols as to leading or trailing edge, particularly if the symbols are mixed on a single logic diagram.

USING COMPUTER SERVICE LITERATURE

13

Unlike some other electronic equipment, it is almost impossible to troubleshoot computer circuits without adequate service literature. There are two prime reasons for this.

Although all computers use the same basic circuits (gates, FFs, delays, etc.), the way in which these circuits are arranged to perform an overall function is unique to each computer. Thus it is absolutely essential that you know exactly what the computer is to do from an operational standpoint. Further, you must know what pulse will appear at what point and under what conditions.

Another reason for good service literature is that in servicing computers you are dealing with failure rather than poor performance. For example, a television set may have a weak picture or some distortion in the audio. This may pass unnoticed or be ignored during normal operation. On the other hand, the counter section of a computer will either read out a correct count, fail to read out a correct count, or not provide any readout. Anything less than the correct count is not acceptable. You *must know* what is correct in every case.

This "knowing the equipment" can come only after a thorough study of the service literature. In the case of most computers, you must also receive factory training before you can hope to do a good trouble-shooting job.

All the information found in service literature is of value, but the most important pieces of information for troubleshooting are the logic diagrams, the theory of operation, and the self-check procedure. A timing diagram can also be of considerable help.

The value of logic diagrams and the theory of operation for trouble-shooting is obvious. To trace pulses throughout the equipment, you must have a logic diagram, preferably supplemented with individual schematics that show the internal circuits of the blocks on the overall diagram. The individual schematics are often omitted when the blocks are IC packages, as is often the case with modern computers. To understand the logic diagram, you must have a corresponding theory of operation (unless you are very familiar with similar equipment or just happen to be a genius).

The value of a timing diagram is somewhat less obvious. However, trouble can often be pinpointed immediately by comparison of circuit pulses against those shown in the timing diagram. Also, unusual problems can show up when pulses are compared with the timing diagram. For example, assume that a computer counter circuit receives input (or count) pulses and reset pulses, both of which originate from a common clock or master oscillator. The reset pulses are supposed to arrive at the counter at some specific time interval, thus allowing given maximum number of clock pulses (say 100) to be read out. Further assume that a defect in the circuit has caused the reset pulses to be delayed slightly in relation to the clock pulse so that the reset pulse coincides with the first count. The counter circuit will never be able to reach a second count, and the readout will always remain at 0, even though all the circuits appear to be good.

The value of the self-check procedure is dependent on the complexity of the computer. On simple computers, an ingenius technician can sometimes devise a check procedure that will eliminate groups of circuits from suspicion or pinpoint the problem to a group of circuits. As an example, assume that the same computer counter circuit is to be checked. The counter gate can be set to open for 1-second intervals, and a 1-kHz pulse signal can be introduced at the counter circuit input. If the counter is operating properly, the readout will be 1000. (From a practical standpoint, if the readout is 999 or 1001, the counter may still be functioning properly. Most computer counters have a ± 1 count ambiguity.) The gate time is then shortened or lengthened and the input pulse frequency changed (increased or decreased) to check all the digits in the readout or each digit one at a time, whichever is convenient.

The self-check procedure must be carefully thought out, even on relatively simple computers. Unless you are completely familiar with every logic equation, you will do much better to follow the service literature. Usually, a computer self-check involves inserting a series of mathematical problems to be solved and then noting the corresponding readout. On those computers with banks of interpolation lights (front-panel register lights), problems are inserted, and the lights are checked as to their state. On other computers, the readout is printed on a typewriter or tape punch. Either way, the problems and corresponding readouts are compared, line for line, until an abnormal readout is found. The service literature usually contains some means of relating the problem and/or readout to a specific circuit or group of circuits.

A. EXAMPLES OF SERVICE LITERATURE

The following paragraphs show typical examples of information found in computer service literature. These data are extracted from the operating and service manual for a Hewlett-Packard scanner. The scanner is part of a computer-controlled data acquisition system. The following information is summarized. Full data appear in the manual. However, the data presented here are sufficient to familiarize the reader with what is available in well-prepared service literature and how the data can be related to troubleshooting.

The purpose of the scanner is to sample several channels of information and pass this information to a single output on a time-sharing basis (channel after channel). In addition to many other controls and circuits, the scanner has a digital readout consisting of three Nixie tubes. The readout indicators show the particular channel (or address) being monitored.

1. Logic Diagrams and Supplementary Troubleshooting Data

Figure 13-1 shows portions of the scanner logic diagram, particularly those portions covering the digital readout circuits. Note that each

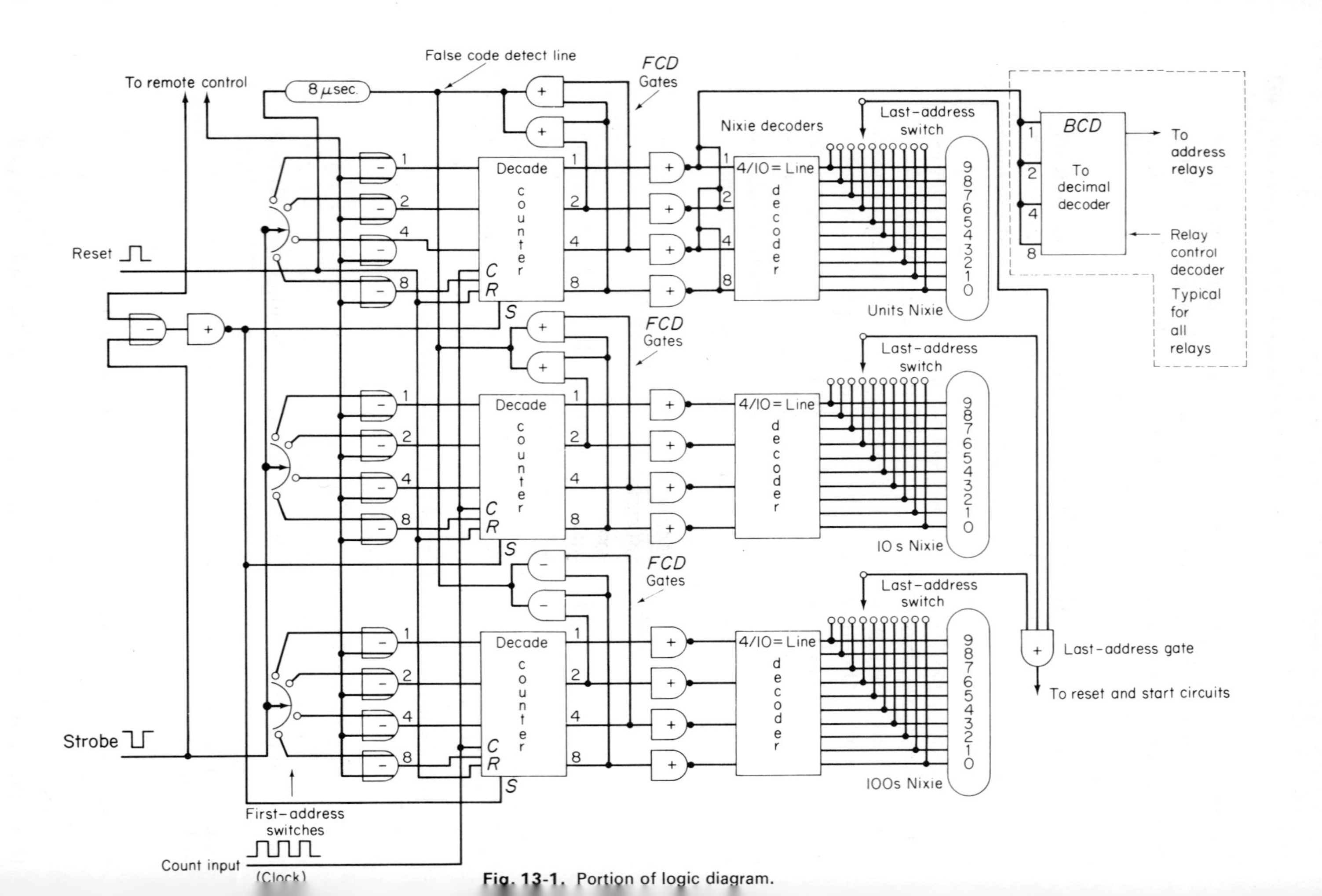

Fig. 13-1. Portion of logic diagram.

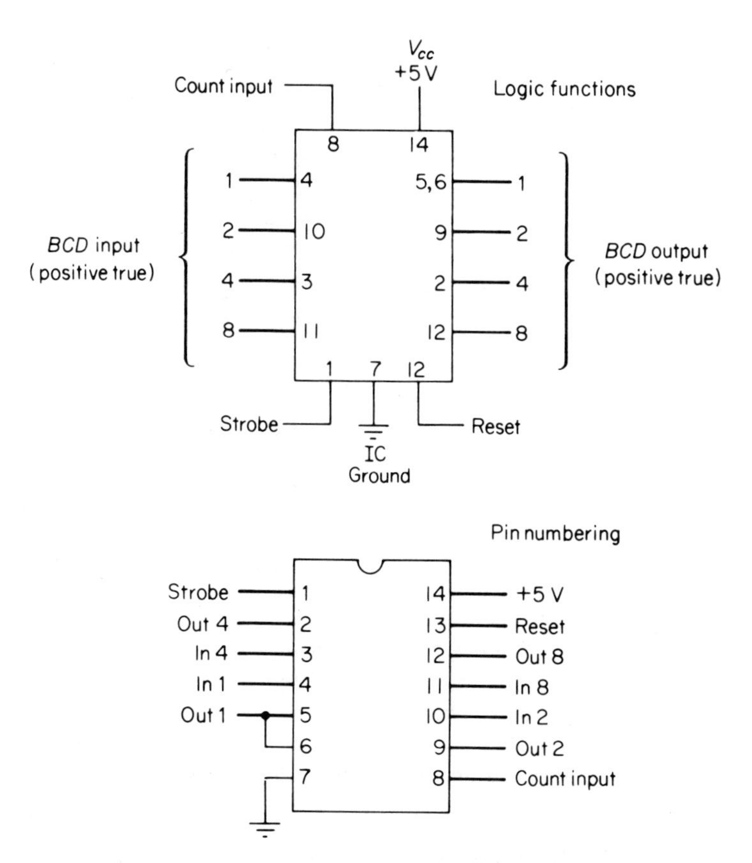

Fig. 13-2. Logic functions and pin-numbering diagram of decade counter.

Nixie tube has a separate 4/10 line decoder (four-digit BCD to decimal) and a decade counter. These are shown as blocks in Figure 13-1, since they are IC packages. The internal circuitry of these particular blocks is not shown anywhere in the manual, since the ICs must be replaced as a package. However, the logic diagram is supplemented by two diagrams, Figures 13-2 and 13-3, which show the IC package terminal arrangements and the outputs or logic states to be expected for a given set of input conditions. By using these supplementary data, it is possible to check the IC packages on an individual basis with real-time pulses (using a logic clip or oscilloscope). Or the IC packages can be checked in operation by monitoring pulse trains at the inputs and outputs.

The following are examples of how the IC packages can be checked on an individual basis (while still installed in the circuit). This is done

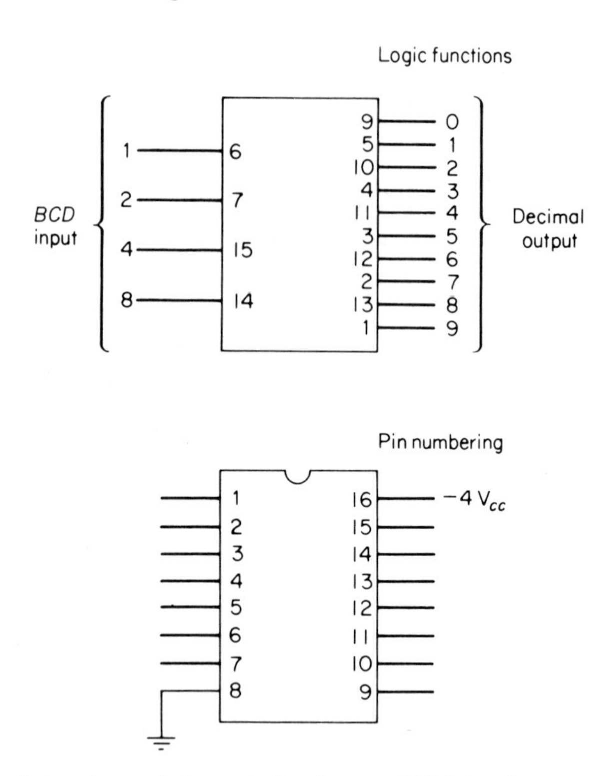

Fig. 13-3. Logic functions and pin-numbering diagram of 4/10 decoder.

when a particular IC is suspected of being defective (as a result of self-check and/or logical deductions, described in later sections).

To check the decade counter of Figure 13-2 on a real-time basis using a logic clip, proceed as follows.

Install the logic clip on the IC to be tested by squeezing the thick end of the clip to spread the contacts and placing the clip on the IC.

Reduce the clock frequency to some rate that can be seen easily (about 1 Hz or slower) by substituting a pulse generator input for the clock oscillator. The scanner in question can be slowed down (by a front-panel control) so that there is about 10 seconds between each channel. Thus no external pulse is required to produce a slow clock rate. As an alternative to slowing the clock rate, remove the IC package connections to the input (IC pin 8), strobe (IC pin 1), and reset (IC pin 13). Then inject pulses at these inputs using a capacitor generator or whatever is convenient.

Inject a pulse at reset (IC pin 13) and check that all four output pins are false (LEDs on the logic clip go out).

Inject a series of pulses at the input (IC pin 8) and check that the output pins go true (LEDs go on) in accordance with the logic of Figure 13-2. For example, with one input pulse, the 1 output goes on. With two input pulses, the 1 goes out and the 2 goes on. With three input pulses, the 2 remains on and the 1 goes back on.

Inject a pulse at the strobe (IC pin 1) and check that the BCD output pins assume the same states as the BCD input pins. Note that the strobe function is synonymous with an enable function. That is, the outputs assume the same states as the inputs whenever the strobe or enable pulse is applied. If all the inputs are false, inject a pulse at one of the inputs and make sure that the corresponding output assumes the same state. For example, if a pulse is applied to the 8 input (IC pin 11) and the strobe (IC pin 1) simultaneously, the 8 output (IC pin 12) should go true.

To check the decade counter of Figure 13-2 on a pulse-train basis with a dual-trace oscilloscope, proceed as follows.

Monitor the input (IC pin 8) and the reset (IC pin 13). If there are no reset pulses, it is safe to proceed with the next step. If there are reset pulses, count the number of input pulses between reset pulses. If the count is ten or more, the decade can reach a full 10 count. If there are less than ten input pulses between reset pulses, this sets the maximum count. For example, if there are seven input pulses between reset pulses, the counter can reach a maximum count of seven. Thus the 8 output (IC pin 12) will not show any pulses (unless the counter is defective).

Monitor the strobe (IC pin 1) and each of the BCD inputs, in turn. If there is a strobe pulse that coincides with any of the BCD input pulses, check that the corresponding BCD output line also has pulses that coincide with the strobe pulses.

2. Timing Diagrams and Theory of Operation

The test procedures just described establish that the IC decade package responds properly to a set of pulses. However, the tests do not show that the pulses are correct (arrive at the right place at the right time). This can be determined only by reference to the timing diagram, logic diagram, and theory of operation. Figure 13-4 is a timing diagram for that portion of the scanner logic shown in Figure 13-1. The following is a summarized theory of operation that applies to the same circuits.

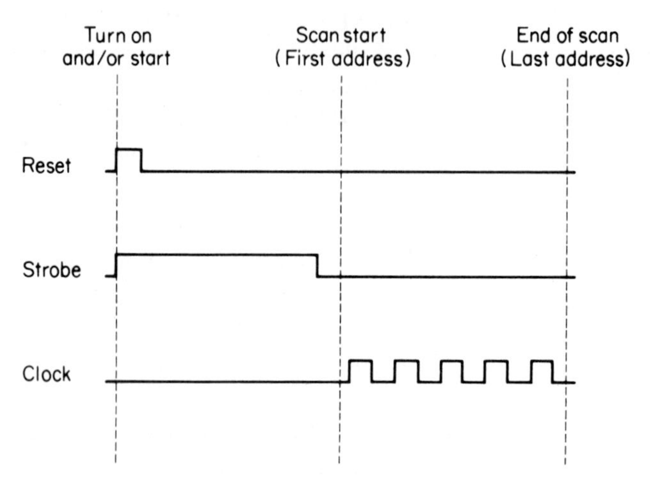

Fig. 13-4. Timing diagram for decade counting function.

Information to be scanned is applied to the common output through relays. There is one relay for each channel. Each relay is connected to a separate line on the BCD-to-decimal decoder. When an output (pulse or continuous voltage) is operated, and the information on that channel is passed to the common output. The address being monitored at any given time is indicated by the Nixie readout tubes (which are operated by separate decoders).

Several modes of operation are available. In the continuous scan mode, a first and last channel (or first and last address) are selected by front-panel switches. The scanner starts by monitoring the first address and then monitors each address in turn until the last address is reached. At that point, the cycle is repeated.

Both the Nixie and relay control decoders receive BCD data from the decade counters. These counters are advanced, an address or count at a time, by pulses from the clock. The decades can also be advanced to a given count by pulses applied through the first address switches when there is a strobe input. All the decade counters are set to 0 when there is a reset pulse.

When the equipment is first turned on, a short-duration reset pulse is applied, together with long-duration strobe and address pulses (Figure 13-4). The reset pulse sets the decade counters to 0. The strobe pulse enables the counters so that the first address pulses can be applied. The counters then advance to the first address. When the scan is started (automatically or by a front-panel switch), the clock pulses are applied, advancing the counter one step at a time. This count is converted to a BCD code and applied to the Nixie and relay control decoders, which produce corresponding decade outputs.

When the counters reach the last address, a pulse will appear simultaneously on all three of the last address switches. These pulses operate the last address AND gate. Output of this gate is applied to other circuits (not shown) that initiate the reset and start functions over again. Thus the channels are scanned continuously between the first and last address.

The function of the false code detect (FCD) gates is to prevent two channels from being addressed simultaneously. When any number greater than 9 is generated by a decade counter, the BCD gates for that counter drive the FCD line true. After an 8-μS delay, the FCD line resets the decade counters to 000.

3. Self-Check Information

The following partial self-check procedure is taken from the Hewlett-Packard manual. Note that the self-check procedure involves the three basic elements of troubleshooting: operating the controls in a given sequence, analysis of symptoms, and measurement of circuit conditions at test points.

CHECKOUT AND TROUBLESHOOTING DIAGRAM

START

Turn on POWER:

OK: Nixies indicate 000: Rear-panel fan operates

BAD: Nixies remain off:

Check a-c power connections

Check rear-panel fuse

Check 115/230 VAC slide switch
Check d-c voltage at plus side of A26C1 for 190 VDC ±10%

BAD: Nixies show blurred display: Check fuse A26F1 and press RESET after replacement

BAD: Nixies indicate number other than 000:
Press RESET
Turn POWER off and on again
Check FIRST ADDRESS switches for setting of 000
Using oscilloscope, monitor test point A22TP1; turn POWER off and on to observe pulse; negative-going, +4.5 to 0 V, 0.4 μS; if pulse is absent, trouble is probably on card A22; if present, trouble is probably on A17

Press RESET:

OK: Nixies display 001

BAD: Nixie display remains at 000:
Monitor A21TP2 for negative-going 10-μS 4.5-V pulse each time STEP is pressed; if pulse is absent, trouble is probably on card A19 or A21
Monitor A17TP1; press STEP repeatedly; level shift of 2.5 V occurs on eight and tenth pressing; if level shifts are absent, trouble is probably in units decade counter or A17; if shifts are present, trouble is probably on card A12

Press RESET again:

OK: Nixies reset to 000

BAD: Nixies remain at 001: Monitor A22TP1 while pressing RESET; negative-going 4.5-V pulse occurs (contact closure); if pulse does not occur, trouble is probably on card A18; if pulse occurs but Nixies do not reset, trouble is probably on card A22

Press START:

OK: CONTACTS CLOSED lamp lights

BAD: CONTACTS CLOSED lamp does not light: monitor A22TP1 while alternately pressing START and

RESET buttons; 5-V shift should occur; if shift is present, lamp or lamp-driver circuit is probably bad; if shift absent, trouble is probably on card A21.

B. EXAMPLES OF COMPUTER TROUBLESHOOTING

Practical computer troubleshooting is a combination of "detective work" or logical thinking and step-by-step measurements. Thus far, we have described what test equipment is available for computer work, how to use the equipment effectively in testing computer circuits, and how to use service literature effectively. The following paragraphs describe the final step: combining all these practical techniques with logical thinking to solve some problems in computer troubleshooting.

Two circuits are discussed, one very simple (the half-adder) and one more complex (a complete decade counter and readout). All three aspects of computer troubleshooting are included: self-check, pulse measurement, and logical thinking.

1. Half-adder Troubleshooting

Figure 13-5 shows the diagram and truth table for a half-adder circuit. Assume that this circuit is made up of replaceable gates, mounted on a plug-in printed-circuit card, and is part of a computer. That is, the entire half-adder circuit can be replaced as a unit by replacing the plug-in card (as a field-service measure to get the computer operating immediately). Then the card can be repaired by replacing the defective gates (as a factory or shop repair procedure).

Further assume that the computer failed to solve a given mathematical problem during self-check and that the trouble is localized to the half-adder card, the card is replaced, and the computer then performs its function normally. This definitely isolates the problem to the half-adder card.

Now assume that the card can be connected to a power source (to energize the gates) and that pulses of appropriate amplitude and polarity can be applied to the two inputs (addend and augend). The sum and carry output, as well as any other points in the circuit, can be monitored with an oscilloscope or logic probe.

Some service shops have special test fixtures that mate with printed

Addend (Digit *A*)	Augend (Digit *B*)	Sum	Carry
0	0	0	0
0	1	1	0
1	0	1	0
1	1	0	1

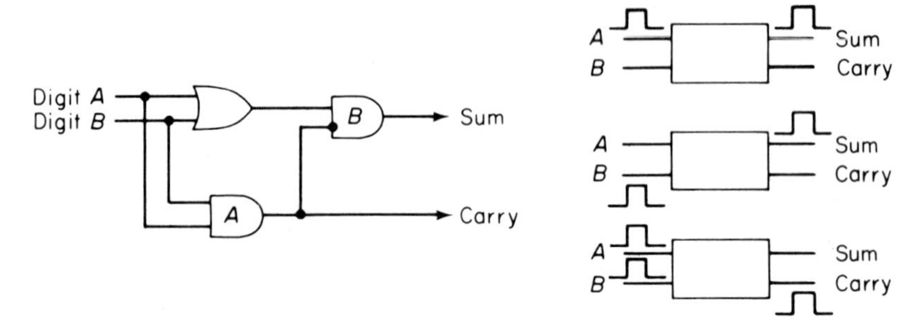

Fig. 13-5. Half-adder troubleshooting.

circuit cards, which provides a mount for the card and ready access to the terminals. In other cases, cards are serviced in the equipment by means of an extender. The card is removed from its socket, the extender is installed in the empty socket, and the card is installed on the extender. This maintains normal circuit operation but permits access to the card terminals and components on the card. These arrangements for printed circuit cards are shown in Figure 13-6.

To test the half-adder circuit of Figure 13-5, inject a pulse (true) at the addend input (digit A) and check for a true (pulse-present) condition at the sum output as well as a false (no-pulse) condition at the carry output.

If the response is proper, both the OR gate and the B AND gate are functioning normally. To confirm this, inject a true (pulse) at the augend input (digit B) and check for a true condition at the sum output as well as a false condition at the carry output.

If the response is not proper, either the OR gate or the B AND gate are the logical suspects. [The A AND gate is probably not at fault, since it requires two inputs (digits A and B) to produce an output.] To further localize the problem, inject a pulse at either addend or augend inputs and check for an output from the OR gate. If there is no output or the output is abnormal, the problem is in the OR gate. If the output is normal, the problem is likely in the B AND gate.

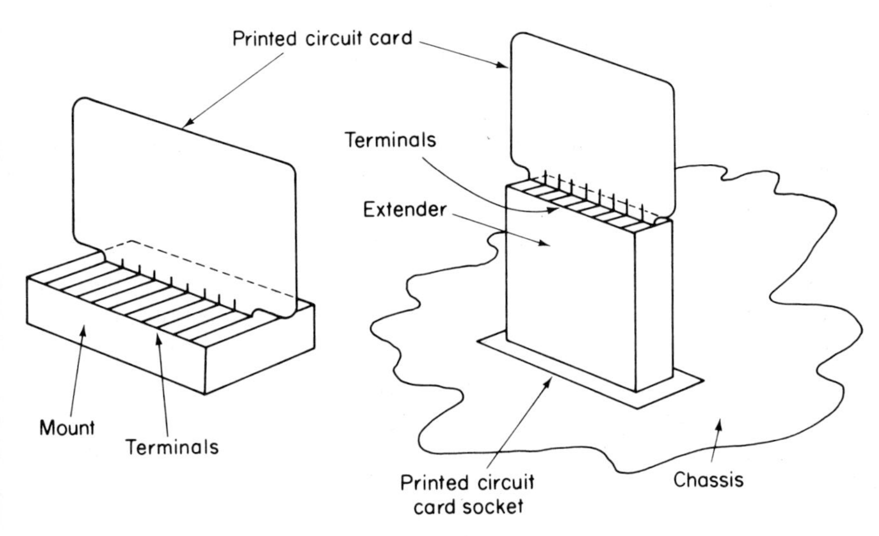

Fig. 13-6. Printed circuit card mount and extender.

To complete the test of the half-adder circuit, inject simultaneous pulses at the addend and augend inputs and check for a true (pulse) at the carry output and a false (no pulse) at the sum output.

If the response is proper, all the gates can be considered as functioning normally. If the response is not correct, the nature of the response can be analyzed to localize the fault.

For example, if the carry output is false (no matter what the condition of the sum output), the A AND gate produces a true output to the carry line when there are two true inputs. Since the test is made by injecting two true inputs, a false condition on the carry line points to a defective A AND gate. A possible exception is where there is a short in the carry line (possibly in the printed wiring). This can be checked by removing all power and checking the resistance of the carry line to ground or common.

As another example, if the carry output is normal (true) but the sum output is also true, the B AND gate is the most likely suspect. The A AND gate produces a true output when both inputs are true. The B AND gate requires one true input from the OR gate and the false input from the A AND gate to produce a true condition at the sum output. If the input to the B AND gate from the A AND gate is true but the sum output shows a true condition, a defective B AND gate is indicated.

2. Decade Counter and Readout Troubleshooting

Figure 13-7 shows the logic diagram for a three-digit decade counter and readout. Each digit is displayed by means of a separate Nixie tube. Each tube is driven by a separate 4/10 line decoder and storage IC package. The three decoder/storage packages are enabled by a clock pulse at regular intervals or on demand. Each decoder/storage unit receives BCD information from a separate decade counter IC package. The counter packages contain four FF and produce a BCD output that corresponds to the number of input pulses occurring between reset pulses. The maximum readout possible is 999. At a 1000 count, the output pulse of the 100 decade is applied to all three counter packages simultaneously, as a reset pulse.

Problem 1

For the first problem, assume that the pulse input is applied through a gate and that the gate is held open for 1 second. The count shown on the Nixie readout then indicates the frequency. For example, if the count is 377, this shows that there are 377 pulses passing in 1 second; the frequency is 377 Hz.

Assume that a 700-Hz pulse train is applied to the input. The counter should then go from 000 to 700. However, assume that the count is 000, 001, 002, 003, 004, 005, 000, 001, 002, 003, and so forth. That is, the count never reaches 006.

One logical conclusion here is that the problem is in the counter function rather than in the readout function (decoder/storage or Nixie). For example, if the units readout is defective so that there is no display beyond 005, the 10 and 100 readouts will be unaffected. That is, the count would go 005, 010, 011, 012, and so forth.

With the problem localized to the counter function, there are three logical possibilities: that the input pulses never reach more than 5 (not likely), that there is a reset pulse occurring at the same time as the sixth input pulse or any time after the fifth input pulse (possible), or that the units counter simply does not count beyond 5 (most likely).

With the detective work out of the way, the next practical step is to make measurements. To confirm or deny the reset pulse possibility, monitor the input pulse line and the reset line of the units counter on a

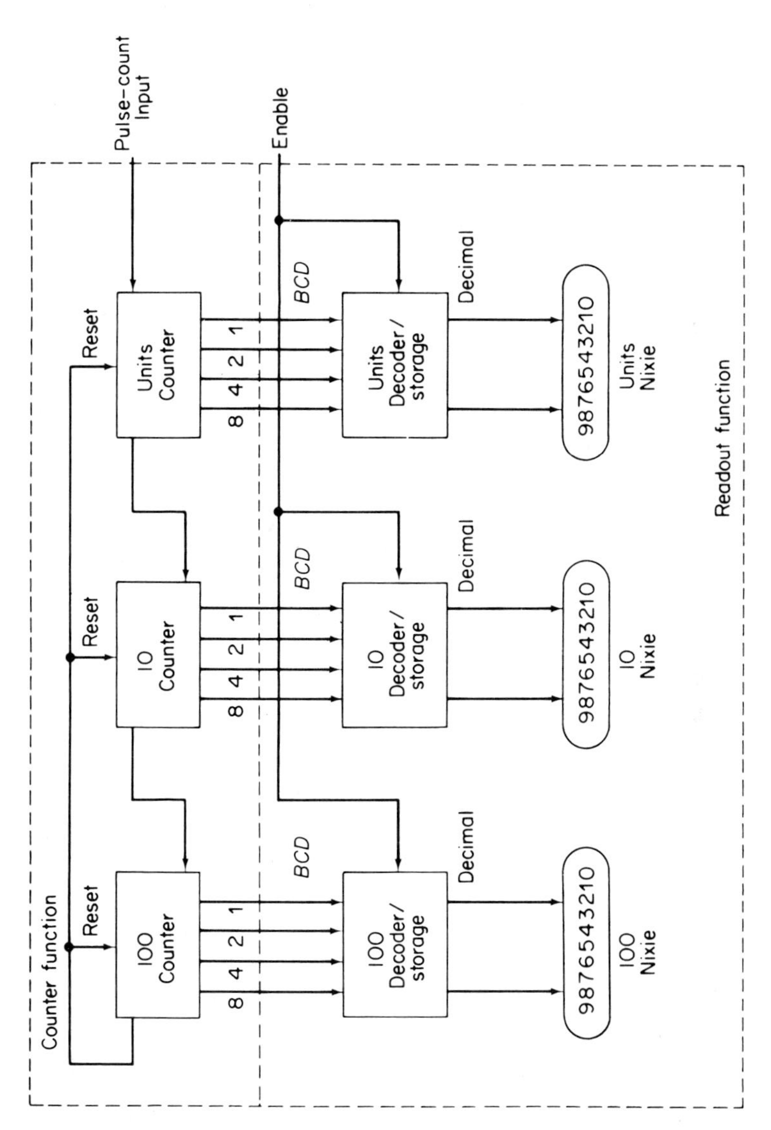

Fig. 13-7. Logic diagram for three-digit decade counter and readout.

dual-trace oscilloscope. Adjust the oscilloscope sweep frequency so that about ten input pulses are displayed.

If a reset pulse does occur after the fifth input pulse, the problem is pinpointed. Trace the reset line to the source of the unwanted (improperly timed) reset pulse.

If there is no reset pulse before the sixth pulse, monitor the input line and the 4 line of the units counter. The 4 line should go true at the sixth input pulse (as should the 2 line). Then monitor the 8 line. In all probability, the units counter is defective: The 4 and 2 lines will show no output or the output will be abnormal.

If a logic clip is available, check operation of the units decade counter on a real-time basis. That is, inject input pulses and check that the 4 and 2 lines go true when the sixth input pulse is injected. If circuit conditions make it possible, disconnect the 4 and 2 lines and recheck operation of the units counter. It is possible that the 4 and 2 lines are shorted or otherwise defective. Unfortunately, with most present-day computer circuits, wiring to the IC modules is in the form of printed circuits, making it impractical to disconnect individual lines or leads. The entire IC must be checked by substitution.

Problem 2

Assume that the test conditions are the same as for Problem 1. However, the readout is 000, 001, 002, 003, 004, 005, 006, 007, 000, 001, 010, 011, 012, and so forth. That is, the 008 and 009 displays are not correct.

The logical conclusion here is that the problem is in the readout function rather than in the counter function. For example, if there is a failure in the counter, the 10 counter will never receive an input from the units counter. Since there is some readout from the 10 counter, it can be assumed that the units counter is functioning.

Assuming that the readout is faulty, there are several logical possibilities: The units counter output lines can be shorted or broken (thus the units decoder receives no input or an abnormal input), the units decoder can be defective, or the units Nixie tube is defective.

The first practical step depends on the test equipment available. Monitor the 8 and 9 lines to the Nixie tube with a logic probe or oscilloscope. If pulses are present, but there is no 8 or 9 display, the Nixie tube is at fault. As an alternative first step, inject a pulse at the 8 and 9 lines of the Nixie and check for a proper display.

If there is no 8 or 9 pulse present at the Nixie input, check for an 8 or 9 input to the units decoder. An 8 input is produced where there is a pulse at the 8 line (between counter and decoder). A 9 input requires simultaneous pulses on the 8 and 1 lines.

If the 8 and 9 inputs are available to the decoder but there are no 8 and 9 pulses to the Nixie inputs, the units decoder is at fault. If a logic clip is available, check operation of the units decoder on a real-time basis. That is, inject input pulses at the 8 line (from the counter), while simultaneously enabling the decoder, and check that the 8 output line (to the Nixie) goes true.

Problem 3

Assume that the test conditions are the same as for Problem 1, except that the input frequency is 300 Hz. However, the readout is 600. That is, the readout is twice the correct value.

The logical conclusion here is that the problem is in the counter function rather than in the readout. It is possible that the readout could be at fault but not likely.

A common cause for faults of this type (where FF are involved) is that one FF is following the input pulses directly. That is, the normal FF function is to go through a complete change of states for two input pulses. Instead, the faulty FF is changing states completely for each input pulse (similar to the operation of a one-shot). Thus the decade counter containing such a faulty FF produces two output pulses to the next counter for every ten input pulses, or the counter divides by 5 instead of 10. All decades following the defective stage receive two input pulses where they should receive one.

The first practical step is to monitor the input and output of each decade in turn. The decade that shows one output for five inputs is at fault.

Problem 4

Assume that the test conditions are the same as for Problem 1. However, the readout is 000, 000, 000, and so forth. That is, the Nixie tubes glow but remain at 000.

The logical conclusion here is that the Nixies are receiving power and are operative. If not, the Nixies could not produce a 000 indication.

The most likely causes for such a symptom are no input pulses arriving at the units counter, a simultaneous reset pulse with the first input pulse (or a short on the reset line), no enable pulse to the decoder/storage packages, or a defective units counter (not responding to the first input pulse).

The practical steps here are to monitor (simultaneously) the input line and the reset line, the input line and the enable line, and the input line and the output of the units counter. This should pinpoint the problem.

For example, if there are no input pulses (or the wiring is defective, possibly shorted, so that the input pulses never reach the units counter input), there will be no output. If the input pulses are present but a reset pulse arrives simultaneously with the first input pulse, there can be no readout. If there is no enable pulse, there will be no readout, even with the counters operating properly. That is, the counters will produce the correct BCD output, which is then stored in the decoders. However, the absence of an enable pulse will prevent the stored information from being displayed on the Nixies. If the input pulses are present and there is no abnormal reset pulse, the output of the units counter should show one pulse for ten input pulses. If not, the units counter is defective.

C. DETAILED COMPUTER CIRCUIT TROUBLESHOOTING

The detailed theory of operation for the ELA/B instruction (E-register circuit operation) of the Hewlett-Packard HP2116 is discussed in Chapter 9 (subdivision M). The following paragraphs describe the detailed procedures to be followed when troubleshooting these circuits involved with the ELA/B instruction. The step-by-step details are those found in the computer service literature.

The following paragraphs provide both a description (from a service or troubleshooting standpoint) and a test procedure for the circuits and process of the ELA/B instruction. Processing operations are summarized in Figure 13-8. Point-to-point signal flow during phase 1 is shown in Figure 13-9.

Servicing Description

The ELA/B instruction reads a number from the A or B register and moves all bits of that number one position to the left. Bit 15 is

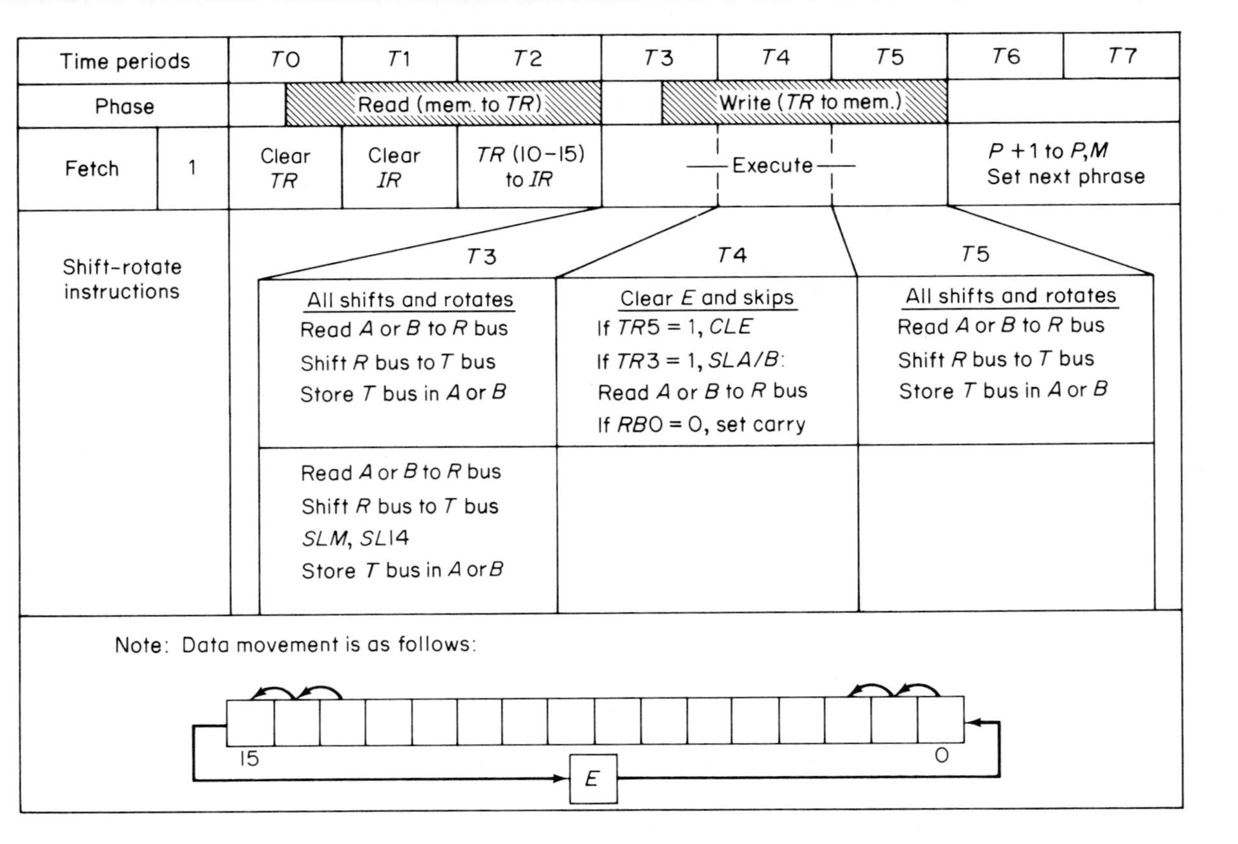

Fig. 13-8. ELA/B instruction processing operations.

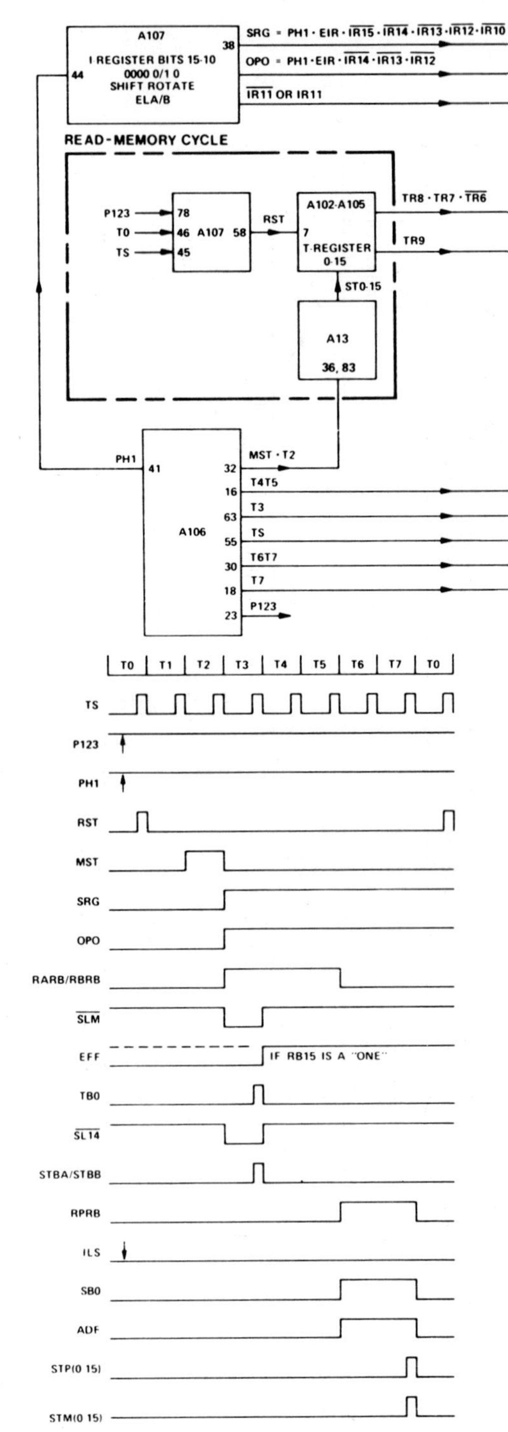

Fig. 13-9. ELA/B instruction processing circuits, servicing diagram.

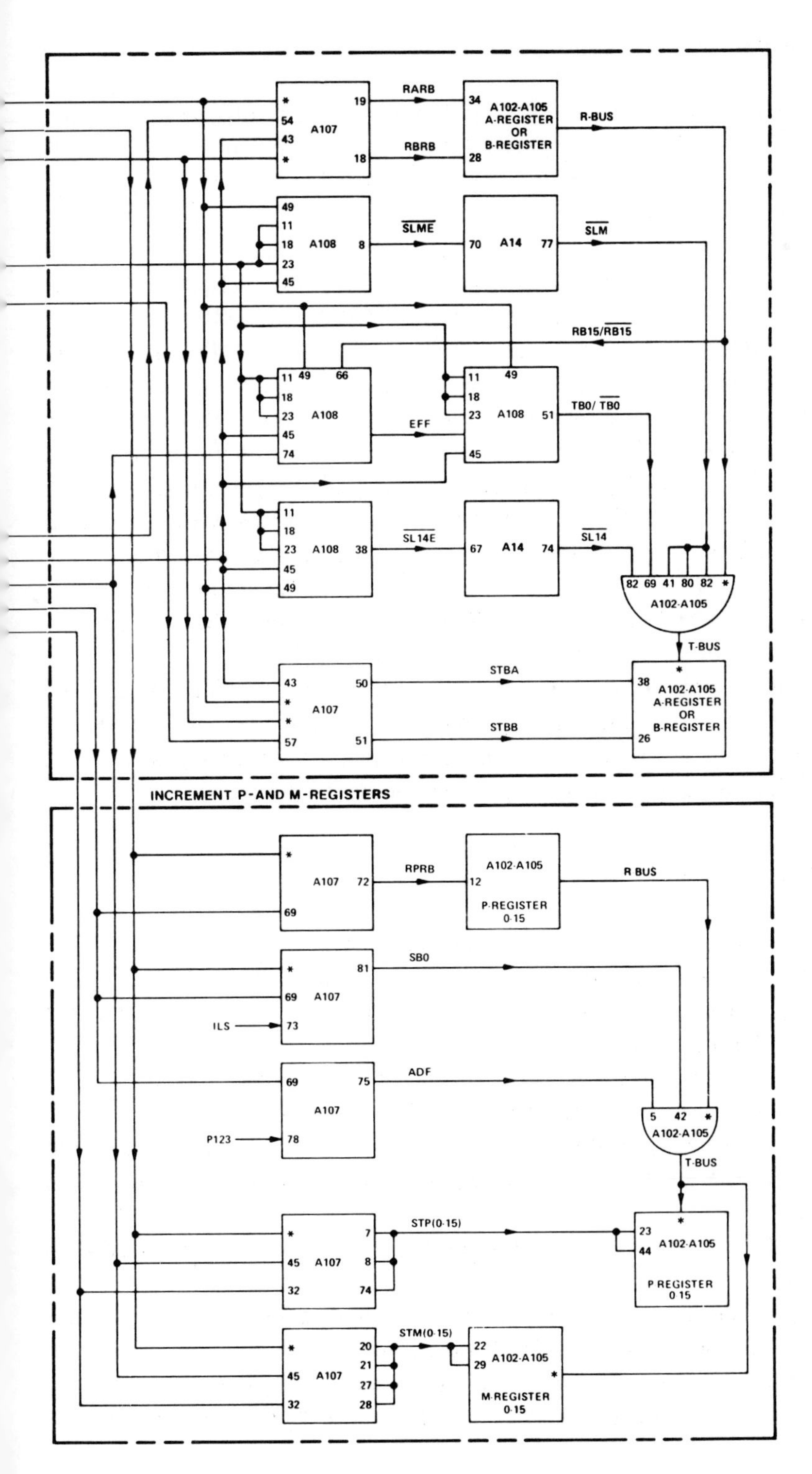
A107
RARB
RBRB
A102-A105
A-REGISTER
OR
B-REGISTER
R-BUS
A108
SLME
A14
SLM
RB15/RB15
EFF
TB0/TB0
SL14E
SL14
T-BUS
STBA
STBB
INCREMENT P-AND M-REGISTERS
RPRB
P-REGISTER
0-15
R BUS
SB0
ILS
ADF
P123
STP(0-15)
P REGISTER
STM(0-15)
M-REGISTER

placed in the E register, and the E register bit is placed in the bit 0 position (see Figure 13-8). At the end of the machine cycle, the P-register number is incremented by 1 and stored in the P and M registers, and the next phase is set.

The ELA/B instruction is read from the memory and executed during phase 1. During time *T*2 of phase 1, the instruction code is read into the I register. Bit configuration 000000 or 000010 (bits 15–10, respectively) in the I register causes signals SRG, OPO, RARB, or RBRB to be generated during time *T*3. (The source and timing sequence of these signals are shown in Figure 13-9.) These signals, in combination with signals TR6, TR7, TR8, and TR9 from the T register, cause signals SLN, SL14, and STBA or STBB to be generated. In turn, these signals cause the A- or B-register number to be read onto the R bus (signal RARB or RBRB), the bits of the number moved one position to the left and the E register cleared or set depending on the state of signal RBO (signal $\overline{\text{SLM}}$ and $\overline{\text{SL14}}$). The number is then stored back into the A or B register (signal STBA or STBB).

During time *T*6*T*7, signals RPRB, SBO, ADF, STP (0–15), and STM (0–15) cause the P and M registers to increment by 1. The next phase (phase 1, or phase 4 if an interrupt is in progress) is then set, and the computer is ready to process the next instruction.

Test procedure

To test the ELA/B instruction circuits, proceed as follows.

At the computer front panel (refer to Chapters 9 and 10 for typical front-panel illustrations), set the switch register to 001000. Press and release the load address switch.

Set the switch register to 001600 (ELA instruction) or 005600 (ELB instruction). Press and release the LOAD memory switch.

Set the switch register to 152525. Press and release the LDA switch if testing the ELA instruction or the LDB switch if testing the ELB instruction.

Set the switch register to 001000. Press and release the load address switch.

Open the door assembly. At display board assembly A501, set the instruction switch to the LOOP position.

At the computer front panel, press and release the single-cycle switch. The P and M registers should retain 001000 in them, the A register should have 125252 or 125253 in it, and the E register should be set.

At the computer front panel, again press and release the single-cycle switch. The P and M registers should retain 001000 in them, the A register should have 052525 or 052527 in it, and the E register should be cleared.

At the computer front panel, press and release the run switch.

The computer is now in the run mode, executing the ELA instruction in location 001000. Using a dual-trace oscilloscope, check the signals shown in Figure 13-9.

As an example, assume that the ADF signal (at terminal 75 of plug-in card A107) is monitored on one trace of the oscilloscope, with the timing pulses (TS, at terminal 45 of plug-in card A107) monitored on the other trace. As shown by the timing diagram, the ADF pulse should appear during time periods *T*6 and *T*7. If the ADF pulse is absent or abnormal, the problem could be on plug-in card A107. However, before substituting a new A107 card, a practical approach would be to monitor the *T*6*T*7 pulses (at terminal 69 of A107) and the P123 voltage level (at terminal 78 of A107). If both of these points show a correct oscilloscope display but the AFD signal is incorrect, then substitute a new A107 plug-in card. If a substitute A107 is not available, the next practical step is to check the A107 circuit components and wiring between terminals 69, 78, and 75. Note that the servicing diagram of Figure 13-9 does not show the internal wiring of the card. Instead, such wiring is shown on a card schematic diagram. Owing to its complexity,

Fig. 13-10. Portion of wiring on instruction decoder card A107.

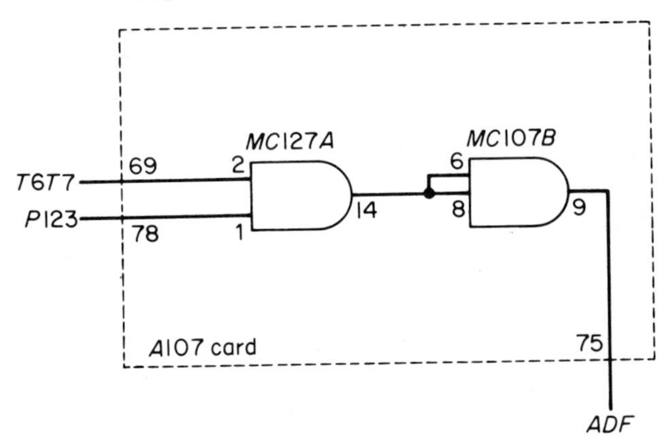

the card schematic is not reproduced here. However, Figure 13-10 shows that portion of the wiring and circuits between terminals 69, 78, and 75.

As shown, the P123 voltage and the *T6T7* pulses form the input to an AND gate (MC127A). The output of this AND gate is applied to another AND gate (MC107B). The second AND gate acts as a buffer and delivers its output (the ADF signal) to terminal 75.

If both P123 and *T6T7* signals are present but there is no output from the first AND gate, the problem is in MC127A. (Note that MC127 is a microcircuit or integrated circuit containing several gates. MC127 must be replaced as a package on card A107.)

If the output from MC127A is correct, the problem is in the buffer AND gate, and MC107 must be replaced on the card.

GLOSSARY

ABACUS: An ancient calculating device using beads strung on wires to indicate decimal values.

ABSOLUTE: Pertaining to an address fully defined by a memory address number or to a program that contains such addresses (as opposed to one containing symbolic addresses).

ACCESS TIME: The time required to extract information from or store information into the computer's memory. *Read time* is access time required to extract information. *Write time* is time required to store information.

ACCOUNTING MACHINE: Any device that prepares accounting records. Usually an accounting machine is keyboard-operated and is not necessarily computerized.

ACCUMULATOR: See *register*. A register in which numbers are totaled or manipulated or temporarily stored for transfers to and from the memory or external devices. Generally, an accumulator is a register used in arithmetic circuits, such as the totalizing circuit of an adder.

ADDER: Circuit used to perform addition in arithmetic section of computer. Generally, the output of an adder circuit represents the sum of the inputs.

ADDRESS: A number (noun) that identifies one location in memory. Also (verb), the process of directing the computer to read a specified memory location (synonymous with *reference*). Address can also refer to a specific channel of information.

ADDRESS MODIFICATION: A programming technique of changing the address referred to by a memory reference instruction so that each time a particular instruction is executed it will affect a different memory location.

ADDRESS WORD: A computer word that contains only the address of a memory location.

ALGOL: Algolrithmic-oriented language; a computer language similar to FORTRAN, but with modifications.

ALTER: A modification of the contents of an accumulator or extend bit (for example, clear, complement, or increment).

ANALOG: Pertaining to information that can have continuously variable values, as opposed to digital information, which can be varied in degrees no smaller than the value of the least significant digit.

ANALOG COMPUTER: A computer that solves problems by translating physical conditions (position, flow, temperature, etc.) into electrical quantities, manipulating the electrical values (by addition, subtraction, integration, differentiation, etc.), and then translating the electrical quantities into a readout or display. Analog computers do not use digital techniques. However, there are "hybrid" computers using both analog and digital methods.

AND: A logical operation in which the resultant quantity (or signal) is true if all the input values are true and is false if at least one of the input values is false.

ARITHMETIC LOGIC: The circuitry involved in manipulating the information contained in a computer's accumulators.

ARITHMETIC OPERATION: (General) Any manipulation of numbers. (Specific) A mathematical operation involving fundamental arithmetic (addition, subtraction, multiplication, and division) but specifically excluding logical and shifting operations.

ARITHMETIC SECTION: That portion of the computer used to perform arithmetic operations on the information being processed by the computer.

ASSEMBLE: A procedure used by programmers to convert programs drawn up in symbolic form (generally flow charts) into a computer language.

ASSEMBLER: A program that converts another program (previously prepared in symbolic form) to binary computer language. The assemble procedure is performed by the assembler.

ASYNCHRONOUS CIRCUIT: Circuits that operate independent of computer master clock or timing signals.

AUTOMATIC CODE: A technique used by programmers where the computer itself is used to code programs (such as using the computer to translate a program in flow-chart form into a computer language program).

AUTOMATION: With regard to computers, automation is any system in which many or all of the processes of production, movement, and inspection of parts and materials are automatically performed or controlled by a computer.

AUXILIARY STORAGE: Any storage system that supplements another storage system. For example, external magnetic tapes can be used as an auxiliary (or secondary) storage to supplement the computer's primary memory section.

BAR PRINTER: A computer readout device using multiple type bars positioned side by side across a single line. Converts computer electrical readout into type printed on paper sheets or rolls.

BASE: The quantity of different digits used in a particular numbering system. The base in the binary numbering system is 2; thus there are two digits (0 and 1). In the decimal system (base 10), there are ten digits (0–9).

BASE PAGE: The lowest numbered page of a computer's memory. It can be directly addressed from any other page.

BASIC: A computer language based upon common English language terms.

BATCH PROCESSING: A technique used by programmers where all information to be processed is coded and collected into groups before processing through the computer.

BINARY: In computers, binary refers to a number system involving only two possibilities (typically high or low, positive or negative, presence or absence of pulses). In mathematics, binary refers to a number system with a base of 2. Any system of numbers or codes involving only two states (typically 1 or 0).

BINARY-CODED DECIMAL (BCD): A number system or form of notation where individual decimal digits are represented by a group of binary digits. Typically, each decimal digit is represented by four binary digits arranged in an 8421 order. For example, the decimal number 37 is represented in BCD form as 0011 (a pure binary 3) followed by 0111 (a pure binary 7).

BINARY COUNTER: A circuit using a group of flip-flops to convert a series of pulses into binary form.

BINARY POINT: The fractional dividing point of a binary numeral; equivalent to *decimal point* in the decimal numbering system.

BINARY PROGRAM: A program (or its recorded form) in which all information is in binary computer language.

BISTABLE: A device or circuit with two opposite stable states (such as a bistable multivibrator or flip-flop).

BIT: An abbreviation for binary information digit. In number systems, a bit is a single character in a group. Thus the pure binary number 10001 has five bits. In computers, a bit is generally the presence (or absence) of a pulse in a group of pulses representing a binary number. The term bit is also used to classify the storage capacity of a memory (such as 50 words of four bits each).

BIT DENSITY: A physical specification referring to the number of bits that can be recorded per unit of length or area (1000 bits/in.^{2} of tape and the like).

BIT-SERIAL: One bit at a time, as opposted to bit-parallel in which all bits of a character can be handled simultaneously.

BRANCH INSTRUCTION: Instructions that direct the computer to leave the basic program at some point and branch to another point in the same program. Also known as *jump*, *skip*, and *transfer* instructions. Usually, branch instructions are carried out between two decision instructions.

BUFFER: Loosely, any electronic device or circuit used between two other devices or circuits. Generally buffers do not translate information into another form (such as an encoder or decoder) but act to hold the information. In specialized computer applications, a buffer is a storage device used to compensate for a difference in time of occurrence of events or a different rate of flow. For example, a paper-tape punch can be considered as a buffer since it permits data to be stored slowly (on a manual keyboard) and then provides for fast read-in to the computer (when the paper tape is played at high speeds).

BUFFER REGISTER: A register used for intermediate storage of information in the transfer sequence between the computer's accumulators and a peripheral (input/output) device. Generally, the buffer register is part of the computer but could be part of the external device.

BUS: A major electrical path connecting two or more electrical circuits.

BYTE: A group of bits, possibly (but not necessarily) making up a complete character or word.

CALCULATOR: Any device capable of performing arithmetic or logic functions (can be mechanical, electromechanical, or electronic).

CARD STACKER: In computers, a readout device that accumulates punched cards in a stack.

CARRY: A digit, or equivalent signal, resulting from an arithmetic operation that causes a positional digit to equal or exceed the base of the numbering system.

CHAIN PRINTER: A computer readout device using a chain of several links, each of which contains alphabetic and numeric characters. The characters are printed on paper by means of electrically operated hammers. Converts computer electrical readout into type printed on paper sheets or rolls.

CHARACTER: The general term to include all symbols, such as alphabetic letters, numerals, punctuation marks, and mathematical operators (+, −, %). Also, the coded representation of such symbols.

CHECKERBOARD: An alternating pattern of zeros and ones stored in a computer for testing purposes.

CLEAR: Reset; the binary 0 condition.

COBOL: Common Business Oriented Language; a computer language developed for business data processing.

CODE: A system of symbols that can be used by machines such as a computer and that in specific arrangements has a special external meaning.

CODING: When used by programmers, coding refers to the translation of a flow diagram into a computer language.

COLLATOR: A data-processing device (not necessarily associated with computers) used to merge sets of cards (or other documents) into a given sequence.

COMB PRINTER: A computer readout device using a set of characters mounted so as to face a paper sheet or roll. The characters are printed on paper by means of electrically operated hammers. Converts computer electrical readout into type printed on paper sheets or rolls.

COMMUNICATION SYSTEM: A computer system having facilities (data sets) for long-distance transfers of information between remote and central locations.

COMPARATOR: An instrument for comparing digitized measurements against presetable upper and lower limits and giving an indication of the comparison result.

COMPARISON CIRCUIT: A circuit used to compare the condition (polarity, voltage level, number of pulses, etc.) present in two devices or circuits (such as comparing the number of information bits in two registers).

COMPILE: When used by programmers, compile refers to the preparation of a computer language program from a program written in another programming language.

COMPILER: A language translation program, used to transform symbols meaningful to a human operator to codes meaningful to a computer. More restrictively, a program that translates a machine-independent source language into machine language of a specific computer, thus excluding assemblers.

COMPUTATION: The processing of information within the computer.

COMPUTER: See *digital computer* and *analog computer.*

COMPUTER WORD: A series of bits (or characters) treated as a unit and capable of being stored in one computer location. Also see *data word* and *word.*

CONFIGURATION: The arrangement of either hardware instruments or software routines when combined to operate as a system.

CONFIGURATOR: A computer program whose purpose is to combine a number of program segments into an integrated whole in a specific, desired manner (or configuration).

CONSOLE: Same as *control panel.*

CONSOLE PRINTER: A computer output printer used primarily for relaying information to the computer operator. Console printers can be part of the computer or an auxiliary printer.

CONTENTS: The information stored in a register or a memory location.

CONTROL: When used by programmers, control refers to programming instructions that determine branch instructions.

CONTROL BIT: A signal, or the stored indication of this signal, that controls the transfer of information to and from peripheral devices. See *flag bit.*

CONTROL PANEL: That part of the computer that contains the operating controls, indicators, and readouts.

CONTROL PUNCH: When used by programmers, control punch refers to a specific code punched into a data card. The code causes the computer to perform a specific function.

CONTROL SECTION: That portion of the computer used to control execution and interpretation of instructions in proper sequence. Sometimes, control section is used synonymously with *control panel* or *console.* However, more accurately, the control section includes both the control panel (operating controls, indicators, and readouts) and those circuits that operate in direct response to the panel controls.

CONTROL STATEMENT: When used by programmers, control statement refers to a form of branch instructions that transfers control of the instruction sequence to a statement elsewhere in the program.

CORE: The smallest element of a core storage memory module. Usually, a core is a ring of ferrite material that can be magnetized in a clockwise or counterclockwise direction to represent the two binary digits, 1 and 0.

COUNTER: A device or circuit used to tally various items of information. Computer counters often include a readout on the control panel. See *program counter.*

CURRENT PAGE: The memory page comprising all those locations that are on the same page as a given instruction.

CRAM: Card Random-Access Memory; a mass storage equipment that uses removable magnetic cards. Each card is capable of storing a large amount of data (in magnetic bit form).

CYCLING TAPE: When used by programmers, cycling tape refers to making a new magnetic tape file by updating old magnetic tapes.

DATA ACQUISTION: The gathering, measuring, digitizing, and recording of continuous-form (analog) information.

DATA PROCESSING: Any operation (such as sorting, selecting, matching, merging, classifying, analyzing) or combination of operations performed on data.

DATA REDUCTION: The transformation of raw information gathered by measuring or recording equipment into a more condensed, organized, or useful form.

DATA SET: A device used for translation of computer language into a form suitable for transmission over communication lines (telephone, telegraph, etc.) and for translation back to computer language.

DATA WORD: A computer word consisting of a number, a fact, or other information that is to be processed by the computer.

DEBUG: A term used synonymously with *troubleshooting*. However, when either term is used by programmers, the terms mean to locate and correct mistakes in a computer program rather than to correct a malfunction in the computer's operation.

DECADE COUNTER: A circuit (usually a group of flip-flops) used to convert a series of pulses into BCD form. Decade counters used in computers may or may not include a readout on the control panel.

DECIMAL: Denoting the numbering system based on the base of 10.

DECODER: A circuit or device used to translate electrical signals from one form to another (BCD to digital, binary to BCD, etc.).

DECREMENT: To change the value of a number in the negative direction. If not otherwise stated, a decrement of 1 is usually assumed.

DELAY: A circuit or device that delays the output signal in relation to the input signal by a fixed amount of time.

DEVICE: An electronic or electromechanical instrument. Most commonly implies measuring, reading, or recording equipment.

DIAGNOSTIC: (Adjective) Relating to test programs for detection of errors in the functioning of hardware or software or the messages resulting from such tests. Also (noun), the test program or message itself.

DIGITAL COMPUTER: An electronic instrument capable of accepting, storing, and arithmetically manipulating information, which includes both data and the controlling program. The information is handled in the form of coded binary digits (0 and 1), represented by dual voltage levels, magnetic states, punched holes, etc.

DIRECT-ACCESS STORAGE: A storage system where information at a particular location can be reached (for read-in or readout) directly. In a true direct-access storage system, the same amount of time is required for access to any location in memory. The term is often used synonymously with *random-access storage*.

DIRECT MEMORY ACCESS: A means of transferring a block of information words directly between an external device and the computer's memory, bypassing the need for repeating a service routine for each word. This method greatly speeds the transfer process.

DISABLE: A signal condition that prohibits some specific event from proceeding.

DISC STORAGE: A means of storing binary digits in the form of magnetic spots on a rotating circular metal plate coated with a magnetic material. The information is stored and retrieved by read-write heads positioned over the surface of the disc.

DOCUMENTATION: Manuals and other printed materials (tables, listings, diagrams, etc.) that provide instructive information for use and maintenance of a manufactured product, including both hardware and software.

DOUBLE-LENGTH WORD: A word that, due to its length, requires two computer words to represent it. Double-length words are normally stored in two adjacent memory locations.

DRIVER: An input/output routine to provide automatic operation of a specific device with the computer.

DRUM PRINTER: A computer readout device using a drum embossed with letters and numbers. The characters are printed on paper by means of electrically operated hammers. Converts computer electrical readout into type printed on paper sheets or rolls.

DUMP: To record memory contents on an external medium (such as magnetic tape).

EDVAC: Electronic Discrete Variable Automatic Computer; an early computer using binary number systems for all data.

EFFECTIVE ADDRESS: The address of a memory location ultimately affected by a memory reference instruction. It is possible for one instruction to go through several indirect addresses to reach the effective address.

ELECTRONIC COUNTER: An electronic instrument used to measure physical quantities by specially controlled counting of electrical pulses.

ELECTROSTATIC PRINTER: A computer readout device using electrostatic printing (magnetized powdered ink, followed by a heat treatment).

ENABLE: A signal condition that permits some specific event to proceed, whenever it is ready to do so. Used synonymously with *strobe.*

ENIAC: Electronic Numerical Integrator and Calculator; one of the first all-electronic computers.

EXCLUSIVE OR: A logical operation in which the resultant quantity (or signal) is true if at least one (but not all) of the input values is true and is false if the input values are all true or all false.

EXECUTE: To fully perform a specific operation, such as would be accomplished by an instruction or a program.

EXECUTE PHASE: A predetermined state of the internal computer logic that causes the computer to *interpret as data* the information read out of the memory during a memory cycle.

EXIT SEQUENCE: A series of instructions to conclude operation in one area of a program and to move to another area.

EXTEND: A register (usually one or two bits) that extends the effective length of other registers in the computer (usually for addition or rotation of bits).

FETCH PHASE: A predetermined state of the internal computer logic that causes the computer to *interpret as an instruction* the information read out of memory during a memory cycle.

FIELD: When used by programmers, the term field represents an area on a data card, paper tape, or magnetic tape assigned to a particular class of data (such as the address portion of a computer word).

FIXED POINT: A numeric notation in which the fractional point (whether decimal, octal, or binary) appears at a constant, predetermined position. Compare with *floating point.*

FLAG BIT: A signal, or the stored indication of this signal, that indicates the readiness of a peripheral device to transfer information. See *control bit.*

FLIP-FLOP: An electronic circuit (usually a multivibrator) having two stable states and thus capable of storing a binary digit. The states are controlled by signal levels at the input and are sensed by signal levels at the output.

FLOATING POINT: A numeric notation in which the integer and the exponent of a number are separately represented (frequently by two computer words), so that the implied position of the fractional point (decimal, octal, or binary) can be freely varied with respect to the integer digits. Compare with *fixed point.*

FLOW CHART: A chart (usually in symbol form) used by programmers to show steps of a program. Generally, a flow chart is drawn on the basis of the particular program requirements and then converted to a language that is compatible with the computer.

FORMAT: A predetermined arrangement of bits or characters.

FORTRAN: Formula Translations; a computer language, or group of languages (FORTRAN I, II, III, IV), developed primarily for scientific and mathematical data processing. Fortran programs are written in a form resembling algebra rather than step-by-step instructions.

FOUR-BIT SYSTEM: A basic computer logic code capable of handling information in groups of four bits or pulses.

GANGPUNCH: A data-processing term indicating that a certain bit of information is punched into all cards in a particular group.

GATE: An electronic switch or circuit that passes or stops the flow of current, signals, or pulses. Gates produce an output on condition of certain rules governing input conditions. For example, a two-input AND gate produces a true output only when input 1 *and* input 2 are true.

HAMMING CODE: An advanced parity scheme.

HARDWARE: Electronic or electromechanical components, instruments, or systems.

HIGH CORE: Core memory locations having high-numbered addresses.

INCLUSIVE OR: A logical operation in which the resultant quantity (or signal) is true if at least one of the input values is true and is false if the input values are all false.

INCREMENT: To change the value of a number in the positive direction. If not otherwise stated, an increment of 1 is usually assumed.

INCREMENTAL MAGNETIC TAPE: A form of magnetic tape recording in which the recording transport advances by small increments, stopping the tape advancement long enough to record one character at the spot located under the recording head.

INDIRECT ADDRESS: The address initially specified by an instruction when it is desired to use that location to redirect the computer to some other location to find the effective address or the instruction.

INDIRECT PHASE: A predetermined state of the internal computer logic that causes the computer to *interpret as an address* the information read out of the memory during a memory cycle.

INFORMATION: A unit or set of knowledge represented in the form of discrete words, consisting of an arrangement of symbols or (insofar as the digital computer is concerned) binary digits.

INHIBIT: To prevent a specific event from occurring.

INITIALIZE: The procedure of setting various parts of a stored program to starting values, so that the program will behave the same way each time it is repeated. The procedures are included as part of the program itself.

INPUT: Information or instructions to be processed, usually transferred from a peripheral device into the computer. Can also apply to the transfer process itself.

INPUT DEVICE: Computer accessory (or peripheral device) designed to bring information into the computer (card reader, tape reader, keyboard, etc.).

INPUT/OUTPUT: Relating to the equipment or method used for transmitting information into or out of the computer.

INPUT/OUTPUT CHANNEL: The complete input or output facility for one individual device or function, including its assigned position in the computer, the interface circuitry, and the external device.

INPUT/OUTPUT SYSTEM: The circuitry involved in transferring information between the computer's accumulators and the peripheral devices.

INPUT SECTION: That portion of the computer used for bringing data into the computer.

INSTRUCTION: A written statement, or the equivalent computer-acceptable code, that tells the computer to execute a specified single operation.

INSTRUCTION CODE: The arrangement of binary digits that tells the computer to execute a particular instruction.

INSTRUCTION LOGIC: The circuitry involved in moving binary information between registers, the memory, and buffers in prescribed ways, according to instruction codes.

INSTRUCTION REGISTER: A register that forms part of the instruction logic. The instruction register generally receives bits from the transfer register when each new instruction is read out of memory and retains these bits for instruction identification. Usually, the instruction register is not a "working" register.

INSTRUCTION WORD: A computer word containing an instruction code. The code bits may occupy all or part of the word.

INTERFACE: The connecting circuitry that links the centeral processor of a computer system to its peripheral devices.

INTERLACED: Multiple functions for the same signal at different times or one signal being dependent on many other signals. A typical condition for digital logic circuits used in computers.

INTERRECORD GAP (IRG): An interval of space or time deliberately left between recording portions of data or records. Such spacing is used to prevent errors through loss of data or overwriting and permits magnetic tape start-stop operations.

INTERRUPT: The process, initiated by an external device, that causes the computer to interrupt a program in progress, generally for the purpose of transferring information between that device and the computer.

INTERRUPT LOCATION: A memory location whose contents (always an instruction) are executed upon interrupt by a specific device.

INTERRUPT PHASE: A predetermined state of the internal computer logic that causes the computer to suspend operation of a program in progress and branch to a specific service routine.

JUMP: See *branch instruction.*

LABEL: Any arrangement of symbols, usually alphanumeric, used in place of an absolute memory address in computer programming.

LANGUAGE: The set of symbols, rules, and conventions used to convey information, either at the human level or at the computer level.

LIBRARY ROUTINE: A routine designed to accomplish some commonly used mathematical function and kept permanently available on a library program tape.

LOAD: To put information into the computer (to the memory, register, etc.). Also, to put an information medium into the device (loading tape into the tape recorder).

LOADER: A program designed to assist in transferring information from an external device into a computer memory.

LOCATION: A group of storage elements in the computer's memory (such as a group of cores in a memory module) that can store one computer word. Each location is identified by a number (address) to facilitate storage and retrieval of information in selected locations.

LOGICAL OPERATION: A mathematical process based on the principles of truth tables (such as AND, OR, NAND, etc., operations).

LOGIC CLIP: A test instrument used to detect and indicate logic levels present at the terminals of IC logic packages.

LOGIC DIAGRAM: A diagram that represents the detailed internal functioning of electronic hardware, using binary logic symbols rather than electronic component symbols. See *schematic diagram.*

LOGIC EQUATION: A written mathematical statement, using symbols and rules derived from Boolean algebra. Specifically (in computer design) a means of stating the conditions required to obtain a given signal.

LOGIC PROBE: A test instrument used to detect and indicate logic levels present in logic circuits.

LOOP: A sequence of instructions in which the last instruction is a jump back to the first instruction.

LOW CORE: Core memory locations having low-numbered addresses.

MACHINE: Pertaining to the computer hardware (machine timing, machine language, etc.).

MACHINE LANGUAGE: The form of coded information (consisting of binary digits) that can be directly accepted and used by the computer. Other languages require translation to this form, generally with the aid of translation programs (assemblers and compilers).

MACHINE TIMING: The regular cycle of events in the operation of internal computer circuitry. The actual events will differ for various processes, but the timing is constant through each recurring cycle.

MACROINSTRUCTION: An instruction, similar in binary coding to the computer's basic machine instructions, that is capable of producing a variable number of machine-language instructions.

MAGNETIC-TAPE RECORDING: In computers, a means of recording information on a strip of magnetic coated material such that binary bits can be represented by reversal of the direction of magnetization.

MAGNITUDE: That portion of a computer word that indicates the absolute value of a number, thus excluding the sign bit.

MARGINAL TEST TECHNIQUE: A troubleshooting technique based upon testing circuits operated at the high and low extremes of their power supply voltage.

MEDIA CONVERSION: The transfer of recorded information from one recording medium to another (such as paper tape to magnetic tape).

MEMORY: In computers, an organized collection of storage elements (typically ferrite cores) into which a unit of information consisting of a binary digit can be stored and from which it can later be retrieved. Also, a device not necessarily having individual storage elements but that has the same storage and retrieval capabilities (such as magnetic discs).

MEMORY CYCLE: That portion of the computer's internal timing during which the contents of one location of the memory are read out (into a register) and written back into that location.

MEMORY MODULE: A complete segment of core storage, capable of storing a definite number of computer words.

MEMORY PROTECT: A means of preventing inadvertent alteration of a selected segment of a memory.

MEMORY REFERENCE: The address of the memory location specified by a memory reference instruction (that is, the location affected by the instruction).

MEMORY REGISTER: The memory address register that controls access to each memory location.

MERGE: In programming, to combine two or more sets of data into one, usually in a specified sequence. In logic circuits, merge is the function performed by the INCLUSIVE OR operation.

MICROINSTRUCTION: An instruction that forms part of a larger, composite instruction.

MNEMONIC: An abbreviation or arrangement of symbols used to assist human memory. For example, CLE stands for "clear the E register." This is easier to remember than, say, "perform instruction 33."

MULTILEVEL INDIRECT: Indirect addressing using two or more indirect addresses in sequence to find the effective address for the current instruction.

MULTIPLE-PRECISION: Referring to arithmetic in which the computer, for greater accuracy, uses too or more words to represent one number.

NINE'S COMPLEMENT: A number so modified that the addition of the modified number and its original value plus 1 will equal an even power of 10. A nine's complement number is obtained mathematically by subtracting the original value from a string of 9s.

NON-RETURN-ZERO: In magnetic-tape recording of binary digits, a technique in which the recording device does not turn off the magnetizing flux between the recording of individual characters. The flux is always at saturation level during recording, and bits are indicated by reversals of flux polarity.

OCTAL: Denoting a numbering system based upon the base of 8. Octal digits are restricted to the values 0–7.

OCTAL CODE: A notation for writing machine language programs with the use of octal numbers instead of binary numbers.

OCTAL POINT: The fractional dividing point of an octal numeral; equivalent to *decimal point* in the decimal numbering system.

OFF-LINE: Pertaining to the operation of peripheral equipment not under control of the computer.

ONE'S COMPLEMENT: A number so modified that the addition of the modified number and its original value plus 1 will equal an even power of 2. A one's complement number is obtained mathematically by subtracting the original value from a string of 1s and electronically by inverting the states of all binary bits in the number.

ON-LINE: Pertaining to the operation of peripheral equipment under computer control.

OPERAND: That which is operated upon. An operand is usually identified by an address part of an instruction.

OPERATION CODE (OP CODE): A code that represents specific operations. Synonymous with *instruction code*.

OUTPUT: Information and/or instructions that have been processed. Information transferred from the computer to a peripheral device. Also can apply to the transfer process itself.

OUTPUT COUPLER: An instrument that provides the interconnecting circuitry between a measuring instrument and a recording instrument.

OUTPUT DEVICE: Computer accessories designed to translate electrical data representing processed information into permanent results (magnetic tape, paper-tape punch, card punch, etc.).

OUTPUT SECTION: That portion of the computer used to translate the processed information into a form suitable for use by an output accessory or device.

OVERFLOW: A register (usually one or two bits) that indicates that the result of an addition has exceeded the maximum permitted value. The addition result will thus be missing one or more significant bits. Also, a signal or alarm that indicates that the capacity of a computer circuit (generally a register) has been exceeded.

PACKED WORD: A computer word containing two or more independent bits of information. This is done to conserve storage when information requires relatively few bits of the computer word.

PAGE: An artificial division of the memory consisting of a fixed number of locations, dictated by the direct addressing range of memory reference instructions.

PAGE ZERO: The memory page that includes the lowest numbered memory addresses.

PARAMETER: A variable that is assigned value for a specific purpose (a maximum voltage, a minimum current, etc.).

PARITY: An equality checking scheme to ensure accuracy of transferred or transmitted data.

PARITY BIT: A supplementary bit added to an information word to make the total 1 bits always be either odd or even. This permits checking the accuracy of information transfers.

PASS: The complete process of reading a set of recorded information (one tape, one set of punch cards, etc.) through an input device, from beginning to end.

PERIPHERAL DEVICE: An instrument or machine electrically connected to the computer but that is not part of the computer itself. Synonymous with *accessory* and *auxiliary*.

PHASE: In computers, one of several specific states of the internal computer logic, usually set up by instructions being executed, to determine how the computer should interpret information read out of the memory.

PHOTOELECTRIC READER: An input device that senses characters (on punched tape, cards, pages, etc.) by optical light detection circuits.

PLANE (BIT): An arrangement of ferrite cores on a matrix of control and sensing wires. Several planes stacked together form a *memory module*.

POWER FAILURE CONTROL: A means of sensing primary power failure so that a special routine may be executed in the finite period of time available before the regulated d-c supplies discharge to unusable levels. The special routine may be used to preserve the state of a program in process or to shut down external processes.

PRIORITY: The automatic regulation of events so that chosen actions will take precedence over others in cases of timing conflict.

PROCESS CONTROL: Automatic control of manufacturing processes by use of a computer.

PROCESSOR: The central unit of a computer system (the device that accomplishes the arithmetic manipulations), exclusive of peripheral devices. Frequently (when used as an adjective) also excludes interface components, even though normally contained within the processor unit (such as input/output registers housed in the same unit as the arithmetic registers).

PROGRAM: A plan for the solution of a problem by a computer, consisting of a sequence of computer instructions. The step-by-step instructions that tell the computer what to do.

PROGRAM COUNTER: A circuit (usually a register) that keeps track of (or "counts") the stored locations of the instructions in a program being executed.

PROGRAM LISTING: A printed record (or equivalent binary output program) of the instructions in a program.

PROGRAMMER: A person who writes computer programs. Also (hardware), an interface device that sets up (or programs) the various functions of one measuring instrument.

PROGRAMMING: The process of creating a program.

PSEUDOINSTRUCTION: A symbolic statement, similar to assembly-language instructions in general form, but meaningful only to the program containing it rather than to the computer as a machine instruction.

PUNCHED TAPE: A strip of tape, usually paper, on which information is represented by coded patterns of holes punched in columns across the width of the tape. Commonly, there are five or eight hole positions (channels) across the tape.

READ: The process of transferring information from an input device into the computer. Also, the process of taking information out of the computer's memory.

REAL TIME: the time elapsed between events occurring externally to the computer. A computer that accepts and processes information from one such event and is ready for new information before the next event occurs is said to operate in a *real-time environment.*

REFERENCE: Shortened form of *memory reference.*

REGISTER: A group of binary circuits (flip-flops, switches, etc.) for temporary storage of information. Unlike mass storage devices such as memory cores, registers can be wired to permit flexible control of contained information for arithmetic operations, shifts, transfers, etc.

RELOCATABLE: Pertaining to programs whose instructions can be loaded into any stated area of memory.

RESET: A signal condition representing a binary 0. Synonymous with a *clear* signal (to a register, flip-flop, etc.).

ROTATE: A positional shift of all bits in an accumulator (and possibly an extend bit as well), with those bits lost off one end of the accumulator *rotated* around to enter vacated positions at the other end.

ROUTINE: A program or program segment designed to accomplish a single function. See *service routine*, as an example.

SAMPLING: The process of taking measurements of a signal existing at a measuring instrument's input during a short (sample) period. The length of the sample period is a predetermined function of the measuring instrument or computer. The term is used most often with computers used in process control systems.

SCANNER: A device for sequentially switching multiple signal sources to one measuring or recording instrument. Used mostly with prccess control computers.

SCHEMATIC DIAGRAM: A diagram that represents the detailed internal electrical circuit arrangement of electronic hardware, using conventional electronic component symbols. See *logic diagram*.

SELECT CODE: A number assigned to input/output channels for the purpose of identification in information transfers between the computer and external devices.

SERVICE ROUTINE: A sequence of instructions designed to accomplish the transfer of information between a particular device and the computer.

SET: A signal condition representing a binary 1. The opposite of *reset* or *clear*.

SEVEN'S COMPLEMENT: A number so modified that the addition of the modified number and its original value plus 1 will equal an even power of 8. A seven's complement number is obtained mathematically by subtracting the original value from a string of 7s.

SHIFT: In general computer arithmetic, any positional shift of information bits. In most binary systems, a shift implies a manipulation (by the power of 2) to multiply or divide the magnitude portion of a computer word.

SHIFT REGISTER: A register capable of shifting stored information to the right or left (as in multiplication and division).

SIGN: The algebraic plus or minus indicator for a mathematical quantity. Also, the binary digit or electrical polarity representing the same.

SIGNIFICANT DIGIT: A digit positioned in a numeral so as to contribute a definable degree of precision to the numeral. In conventional written form, the *most significant digit* in a numeral is the leftmost digit, and the *least significant digit* is the rightmost digit.

SKIP: An instruction that causes the computer to omit the instruction in the immediately following location. A skip is usually arranged to occur only if certain specified conditions are sensed and found to be true, thus allowing various decisions to be made. A skip instruction is a form of *branch instruction* or *jump instruction*.

SOFTWARE: Computer programs. Also, the tapes or cards on which the programs are recorded.

SOFTWARE PACKAGE: A complete collection of related programs, not necessarly combined as a single entity.

SOROBAN: A variation of the abacus.

SOURCE PROGRAM: A program (or its recorded form) written in some programming language other than machine language and thus requiring translation. The translated form is the *object program.*

STARTING ADDRESS: The address of a memory location in which is stored the first instruction of a given program. The starting address is not always the lowest numbered address. Generally, a block of number addresses are researved for some specific purpose other than the normal program.

STATEMENT: An instruction in any computer-related language, other than machine language.

STORAGE REGISTER: A register designed primarily for temporary storage of data. May or may not include a shift function. See *register* and *shift register.*

STORE: (Noun) Retention of information in the memory section of the computer or in computer accessories. (Verb) To put information into a memory location, register, or device capable of retaining the information for later access.

SUBROUTINE: A sequence of instructions designed to perform a single task, with provisions included to allow some other program to cause execution of the task sequence as though it were part of its own program. Any routine that can be a part of another routine.

SUBTRACTOR CIRCUIT: Circuit used to perform subtraction in the arithmetic section of the computer. Generally, the output of a subtractor circuit represents the difference between inputs.

SYMBOLIC ADDRESS: A label assigned in place of absolute numeric addresses, usually for purposes of relocation. Sec *relocatable.*

SYSTEM: An assembly of units (hardware instruments or software routines) combined to perform an overall function.

TIME PERIOD: The smallest division of time in the computer's internal timing cycle. See *machine timing.*

TIME SHARING: A system where a central computer is used by several operators at remote locations.

TRANSFER REGISTER: A register that directly receives words from memory and directly applies words to memory.

TRUTH TABLE: In mathematics, a table listing all possible configurations and resultant values for any given Boolean algebra function. In logic circuitry, a table or chart used to show relationships of input and outputs for logic circuits used in computers.

TWO'S COMPLEMENT: A number so modified that the addition of the modified number and its original value will equal an even power of 2. Also a kind of arithmetic that represents negative numbers in two's complement form so that all addition can be accomplished in only one direction (positive incrementation). A two's complement number is obtained mathematically by subtracting the original value from an appropriate power of the base 2 (that is, from 1_1, 10_2, 100_2, etc.) and electronically by inverting the states of all binary bits in the number and adding 1 (complement and increment method).

UPDATED PROGRAM: A program to which additions, deletions, or corrections have been made.

USER: The person or persons who program and operate a particular computer.

UTILITY ROUTINE: A standard routine to assist in the operation of the computer (device driver, sorting routine), as opposed to mathematical (library) routines.

WAITING LOOP: A sequence of instructions (frequently only two) that is repeated indefinitely until a desired external event occurs, such as the receipt of a flag signal.

WORD: A set of binary digits handled by the computer as a unit of information. Word length is determined by hardware design (number of cores per location, number of flip-flops in a register, etc.).

WORKING REGISTER: A register whose contents can be modified under control of a program. Thus a register consisting of manually operated switches is not considered a working register.

WRITE: The process of transferring information from the computer to an output device. Also, the process of storing (or restoring) information into the computer's memory. See *memory cycle*.

INDEX

DATE DUE